The Economics of Air Pollution

The Economics of
Air Pollution

A Symposium

EDITED BY HAROLD WOLOZIN

W · W · NORTON & COMPANY · INC · NEW YORK

First Edition

1 2 3 4 5 6 7 8 9 0

Contents

Preface

THE ROLE OF economic analysis in formulating policies to promote overall economic prosperity is now widely understood and appreciated. There is a broad and growing consensus—among the public as well as among economists—that fiscal, monetary and other policies can and should be used to promote full employment, a stable price level, and rapid economic growth. Lively discussion continues in public and in the learned journals, but disagreement is now, much more than previously, about matters of degree and emphasis. Since 1961, vigorous expansionary policies have been pursued to reduce the slack that had built up in the economy since the mid-1950's. These policies have helped to balance and sustain the current expansion, now well into its fifth year. That the stimulus has been achieved at the same time the Federal Government's deficit was being gradually reduced, and without increasing the Government's share of economic activity, attests to the variety and flexibility of available policies.

There are, however, many other areas of public responsibility in which careful economic analysis is needed. Although their goals may go well beyond the narrow confines of economics, most government programs have important economic aspects. What is the most productive way for the Federal Government to help finance education? Which are the most efficient weapons in the war on poverty? How can governments best help to improve the quality of the urban and rural environment? There are many possible approaches to each such problem, and they may differ greatly in their cost and in their effectiveness. Economic analysis can help in making wise choices among alternatives.

In spite of considerable past and present effort, economic analysis has not yet been applied with full effectiveness to these problems. The goals being pursued are numerous and sometimes contradictory. Tools of analysis and available data—both technical and economic—may be inadequate. Often, there are complex relationships between public and private responsibilities, and among the responsibilities of Federal, state, and local governments. New political or administrative machinery may be required to carry out a policy that seems in other respects feasible. Sometimes, groups acquire vested interests in particular approaches to problems, although they may be more costly or less effective than alternative approaches. Much more work needs to be done—in sharpening the economist's tools, and in seeking ways to bring the best analysis to bear through the political process—in order to realize the full potential of economic analysis in public policy.

Air pollution, the subject of the papers in this volume, is an important example of a problem in which the goals of public policy are mainly non-economic, but have important economic aspects. Federal, state, and local governments now have major programs to prevent and abate the pollution of the atmosphere. Yet many economic issues related to these programs are inadequately understood or documented. What are the benefits from cleaner air in improved health, reduced property damage, and increased aesthetic satisfaction? How much are these benefits worth? What are the costs of various methods and degrees of pollution abatement? Would it be cheaper and more effective to disperse activities that pollute the atmosphere, to burn higher quality fuels, or to remove pollutants before effluents are discharged to the atmosphere? How can public policy help to increase private incentives to abate air pollution? What would be the direct and indirect effects of efforts to reduce the discharge of pollutants to the atmosphere from government-operated sources? What data need to be collected to improve our understanding of problems of air pollution?

At present, answers to these and similar questions are inadequate or nonexistent. As the papers that follow make clear, almost none of the relevant questions has an easy answer. Finding better answers, and implementing them through governmental processes, are major challenges to the economics profession, to students of public administration, and to elected officials.

The Public Health Service is to be commended for its support of the seminar at American University in which these papers were presented. Many complex and controversial issues are raised. Proposals are put forward, some of which will be the subject of lively controversy. Most important, the papers help to define the dimensions of the problem and to indicate desirable directions for further work.

GARDNER ACKLEY

Chairman
Council of Economic Advisers
Washington, D. C.

Foreword

ALTHOUGH air pollution has been a problem in industrialized cities since the dawn of the industrial revolution, only within the past decade have scientists, legislators, and the public come to recognize it as a serious hazard to health and a costly economic burden which merits national attention in the United States. This new recognition results fundamentally from the merging of two important trends in our society, both of which tend to intensify the quest for more rational means of dealing with a problem which can no longer be regarded as a mere nuisance. First, technological, industrial, and urban growth, which continue to accelerate, have forced onto our attention the fact that air pollution, already more extensive and more damaging on a national basis than ever before, is destined to get worse. Second, knowledge of the nature, causes, and many adverse effects of air pollution, while still incomplete, has been increasing substantially in recent years. This knowledge, combined with the inevitable growth of those factors which produce the problem, makes the need for intensified control action inescapable.

The first comprehensive Federal legislation on air pollution was enacted in 1955. During the ten years since then, air pollution has received increasing attention from the scientific community—from physicians, engineers, chemists, meteorologists, biologists, and others. Those engaged in the social sciences, however, have barely begun to include air pollution within the broad scope of their interests—despite the fact that air pollution is fundamentally a social problem, the solutions to which will need to be worked out in the complex milieu of our contemporary urban environment.

The present volume, therefore, is something of a milestone. It is the first book, to my knowledge, devoted entirely to the task of attempting to define some of the social, political, and economic problems bearing on air pollution. More questions are raised than are answered, which is to be expected at this early stage in our search for solutions to the scientific and social perplexities posed by the problem. Nor are all of the contributions to this volume equally germane to the issues which must be resolved in our struggle to maintain modern man in an environment more compatible to his real needs than that which now exists. But the issues are brought into the open and that is worth a great deal. I am reminded of one of the statements made by Dr. Luther L. Terry, former Surgeon General of the Public Health Service, at the 1962 National Conference on Air Pollution, "We cannot," Dr. Terry said, "confine our great accomplishments to the calm and dispassionate atmosphere of the laboratory. We must move out, into the sun and the smog, where ugliness blights our fairest cities. . . ." This volume represents another worthwhile step in the direction in which Dr. Terry reminded us we ought always to be moving.

V. G. MacKenzie
Assistant Surgeon General
Chief, Division of Air Pollution
Public Health Service
U. S. Department of Health, Education, and Welfare

Introduction

THE ECONOMICS OF air-pollution control, research, and policy formulation is the subject of the papers in this volume, most but not all of which were commissioned for delivery in a graduate seminar on national economic policy. The aspect of the air-pollution problem which commands the economist's attention is the fact that clean air is a resource; it is either a final product or an intermediate one in the language of national accounting, and it is becoming increasingly scarce. The sum of this volume on air pollution is a stimulating and sometimes provocative application of the techniques evolved by economists to analyze economic decisions of individuals, households, business firms, and society as a whole, and an attempt to identify the areas where the techniques fail, where work must be done. Taken as a whole, this volume is much more than a pedantic application of economics (microeconomics, public finance, the "new" welfare economics) to air pollution.

One might have expected that the traditional economic approach to the problems of resource allocation would provide adequate guidelines. Quite the contrary! As one of the contributors points out, the application of economic principles presents special difficulties which are not only far from resolved, but continue to present a vexing challenge to the traditional economics. It may well be that certain economic aspects of the problem can be coped with adequately only if the traditional boundaries of economic science are transcended. This, we feel, is a major contribution of our volume.

Most of the contributors to this book were invited because they are singularly qualified either because of direct experience with the problems of pollution research and pollution-control policy or because of their work in closely related areas. Not only do they represent several disciplines, but they range from theorist to practitioner, in government, university, and research institute. At the seminar, they demonstrated a ready willingness to extend their horizons, and produced new and valuable insights. Their contributions made it increasingly clear that the economic aspects of air pollution can not be divorced from social, political, and psychological considerations. The experience they brought to bear on the problem ranged from a closely related field, the economics of water pollution, to the use of consumer-expenditure data. There were discussions on the obtuse machinations involved in the politics of forging effective air pollution control legislation—machinations in which rational economic considerations came out second best, if they were not ignored entirely. Like the speakers, the students in the seminar had a wide range of backgrounds and interests. One graduate student, for example, had had intimate experience with air pollution in South America; another had studied the problem in India.

At this point the reader may well ask, What is it about air pollution that makes it so difficult to deal with; why is it more knotty than conventional problems in resource allocation? Allen V. Kneese comes to grips with this problem in his perceptive paper. He attributes a good share of the burden to "external" effects (externalities, neighborhood effects) of consumption and production—like blowing soot over one's neighbors. The existence of these external effects is "one major reason" why the economy in many instances fails to produce automatically what is wanted; it is in a sense the nub of the air-pollution problem. Air pollution also involves a heavier burden of control than water pollution, Dr. Kneese emphasizes, because it is more localized. This makes it less tractable to regional solutions such as watershed arrangements which some experts favor because, in addition to their administrative advantages, such arrangements spread the cost of remedies.

Another aspect of the problem is that polluters often inflict costs, reciprocally, on each other. This is analogous to a "common pool" problem, a situation in which benefits are easily identified with the areas where they are received. These are but some of the valuable insights contributed by Allen Kneese. It should be emphasized that his pioneering work in the economics of water pollution qualifies him uniquely to draw parallels and identify the significant differences between the economics of air and of water pollution. A careful reading of this excellent and suggestive survey of the problem will prepare the reader for the other papers in this volume.

Some readers, however, may well question whether the external costs and benefits of the abatement of air pollution are as measurable as might be inferred from a first reading of Dr. Kneese's paper. He is, it should be apparent, very well aware of the complexities of measurement, a problem to which some of the other papers in this volume address themselves in considerable depth. Dr. Kneese makes the telling point, for example, that although a great many external costs resulting from air pollutants are "readily measurable," we have not yet attempted to isolate them. The reader will see, however, that two of the papers in this volume do attempt, on a small scale, to deal directly with two of the externalities mentioned by Dr. Kneese, namely reduction in property values and agricultural losses, and two more papers are concerned with certain aspects of the measurement of such external costs.

Drawing upon his broad experience in dealing with water pollution, Dr. Kneese contends that compared with the ways available to deal with water pollution, the economically feasible means of dealing with air pollution are relatively few. He offers two principal reasons for this. First, it is easier to control "hydrological events" (water flows and contamination) than weather, or "meteorological events." Second, air pollution can best be treated at the source, in contrast to water pollution, where there are alternatives. One significant conclusion which follows is that the locations of industry, housing, and recreation areas, warrant careful study in terms of controlling them effectively to cope with the air-pollution problem.

Edwin S. Mills takes on the formidable task of asking how free enterprise can be restructured to cope with the problem of air-pollution abatement. He is not willing to accept the proposition that because the market misallocates resources (i.e., does not correctly value clean air), just any kind of intervention is justified. Dr. Mills distinguishes between direct and indirect intervention, and then analyzes techniques for achieving the latter within the framework of the market mechanism. He offers two alternative schemes: payments (subsidies) for reducing pollution levels, or charges (fines) according to the amount of pollutants emitted. Dr. Mills has three reasons for preferring to levy charges rather than subsidize abatement undertakings. First, it would be extremely difficult to decide how much to pay whom for what level of pollution reduction. All of the problems encountered in administration of the government's agricultural crop-reduction policy would develop. Because, as Mills says, "there is no natural 'origin' for payments," a multitude of abuses might result. Second, according to Dr. Mills, "feelings of equity" would be violated by subsidies. People feel that consumers receiving the benefit of clean air ought to pay for it insofar as it is a cost of production—an input like labor and capital. Third, he feels that creating a credit against tax liability as a reward for reducing the discharge of pollutants would introduce a "gimmick"; the funds required would have to be raised by increasing taxes elsewhere. He thinks that this would lead to resource misallocation. His conclusion is, ". . . a strong presumption for the use of discharge or effluent fees as a means of air-pollution abatement." To implement this approach, Dr. Mills proposes that "air pollution control authorities be created with responsibility to evaluate a variety of abatement schemes, to estimate benefits and costs, to render technical assistance, to levy charges for the discharge of effluents, and to adopt other means of abatement." This proposal is discussed in considerable detail in this paper and is worth serious attention by the reader.

The thought-provoking paper by Leslie A. Chambers illustrates the difficulties of attempting to consider the risks and costs of public-health practices. As the problems and complexities of environmental health hazards increase, the interrelationships of these threats to existence become more apparent, and the need for coordinated, interdisciplinary solutions becomes more acute. Dr. Chambers explores the new demands upon existing institutions of the developing environmental-health sciences, and the challenge of giving birth to new approaches. His call for "academic centers of excellence" for broadgauged research and education should be heeded immediately.

The next two papers are written by two university economists, Thomas D. Crocker and Ronald G. Ridker, who are conducting research in the economics of air pollution for the Public Health Service. In his paper, Thomas Crocker is particularly interested in the role of an air pollution control authority. He is concerned with the extent to which it becomes necessary for such an authority to substitute for the market mechanism, to decide upon the precise quality of air to be achieved rather than to accept a market-determined decision that would reflect bargaining between those who contaminate the air and those who suffer the contamination. Ignorance plays a key role in the problem, says Crocker. The less the central authorities know about what individuals want, the more the authorities have to assert their own preferences for levels of air purity. Crocker concludes that "the signaling potential of a price system has not yet been given its due in most atmospheric pollution problems." This does not mean that he wholly rejects any role for a control authority; he accepts such a need. The problem in control, as he sees it, is to gauge the proportions in which private and collective decisions are to be meshed. "The choice is not between two systems of control," writes Crocker, ". . . but between two imperfect systems, each with its own set of errors." His solution is to determine what "optimum results" would be and then to "test each possible mix of the two alternatives" (public control and private, market-influenced decision-making) against these and accept the best combination.

Ronald G. Ridker's paper is a first report on his research project, sponsored by the Public Health Service, in which he attempts to measure the costs of air-pollution damage. His paper is significant because it demonstrates the frustrating difficulties which beset the researcher in this area and the kind of uneasy compromises he is forced, sometimes unconsciously, to make. The reader may disagree with Dr. Ridker's approach, but this is in itself salutary, for it can only stimulate thought and further work on the difficult task of measurement. Ridker's plea for disaggregation, for example, merits serious thought. His confidence—by no means self-evident—that changes in property value attributable to air pollution can be measured accurately, his preference for cross-section data rather than time series, his disenchantment with existing data, his approach to the measurement of "psychic loss," all of these merit serious evaluation and discussion, for Ridker is much more confident of the possibility of quantifying in this area than others are.

Both Helen H. Lamale and Edward T. Crowder have had long association with, and have made significant contributions to, the economic statistics programs of the United States Government. Mrs. Lamale, in addition, has been consulted by the Division of Air Pollution of the Public Health Service on the use of consumer-expenditure data for measuring costs and effects of air pollution. Dr. Crowder, who is associated with the Division of Statistical Standards of the Bureau of the Budget, brings to his discussion of the use of government statistics in air-pollution control the fruits of a long and effective career in evaluating and organizing statistical programs.

Dr. Crowder's conclusions are bound to stimulate considerable discussion. He feels that air-pollution control is a local problem; the relevant statistical universe is the city, the county, or the metropolitan area. In many instances, the "well-known bodies of social and economic statistics" cannot supply the data needed for air-pollution control—meteorological data, for example, and the results of medical, engineering, and chemical research. All of this has broad implications, which Dr. Crowder expands upon. The statistical needs in the air-pollution field reflect a growing need for more data at the local level. This stands in contrast to the traditional statistical programs of the Federal Government, which are largely designed to provide numbers for the analysis of problems at the national level. This growing interest in local data for air-pollution analysis will inevitably stress the Standard Metropolitan Statistical Area as the most efficient unit of analysis. Dr. Crowder is of the opinion that because of its nature, any data gathering sponsored by the Federal Government for purposes of air-pollution control will by and large be "carried on under contracts or grants rather than as part of the regular activities of an established statistical agency." At the end of his paper, he raises a very pointed question: ". . . if a survey is to be made at all," how accurate must the data be? Accuracy costs money. Therefore, he asserts, "The policy maker must ask to what extent the statistics actually affect his decision." Dr. Crowder ends on an optimistic note, however, pointing out that the air pollution abatement problem is one which "at many points lends itself to more precise measurement" than many economic problems he normally encounters.

Up and beyond the design of her paper, "The Use of Consumer-Expenditure Data in Air-Pollution Control," Helen H. Lamale has contributed a succinct and masterful account of the Bureau of Labor Statistics' consumer-expenditure studies. Even though she modestly refuses to recommend the use of this data "for such special purposes as air-pollution cost analyses," a reading of her paper cannot but leave the reader with the strong impression that the experience and data yielded by the consumer-expenditure surveys can be very helpful in the air-pollution area. The data provide the investigator with "a framework within which to consider the effects of air pollution and their impact upon consumption expenditures." They are helpful in deciding where information is needed, according to Mrs. Lamale, and supply the kinds of information required "to build the bridges between the expenditure data and air-pollution effects." They also are valuable guides for the designing of special air-pollution surveys that can then be related to the general consumer-expenditure data.

The paper entitled "Air-Pollution Control in the Metropolitan Boston Area" is by a specialist of the Division of Air Pollution of the Public Health Service, Lester Goldner, a man who makes air-pollution problems his everyday business. Although his is primarily a case study, a skillful and perceptive account of the problems confronting an area whose air has gone bad, it might be the story of the difficulties besetting any of our nation's metropolitan areas. Some have solved them much more successfully than the area he describes, others less so. In many ways this is an alarmingly sobering report; for, as the author points out, the situation is summarized in the words of a colleague who was tempted to call an article on this subject "On the Difficulty of Being Reasonable." In another sense, this careful and detailed study can serve as a primer for both the public servants and the involved "sources" of air pollution, as well as the public's representatives in any community.

The final paper in the volume, "Setting Criteria for Public Expenditures on Air-Pollution Abatement" is my attempt to appraise and summarize that body of theory which economists draw upon in determining how much should be spent in what directions by public bodies in areas such as air-pollution abatement and control. I am more pessimistic than many about the success of efforts to enlist the private sector of the economy to shoulder the burden of air-pollution abatement. The constraints on any actions by government which are implicit in most policy programs must be identified so as to avoid impractical proposals for public action. Economic criteria must be integrated with the social, economic, and psychological factors which are part of the total problem of air-pollution control. Finally, in air pollution the use of benefit-cost analysis is extremely difficult. At the conclusion of my paper I present certain concrete proposals for further study of the principles and practices which serve as guides to public expenditure on the control and alleviation of air pollution.

HAROLD WOLOZIN

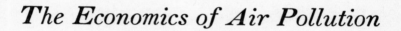

The Economics of Air Pollution

Air Pollution—General Background and Some Economic Aspects [1]

ALLEN V. KNEESE
RESOURCES FOR THE FUTURE, INC.

Allen V. Kneese is director of the Water Resources Program of Resources for the Future, Inc., Washington, D. C. He has written extensively on the economics of both water and air pollution.

AIR POLLUTION has occasionally reached deadly proportions. Among the recorded instances is the case in the Meuse Valley, Belgium, in which 100 persons were made ill and 63 died in 1930. In 1948 the horseshoe-shaped valley of the Monongahela River in Pennsylvania was covered by a fog and a low-level temperature inversion. In the valley area around the town of Donora nearly half the population became ill and 17 died. In London in 1952 an estimated 4,000 excess deaths were recorded during a two-week period in December. In December, 1962, a national air-pollution conference was held in the United States almost at the very time air pollution caused the deaths of more than 300 people in London.[2]

Occasional instances of deadly gases and particles engulfing a city do not begin to define the magnitude of the problem, however. The greatest health problems and the greatest property damage appear to arise from persistent exposure at many different locations. One survey has indicated that air pollution to one or another degree affects at least six thousand American communities. It ranges from highly localized effects, perhaps the smoke and gases of a single factory chimney, to smogs that blanket entire metropolitan areas. Los Angeles provides the extreme example of the latter. Because the character of air pollution has undergone radical change in recent years, it is not possible to formulate a simple meaningful index of past change in its magnitude.

Polluting substances often are divided into two categories. The first of these consists of stable *primary pollutants* that are not changed in the air and consequently are traced with comparative ease to their source. These arise from industrial, commercial, domestic, transport, and agricultural activities, and are in the form of dust, smoke, fumes, and droplets (aerosols). They obscure sunlight and visibility; they dirty buildings and other articles, corrode metals, and affect life processes. The burning of coal used to be responsible for large amounts of dust and smoke—called "particulate pollutants" in the United States—and still is the major cause of air pollution at numerous locations in Europe.

An extreme example of this type of pollution is to be found in the Ruhr Basin of West Germany, which is intensively industrialized and heavily populated. An area stretching along the Rhine from Duisburg to Dinslaken, however, contains a particularly large and concentrated industrial complex. Despite efforts of the land-planning authority for the Ruhr area to separate industrial from residential activities, this area still has a considerable residential population as well. Probably there is greater continuous pollution of the air by primary pollutants in the Ruhr than in any other sizable area on earth.

Along with such interesting details as the fact that the waiters in Duisburg restaurants change their collars three times a day, it is also reported that over 15 per cent of the children in the most concentrated part of the Ruhr area show symptoms of rickets, while only half as high a percentage do so in a control city in the Rhine Valley. The same study also shows that teen-age children in the Ruhr weigh less and are shorter than children in the control city. In addition to these physiological effects, there is a large amount of property damage. It should be noted, of course, that a substantial reduction of pollution discharge in this mammoth industrial area might be extremely expensive.

In recent years primary particulate forms of pollution in the United States appear to have declined greatly. For example, dust fall in Chicago has decreased from 395 tons per square mile per month in 1928 to an average of 43 tons in 1962.[3] The decline in dust fall is said to be comparable throughout the country. The national monitoring network of the Public Health Service shows that suspended particulate matter in the atmosphere decreased from 1957 to

1961. A study by the United States Weather Bureau indicates that visibility in many urban areas of the United States is improving. The reduction in particulate matter and primary pollutants results basically from two causes. One is a greater use of liquid and gaseous fuels, which reduces these types of pollutants. The other is the large-scale introduction of abatement devices by industry, especially the steel industry.[4]

The shift to the newer fuels is by no means an unmixed blessing, however, for the pollutants arising from them are in some respects more difficult to deal with. The residuals from the combustion of the newer fuels are particularly important contributors to what have been called *secondary pollutants,* the other major class of air pollutants.

Generally speaking, secondary pollutants are more intractable, of less predictable effect, and possibly more dangerous to health than primary pollutants. They do not arise directly from any industrial, municipal, or household source, but are produced by photochemical or physiochemical interactions between primary pollutants within the atmosphere. The most objectionable pollutants of this type appear to arise from the oxidation (often produced by ozone which is generated by the photochemical reaction between organic substances and oxides of nitrogen) of hydrocarbons which are present in incompletely burned fuel fumes.

An extreme example of secondary pollution is Los Angeles smog, which is largely the result of unburned fuels being irradiated in stagnant air by sunlight. There are over 3,000,000 automobiles in Los Angeles County, which consume well over 6,000,000 gallons of gasoline a day. The January, 1963, figures of the Los Angeles County Air Pollution Control District indicate that the automobiles emit some 8,050 tons of carbon monoxide and almost 1,650 tons of hydrocarbons each day. About 850 tons of oxides of nitrogen combine with other ingredients to form an atmosphere which can be eye-irritating, ugly, and literally breathtaking.[5] Primary pollutants have virtually been eliminated in the Los Angeles area, for it has the strictest controls on industrial emissions and household sources of pollution found anywhere in the world.

The situations in other urban communities of significant size in the United States fall between the extremes which have been described. There is generally a sizable but diminishing amount of particulate substance in the air. Secondary photochemical products are becoming noticeable during some periods, and in some instances have become highly significant. Since no systematic data over any length of time are available on the secondary pollutants, one cannot say precisely what has been happening. It is clear, however, that this form of pollution has been rising rapidly.

What can we say about the future direction of air pollution? Unfortunately, we must rely on the most general kind of indicators. Since 1940, the use of mechanical energy in the United States has doubled and the urban population has grown by half. Further rapid increases in these factors, affecting air pollution, appear inevitable. Recent projections indicate that the United States may have a population of over 300,000,000 by the end of the century, and that more than three-quarters of these people will live in urban areas. Indeed, the entire population increase promises to be in urban areas. Also, a striking increase in the use of energy is projected by a Resources for the Future study. For example, it is forecast that in the twenty years from 1955 to 1975 the use of coal will increase by over 70 per cent, the use of oil by over 85 per cent, and natural gas utilization by over 100 per cent. What can we infer from these projections? One certainty is that unless efforts to control particulate pollution continue at a high level, the recent downtrend will be reversed. Another is that secondary pollution resulting from the combustion of fuels, primarily liquid and gaseous fuels, will continue to increase rapidly in the absence of enhanced control efforts.

The costs which may be involved in control efforts, especially as they relate to automobiles, may again be illustrated in rather extreme form by some projections for Los Angeles. California has pioneered in attempting to control automobile-exhaust emissions. In 1960, the legislature set up the Motor Vehicle Pollution Control Board to review and pass on devices for controlling exhaust gases. In 1964, the Board approved four afterburner devices to help eliminate unburned hydrocarbons from auto exhausts. All 1966 cars sold in California must be equipped with an approved device. In several years they will probably be mandatory on old cars as well. Several manufacturers have announced that most of the 1966 cars marketed in California will be equipped with an engine mechanism which will meet the established standards without a device mounted on the exhaust pipe. It has been estimated that the cost of automobile-exhaust controls in California will be several hundred million and may be as high as a billion dollars.[6] While these controls will unquestionably improve the situation, it has been estimated that if the present pattern of automobile use continues in Los Angeles, and if the area's population continues to grow at its present rate, auto pollution will be as bad in a decade as it is now unless control standards are raised.

Differences Between Air and Water Pollution

In addition to providing some general background, an objective of this paper is to point to various economic and management problems in regard to air pollution and to suggest research which is needed to deal with them. In doing this, I would like to draw some parallels and make some contrasts with water pollution. The latter is now the subject of a small but reasonably systematic program of research in economics and management.[7]

From the point of view of the economic theory of resources allocation, air and water pollution have some strong common elements. Perhaps the most significant is that both are excellent cases of what the economist rather forbiddingly calls "technological externalities." This concept is so important in the economist's view of the matter that a somewhat extended explanation may be in order—even at the risk of traversing well-understood ground for some.

A market economy can produce precisely those goods and services wanted by consumers, produce these in just the quantities wanted, and produce these quantities in the cheapest possible way. But one of the important conditions necessary for this result is that the quantities of *all* parts of an individual's consumption be under his control and that *all* the inputs of each business—such as labor, services of machines, and so on—be under its control. If we further imagine an economy in which both consumers and producers know precisely what they are doing, and in which no industry is dominated by a few firms, we can envision a succession of adjustments which would yield these happy results. Adam Smith, who was perhaps the first to perceive clearly the possibility of an economic system functioning in this way, used the term "invisible hand" to describe the process. The importance of this perception remains undiminished even today, for it serves to isolate for us and permit us to understand the basic function of a market economy—the organization of production so as to produce what each consumer wants produced within the limit of his income.

Things actually don't work out quite that way, a fact which will not be news to anyone with even a small interest in the operation of the economy. In the process of constructing an abstract model of the economy (on paper) which will clearly exhibit these properties, it has been found necessary to imagine a world which is different from the real world. Hence, the automatic functioning of the invisible hand of the market, which can be seen so clearly in this simplified model, becomes obscured when we look at the real world and ask how well the economy succeeds in producing what is wanted. While observers will differ on the degree to which the economy falls short in performing this function, all are agreed that it does fall short.

A little reflection will indicate that one major reason is that "external" effects occur in many production and consumption processes. What this means simply is that there are flows of some goods or services that come to the consumer or business whether he wants them or not and without his paying for them. This situation may be described by saying that a change in the output of one economic unit (a firm or consumer) *necessarily* affects the inputs (and hence the output) of some other economic unit. That is, the activities of one economic unit may generate "real" effects that are *external* to it. These effects, which may take the form of air and water pollution, in a basic sense are the source of the "problem." For example, an increase in the output of a cannery may increase stream pollution, which in turn will require downstream firms or communities to spend more money to clean up the water they use. They have experienced an unwanted increase of certain inputs—pollutants in this case. The parallel in air pollution is obvious.

If external effects are present, a misallocation of resources is likely to be the result whether the external effect is beneficial or detrimental to its recipient. The reasons are most easily explained with respect to industrial firms. The signals which tell a firm how much it should produce—price and cost—do not work properly in the presence of external effects. With no external effects present, we may think of a firm comparing the price it will get from making and selling another unit of its product with the associated cost. As long as price is greater than this cost, it will pay to expand output. When the two are equal, it will not pay to expand output any further, for that would diminish profit. This output happens also to be the right output from the point of view of the consumers viewed as a group, for the value of the article to them as measured by price is just equal to the costs of making it. These costs are equal to the value of *other* articles that could have been produced alternatively with the same resources and hence measure what consumers have had to give up in order to obtain the article in question. If labor services are used to produce shoes, they can't be used to produce furniture, but just the right proportions of the two will tend to be produced.

If external effects are present, this nice balance may be upset. Suppose that a business pollutes the air and thereby increases the costs to another firm. If the firm responsible for polluting the air is not induced to take account of this effect, it will neglect these possibly important costs in deciding how much to produce and what technology to use. From the point of view of consumers (again viewed as a group) the firm is producing too much or with a technology that produces too much waste, for the costs associated with the production of another unit of product are now greater than price. If all costs are taken into account, including the off-site costs associated with the pollution, consumers will be giving up *other* products that could have been produced (the value of which is measured by all costs) in return for a unit of product that is less valuable. This is a misallocation of production.

Misallocation of production—this is the problem that may result when external effects are present. The producer may be not a manufacturing firm, but an automobile driver producing transportation services for himself, or a householder providing space heating.

It does not follow, however, that detrimental external effects should be completely eliminated, for this might entail the elimination of other associated effects or products whose value to consumers outweighs the harm done. In dealing with the allocation problem arising from external effects [8] the goals is to find some means whereby decisions on how much to produce and what technologies to employ take proper account of *all* the costs and benefits flowing from the economic activity in question.

There are three ways to get this result. One is for the unit that generates the effect to reach agreement with the recipient on the proper level of the effect—perhaps with a payment from one to the other. Where the effect is measurable, property rights are clearly defined, and the number of units involved is small, this solution may be feasible.

A second method is to "internalize" the effect so that the same economic unit both generates and receives it. This will insure that output decisions will take into account the costs or benefits associated with the effect. One way to do this is to enlarge the size of the economic unit. Another way is to change the limitations under which the initiator of the effect is operating. This could be done by imposing a tax on the effect that is emitted, in which case the firm might decide to reduce the effect either by cutting the output of its main product or by spending some money to minimize the external effect, for example, by treating waste solutions in the plant. Still another way is directly to regulate the effect emitted. For example, it might be required that an undesirable effect be kept below a certain specified level. "Internalizing" the effect by means of levying a charge on it has the advantage of letting the economic units involved decide on the best adjustment to be made in the light of all costs and benefits. It may be possible and desirable to eliminate or reduce the effect, but there will be some cases in which the best thing to be done is simply to bear it.

A third method is to regulate the allocation of production directly, perhaps by governmental operation of the activity that produces the external effect.

In the search for ways to improve the misallocation resulting from external effects, care must always be exercised to take into account any additional costs or penalties associated with the remedy. It is quite possible, for example, to set standards designed to reduce external effects so strictly that there will be a loss to national product rather than a gain. Nor should it be assumed that governmental regulation is costless, for it sometimes requires large regulatory staffs and may involve other types of costs, some of which are not obvious and may be hard to measure.

However, there may be instances where even the practice of having external costs reflected in individual decisions cannot by itself produce optimal results. These are instances where large-scale measures beyond the scope of any individual decision unit may turn out to be an efficient adjunct to control at the source. In the case of water pollution, examples are reservoirs to control the flow of streams and thereby improve their waste-assimilative capacity, or artificial reaeration of streams to achieve the same objective. Analogous opportunities may exist in regard to air pollution. Increasingly, consideration of such alternatives enters research on optimal management of streams and to a minor extent these options have been brought into practice.

Four main ideas emerge from the preceding discussion:

The generators of external costs must systematically weigh these costs in their decision-making if the overall result of decentralized decisions is to be optimal.

To insure that this occurs, some sort of collective entity must exist which is at least large enough to "internalize" the major effects of decisions made within its purview.

An economically rational system for controlling externalities requires knowledge by the management agency of the external cost imposed by various levels of activity and of the cost of alternative ways of mitigating the external effects.

The management agency should seek systematically to identify, evaluate, and implement any large-scale alternatives which can efficiently be brought into the management system.

While these concepts are fully as meaningful in regard to air pollution as they are with respect to water pollution, their application to air-pollution matters presents somewhat different and usually more difficult problems.

Let us look at various aspects of air pollution in the economic-management context and compare them with analogous features of the water-pollution problem.

1. Air pollution is heavily implicated as a factor affecting public health, both in the United States and abroad. Although water pollution may be more costly in terms of nonhuman resources than air pollution, the current link of water pollution to public-health problems on any large scale in the United States is based on suspicion concerning chronic effects rather than on firm evidence. The somewhat stronger evidence which links air pollution and health has been summarized by a former surgeon general of the United States Public Health Service in part as follows:

Comparison of morbidity and mortality statistics with indices of air pollution suggests that communities with the heaviest air-pollution loads tend to rank high in death rates from a number of diseases.

Also, there is a significant correlation between air pollution and cancer of the esophagus and stomach, lung cancer, and arteriosclerotic disease.

Even so, the speculative character of these findings is striking. We are far from being able to trace specified causes and effects and to relate them to the most efficient means of control. For example, while Los Angeles smog has been the subject of almost endless writing and a great deal of research, no one is quite sure what the eye-irritating agents in the smog actually are. Also, evidence is accumulating that there occur between pollutants certain synergistic or multiplicative effects, which make forecasting of the consequences for health especially difficult. It has been seen in animal studies that many aerosols found in urban air may potentiate or increase the toxic effects of sulfur dioxide—a common product of the combustion of fossil fuels.[9] Until these effects are better understood, any efforts to estimate benefits and costs will be impeded.

Moreover, as in the case of water pollution, explicit evaluation of the effects upon health of air pollution—despite considerable imaginative research in the economics of health—does not appear currently feasible.

Nevertheless, given more precise knowledge of physical effects, valuable tests to determine the cost of achieving various levels of standards and their associated physical effects could be performed to aid the social decision process. A point that canot be repeated too often is that the assignment of an environmental standard implies a value which can be measured in dollars.[10] This is the cost of achieving a marginal or incremental change in the standard. Making explicit this value, which is almost always implicit, can be very useful. First, it can lead to a better-informed judgment as to whether the standard should be higher or lower. Second, it makes possible the performance of certain tests of consistency, i.e., of whether the effect accomplished per incremental dollar of cost to achieve one protective standard is at least roughly equal to the effect of other approaches. If, for example, we as society are spending much more to save a life in one manner than in another, it is easy to show that more lives could be saved by shifting standards without committing a greater value of resources to the effort.

Furthermore, research may help us to quantify aesthetic and to some degree health-based preferences for cleaner air by means of surrogate measurements such as relative land values, expenditures for air purifiers, commuting costs people are willing to incur to avoid polluted air, and certain costs associated with ill health related to polluted air.

2. As in the case of water pollution, a great many of the external costs imposed by air pollutants appear to be rather readily measurable, but little or no systematic measurement has yet been under-

taken. These are, for example, soiling, corrosion, reduction in property values, and even agricultural losses. Crop damage from air pollution has been detected in many states. Damage claims have ranged from a slight reduction in crop yields to loss of entire farm enterprises. Some empirical investigations of these damages are now getting under way.

3. In general there appear to be fewer economically feasible means of dealing with air pollution than of dealing with water pollution. In part, this lack results from the fact that it is easier for man to control hydrological events than meteorological events; for example, he can and does regulate stream flows to improve waste-assimilative characteristics.

In part, it results from the fact that air is not delivered to users in pipes as water frequently is, so that polluted air is treatable only to a limited extent before it is consumed. Therefore, we are in somewhat the same position in regard to polluted air as the fish are to polluted water. We live in it. Accordingly, control of air pollution is largely a matter of preventing pollutants from escaping from their source, eliminating the source, or shifting location of the source or the recipient. Water pollution, on the other hand, is in general subject to a larger array of control measures. Nevertheless, both present intricate problems of devising optimal control systems. For example, we must understand how alternatives like reducing or altering the amount or altitude of industrial discharges, controlling automobile emissions, relying more heavily on mass transportation, and the like would fit into a least-cost system for attaining any given air-cleanliness objective.

Especially, we need to understand much better the role that location controls can play in optimal management. While there is some experience with this in air pollution, especially in the Ruhr area of Germany, in most cities industries and associated activities are now located in river valleys to take advantage of transportation facilities, although these locations are least satisfactory for dispersal of aerial wastes. Also, river-bottom locations are peculiarly subject to flooding, the control of which represents one of our largest categories of public-works investments. We must improve our ability to understand and plan for optimal location of activities in the urban complex in view of *all* the associated costs and benefits—public and private, internal and external.

4. Air pollution, with some notable exceptions, is ordinarily more

localized than water pollution. As streams of wind carry the pollutants for any appreciable distance, dilution is usually sufficient to mitigate their harmfulness. This contrasts with water pollution, where streams are like conduits, carrying persistent types of pollution farther and farther downstream. Thus while air pollution certainly involves substantial external costs, it is more difficult to shift the burden completely to another geographical area. Accordingly, remedies, though costly, are much more clearly related to benefits within comparatively localized political jurisdictions. Moreover, in this regard the problem has much in common with a traffic-congestion or "common pool" problem. To a substantial degree, polluters—particularly automobile users—are imposing externalities reciprocally on each other. This presents a control problem which is analytically more complex than the serial or sequential problems ordinarily associated with water pollution.[11]

Even so, some students of the problem have felt that it could usefully be addressed in terms of regional air sheds analogous to watersheds. These air sheds, of course, do not necessarily correspond to any existing political jurisdictions. One comment along these lines is as follows: "We must learn to think about the finite but variable air supply of metropolitan regions and to plan our uses of air accordingly. It is possible to think, plan, measure and act upon the existences of air sheds in somewhat the same way as we are learning to consider entire river basins as units in the planning and conservation of water resources." [12]

The prevailing wind pattern and terrain in any given area of sufficient size determine to some extent the boundaries of an air shed which bear some resemblance to the boundaries of a watershed or river valley. On the west coast of California, where there is a prevailing westerly breeze, there exist several well-defined urban air sheds, one in the San Francisco Bay area and another in the Los Angeles area. Each is bounded by a rim of mountains or hills but is more or less open to the west. Another "boundary" of an air shed is a ceiling which results from inhibition to vertical mixing due to stability of the air mass. Air temperature normally decreases with increased height in the atmosphere. The rate of decrease of temperature with height is called the "lapse rate." The smaller the lapse rate, the greater the energy required to effect vertical exchange. When temperature increases with height (negative lapse rate) an inversion condition exists which tends to restrict vertical mixing. Shallow inversions may be produced nightly under clear skies and light wind conditions. If the vertical extent of the inversion is great enough, solar heating may not be able to break it. While inversion conditions are indeed important in severe air-pollution episodes, some writing has tended to emphasize them to the exclusion of other equally important factors, particularly wind speed. Generally the higher the wind speed, the greater the dispersion of airborne materials.

The notion of an air shed may be a useful concept for analysis and control of air pollution, but the problems in its use should not be minimized. In the case of water pollution, the stochastic character of streamflow presents difficulties in measuring costs associated with water pollution and in designing and operating optimum systems for water-quality control. The air shed adds more dimensions to this problem. It may be likened to a stream which varies its course rapidly (within defined boundaries), changes specific gravity, and from time to time decides to flow uphill. We must learn to understand, and at least in a probabilistic sense, forecast these phenomena. Will ordinary concepts such as mathematical expectation be relevant and practical, as they are in regard to hydrological events? Will the complicated stochastic processes involved and the range of alternative means of abatement, including land-use regulations, mean that analytical solutions to the optimization problem will not be feasible and that we must depend upon behavioristic approaches like large-scale computer-system simulation? What kind of information would be needed to do this?

To the extent that air sheds are definable, air-shed authorities or compacts or districts are conceivable and may be useful administrative devices. There is some precedent here, for example, in the form of the San Francisco Bay Area Air Pollution Control District. In the Ruhr Valley of Germany an important part of the work of the *Siedlungsverband* (Land Planning Authority) is to deal with problems of air pollution. The primary means used in Germany is control of the location of industrial activities. Efforts of this kind present useful laboratories for studying the costs and effectiveness of various approaches.

5. As in the case of water pollution, some administrative and regulatory alternatives to protective standards may demand serious consideration—for example, some variety of air-pollution charge or tax. This would be levied on the theory that the use of a congested facility—air—should be reduced by putting a price on that use.

Such a tax would be based on some measure of pollutants discharged at the source and could be weighted according to location of the source, the external costs of specific pollutants, timing of releases in relation to peak loads of air congestion, wind direction, and so on.

These approaches need looking into from the point of view of administrative feasibility. As in the case of water pollution, it may sometimes be more feasible and economical to alter the character of some manufactured input, the use of which results in pollution, than to deal with the immediate source of pollution itself. This suggests that taxation or other means of regulation of particular manufactured products may be useful and effective. For instance, it would not have been feasible to regulate each commercial and household user of "hard" water-polluting detergents, but it was feasible to put pressure upon manufacturers to produce bio-degradable types. Similarly, it appears that desulfurization of residual fuel oil at the refinery may cost about the same as scrubbing stack gas at utilities for removal of sulfur dioxide.[13] It may be the only economically feasible way to eliminate this major pollutant from certain other emissions, such as those of household heating plants. There is need for investigation of various means of controlling the character of inputs used, including the taxation of those with especially destructive effects—say high-sulfur fuel oils. The advantage of the taxation route is that it can achieve the "optimal" or desired degree of control while leaving specific production and consumption decisions decentralized, in individual hands. This means that the destructive substance will be automatically eliminated from its least valuable uses —ordinarily by the introduction of substitutes—but will continue in those uses where it is unusually economical.

In general, the practical problems in administering any scheme of optimal pricing to deal with air pollution appear to be greater than those involved in dealing with water pollution. Perhaps a better parallel is the attempt to use pricing of transport services for the control of urban transportation congestion. Here too there are great practical problems in administering any scheme of optimal pricing, in this instance because of the complexity of an optimal price structure and the costs of price or toll collections. Researchers have thus been led to the search for a price base that can serve as a surrogate for travel. Hence, in place of an intricate system of tolls, consideration is given to the use of vehicle taxes, parking charges, and gasoline taxes (in the case of motor vehicles). Thus, the choice becomes one among highly imperfect but feasible means of rationing urban transport among potential users. Useful exchange between the fields of transportation and air pollution should be possible.[14]

The Problem of the Carbon Dioxide Buildup

I cannot end this discussion without mentioning one other problem, one about which comparatively little is known, but with possible implications so vast that they involve a realm of discourse wholly different from those with which we have been dealing. This is the accumulation of carbon dioxide in the air due to the combustion of fossil fuels. Within a comparatively few years man is oxidizing (through burning) carbonaceous materials which have accumulated through geologic time. The result has been a measurable increase in the carbon dioxide content of the air.[15] If the use of fossil fuels continues to climb commensurately with the growth of economic activity, the amount of carbon dioxide in the atmosphere could rise by more than half by the end of the century. In the very long run the carbon dioxide content of the atmosphere must be in equilibrium with water reservoirs (principally the oceans) and therefore any excess tends to be absorbed into the water. It is thought, however, that this process would take hundreds of years to restore equilibrium should the anticipated increase in carbon dioxide come to pass.

What is the significance of this? No one really knows. It is known that atmospheric carbon dioxide is one of the substances which help to retain the heat of the sun in the atmosphere and thus may be an important factor in determining the earth's climate. Some scientists believe that measurable increases in temperature have already occurred as a consequence of the carbon dioxide buildup. Small temperature changes, say an increase of one degree on the average, have profound effects on the world's climate. While few, if any, scientists working on air pollution are willing to forecast the dire effects which have sometimes been foreseen in the popular press, all are concerned. Should effects on climate and other aspects of the human environment turn out to be adverse, we would face a problem of control on a global scale, and massive efforts might have to be undertaken to reduce our dependency on fossil fuels, possibly at great cost. About all one can say at this point is that it is urgently important that we observe the situation closely and endeavor to learn more about the role of carbon dioxide in the determination of climate.

NOTES

1. I would like to express my appreciation to Orris C. Herfindahl for help in the preparation of this paper.

2. Gordon M. Fair, "New Factors in Man's Management of His Environment," Chadwick Lecture delivered in the Royal Hall, Harogate, on April 28, 1959, in conjunction with the Health Congress of the Royal Society of Health; and statement by V. G. MacKenzie (Chief, Division of Air Pollution, U. S. Public Health Service), in *Air Pollution Control* (Hearings before the Subcommittee on Air and Water Pollution of the Senate Committee on Public Works, 88th Congress, First Session, September, 1963), Washington, D. C., U. S. Government Printing Office, 1963.

3. *Ibid.*, statement by Erwin E. Schulze.

4. This should not be taken to mean that there are no areas left where primary pollutants are the major concern. This appears to be true of the Kanawha Valley, for example, where coal is the primary fuel used in industrial and thermal electric plants and where the resulting fly ash, sulfur dioxide, and nitrogen constitute the major problems. Jean J. Schueneman and Carl A. Beard, "Charleston-Kanawha Valley Air Pollution Study—A Description," presented at the 55th National Meeting of the American Institute of Chemical Engineers, Houston, Texas, February 7–11, 1965, pp. 5–6.

5. John R. Goldsmith, "Urban Air Conservation," *Bulletin of the Atomic Scientists,* Vol. 27 (November, 1961), pp. 376–9.

6. *Ibid.* The "built-in" devices may be capable of bringing the larger figure down somewhat.

7. See Allen V. Kneese, *Water Pollution—Economic Aspects and Research Needs,* Washington, D. C., Resources for the Future, Inc., 1962. This monograph outlines a program of research which has by now been brought well under way.

8. Note that we are considering here only the allocation problem. But external effects may also create significant distribution-of-income problems. Some attention will be given to this at a later point.

9. M. O. Amdur, "Report on Tentative Ambient Air Standards for Sulfur Dioxide and Sulfuric Acid," *Annals of Occupational Hygiene,* Vol. 3 (February, 1961), pp. 71–83.

10. Harold A. Thomas Jr., "The Animal Farm," *Quarterly Journal of Economics,* Vol. 77 (February, 1963), pp. 143–8.

11. Allen V. Kneese, "Rationalizing Decisions in Water Supply Quality Management in Urban Industrial Areas," in Julius Margolis, ed., *The Public Economy of Urban Communities,* Washington, D. C., Resources for the Future, Inc., 1965.

12. Goldsmith, *op. cit.*

13. Lionel S. Galstaun, Bernard J. Steigerwald, John H. Ludwig, and Howard R. Garrison, "Economics of Fuel Oil Desulfurization," presented at the 55th National Meeting of the American Institute of Chemical Engineers, Houston, Texas, February 7–11, 1965. The authors report that combustion of petroleum products accounts for more than 22 per cent of all sulfur dioxide emitted in this country. About 85 per cent of the total emission of sulfur

dioxide from petroleum products results from combustion of residual fuel oils.

14. I owe this thought to Professor Robert Strotz.

15. See *Implications of Rising Carbon Dioxide Content of the Atmosphere*, New York, Conservation Foundation, 1963.

Economic Incentives in
Air-Pollution Control [1]

EDWIN S. MILLS
COUNCIL OF ECONOMIC ADVISERS

Edwin S. Mills, a professor of Economics at Johns Hopkins University, has been on the faculty of the Massachusetts Institute of Technology and recently served as senior staff economist of the Council of Economic Advisers. He is a specialist in price theory.

SMOKE IS one of the classic examples of external diseconomies mentioned in the writings of Alfred Marshall and his followers. Generations of college instructors have used this form of air pollution as an illustration to help their students to understand conditions under which competitive markets will or will not allocate resources efficiently. By now, the theoretical problems have been explored with the sharpest tools available to economists. The consensus among economists on the basic issue is overwhelming, and I suspect one would be hard-pressed to find a proposition that commands more widespread agreement among economists than the following: The discharge of pollutants into the atmosphere imposes on some members of society costs which are inadequately imputed to the sources of the pollution by free markets, resulting in more pollution than would be desirable from the point of view of society as a whole.

In spite of the widespread agreement on the fundamental issues regarding externalities such as air pollution, there have been remarkably few attempts in the scholarly literature to carry the analysis beyond this point. Most writers have been content to point out that the free market will misallocate resources in this respect, and to conclude that this justifies intervention. But what sort of intervention? There are many kinds, and some are clearly preferable to others.

Too often we use the imperfect working of a free market to justify *any* kind of intervention. This is really an anomalous situation. After all, markets are man-made institutions, and they can be designed in many ways. When an economist concludes that a free market is working badly—giving the wrong signals, so to speak—he should also ask how the market may be restructured so that it will give the right signals.

Thus, in the case of air pollution, acceptance of the proposition stated above leads most people to think entirely in terms of direct regulation—permits, registration, licenses, enforcement of standards, and so on. I submit that this is rather like abandoning a car because it has a flat tire. Of course, in some cases the car may be working so badly that the presence of a flat tire makes it rational to abandon it, and correspondingly the inadequacies of some market mechanisms may make abandonment desirable. Nevertheless, I submit that the more logical procedure is to ask how a badly functioning market may be restructured so as to preserve the clear advantages of free and decentralized decision-making, but to remedy its defects. Only when there appears to be no feasible way of structuring a market so that it will give participants the right signals, should it be given up in favor of direct regulation.

Technical Factors

Technical questions arise with regard to both the sources and the effects of air pollution. Unfortunately, much less is known about the sources and effects of air pollution than about those of water pollution.

Although a large number of substances can pollute the air, it seems that almost all air-pollution problems result from the direct or indirect effects of from five to ten substances. Candidates for inclusion in this group are particulate matter (smoke and dust), sulfur dioxide, carbon monoxide, hydrocarbons, nitrogen oxides, carbon dioxide, hydrogen sulfide, hydrogen fluoride, and lead. Some experts might add one or two others, and some might delete one or two. Most sources of these substances can apparently be identified, and the amounts can be metered, at least on a sample basis, in ways that are not extremely expensive. For most pollutants, there are a large number of control methods, some of which are more effective than others, and some of which are more costly than others. Take sulfur dioxide as an example. Its major source is burning fossil fuels. It can be removed from smokestack gases in a variety of more or less effective ways. Or it can be removed from the fuel before burning (e.g., in the refining process). In addition, fuels with low sulfur dioxide content can be substituted for fuels with high sulfur dioxide content. The time pattern of burning can be altered so that relatively little fuel is burned at times when pollution is serious. The level or location of the activity for which the fuel is burned can be changed. Finally, it can be dispersed by high smokestacks.

These methods of control differ greatly in effectiveness and cost. Some may be more appropriate in one set of conditions than in others. The moral is, There are a large number of ways of doing almost anything, and air-pollution abatement is no exception.

Technical questions also arise regarding the effects of air pollution. Pollution may damage property (including crops and livestock); it may injure people's health; or it may be aesthetically displeasing. Property damage should not be particularly difficult to estimate, but I have seen no very careful attempts to do so. Health damage is much harder to estimate because of the chronic nature of the suspected damage. The aesthetic damage is measured by the number of dollars people are willing to pay to reduce the aesthetic displeasure from air pollution. Like other subjective magnitudes, it is difficult to estimate.

Economic Analysis

The relevance of the above considerations is, of course, that the extent to which it is in society's interests to abate pollution depends on the benefits and costs of doing so.

It is easy to state the principle by which the socially desirable amount of pollution abatement should be determined: *Any given pollution level should be reached by the least costly combination of means available; the level of pollution should be achieved at which the cost of a further reduction would exceed the benefits.*

To clothe the bare bones of this principle with the flesh of substance is a very tall order indeed. In principle, if every relevant number were known, an edict could be issued to each polluter specifying the amount by which he was to reduce his discharge of pollutants and the means by which he was to do so. In fact, we are even farther from having the right numbers for air pollution than we are from having those for water pollution.

In this situation, I suggest that any scheme for abatement should be consistent with the following principles:

1. It should permit decision-making to be as decentralized as possible. Other things being equal, a rule that discharges must be reduced by a certain amount is preferable to a rule that particular devices be installed, since the former permits alternatives to be considered that may be cheaper than the devices specified in the latter.

2. It should be experimental and flexible. As experience with abatement schemes accumulates, we will gain information about benefits and costs of abatement. We will then revise our ideas about the desirable amount and methods of abatement. Control schemes will have to be revised accordingly.

3. It should be coupled with careful economic research on benefits and costs of air-pollution abatement. Without benefit-cost calculations, we cannot determine the desirable amount of abatement. We can, however, conjecture with confidence that more abatement is desirable than is provided by existing controls. Therefore, our present ignorance of benefits and costs should not be used as an excuse for doing nothing. I would place great emphasis on doing the appropriate research as part of any control scheme. A well-designed scheme will provide information (*e.g.*, on the costs of a variety of control devices) that is relevant to the benefit-cost calculations.

Means of Control

We are not in a position to evaluate a variety of schemes that are in use or have been proposed to control or abate air pollution. It will be useful to classify methods of control according to the categories employed by Kneese [2] in his discussion of water pollution:

1. *Direct Regulation.* In this category, I include licenses, permits, compulsory standards, zoning, registration, and equity litigation.

2. *Payments.* In this category I include not only direct payments or subsidies, but also reductions in collections that would otherwise be made. Examples are subsidization of particular control devices, forgiveness of local property taxes on pollution-control equipment, accelerated depreciation on control equipment, payments for decreases in the discharge of pollutants, and tax credits for investment

in control equipment.

3. *Charges.* This category includes schedules of charges, or fees, for the discharge of different amounts of specified pollutants, and excise or other taxes on specific sources of pollution (such as coal).

My objection to direct regulation should be clear by now. It is too rigid and inflexible, and loses the advantages of decentralized decision-making. For example, a rule that factories limit their discharges of pollutants to certain levels would be less desirable than a system of effluent fees that achieved the same overall reduction in pollution, in that the latter would permit each firm to make the adjustment to the extent and in the manner that best suited its own situation. Direct restrictions are usually cumbersome to administer, and rarely achieve more than the grossest form of control. In spite of the fact that almost all of our present control programs fall into this category, they should be tried only after all others have been found unworkable.

Thus, first consideration ought to be given to control schemes under the second and third categories.

Many of the specific schemes under these two categories are undesirable in that they involve charges or payments for the wrong thing. If it is desired to reduce air pollution, then the charge or payment should depend on the amount of pollutants discharged and not on an activity that is directly or indirectly related to the discharge of pollutants. For example, an excise tax on coal is less desirable than a tax on the discharge of pollutants resulting from burning coal because the former distorts resource use in favor of other fuels and against devices to remove pollutants from stack gases after burning coal. As a second example, a payment to firms for decreasing the discharge of pollutants is better than a tax credit for investment in pollution-control devices because the latter introduces a bias against other means of reducing the discharge of pollutants, such as the burning of nonpolluting fuels. Thus, many control schemes can be eliminated on the principle that more efficient control can normally be obtained by incentives that depend on the variable it is desired to influence rather than by incentives that depend on a related variable.

Many of the specific schemes under *Payments* can be eliminated on the grounds that they propose to subsidize the purchase of devices that neither add to revenues nor reduce costs. Thus, if a pollution-control device neither helps to produce salable products nor reduces production costs, a firm really receives very little incentive to buy the device even if the government offers to pay half the cost. All that such subsidy schemes accomplish is to reduce somewhat the resistance to direct controls. Of course, some control devices may help to recover wastes that can be made into salable products. Although there are isolated examples of the recovery of valuable wastes in the process of air-pollution control, it is hard to know whether such possibilities are extensive. A careful survey of this subject would be interesting. However, the key point is that, to the extent that waste recovery is desirable, firms receive the appropriate incentive to recover wastes by the use of fees or payments that are related to the discharge of effluents. Therefore, even the possibility of waste recovery does not justify subsidization of devices to recover wastes.

The foregoing analysis creates a presumption in favor of schemes under which either payments are made for reducing the discharge of pollutants or charges are made for the amount of pollutants discharged. The basic condition for optimum resource allocation can in principle be satisfied by either scheme, since under either scheme just enough incentive can be provided so that the marginal cost of further abatement approximates the marginal benefits of further abatement. There are, however, three reasons for believing that charges are preferable to subsidies:

1. There is no natural "origin" for payments. In principle, the payment should be for a reduction in the discharge of pollutants below what it would have been without the payment. Estimation of this magnitude would be difficult and the recipient of the subsidy would have an obvious incentive to exaggerate the amount of pollutants he would have discharged without the subsidy. The establishment of a new factory would raise a particularly difficult problem. The trouble is precisely that which agricultural policy meets when it tries to pay farmers to reduce their crops. Jokes about farmers deciding to double the amount of corn not produced this year capture the essence of the problem.

2. Payments violate feelings of equity which many people have on this subject. People feel that if polluting the air is a cost of producing certain products, then the consumers who benefit ought to pay this cost just as they ought to pay the costs of labor and other inputs needed in production.

3. If the tax system is used to make the payments, e.g., by per-

mitting a credit against tax liability for reduced discharge of pollutants, a "gimmick" is introduced into the tax system which, other
things being equal, it is better to avoid. Whether or not the tax system is used to make the payments, the money must be raised at least
partly by higher taxes than otherwise for some taxpayers. Since most
of our taxes are not neutral, resource misallocation may result.

I feel that the above analysis creates at least a strong presumption for the use of discharge or effluent fees as a means of air-
pollution abatement.

A Tentative Proposal

It is not the purpose of this paper to make detailed proposals of an
institutional or legal nature. Nevertheless, implementation of any
scheme of air-pollution abatement requires an institutional framework, and some discussion of criteria for such a framework seems
desirable. Furthermore, an interesting suggestion has been made by
another contributor to this symposium of an institutional arrangement for dealing with water pollution.[3] It therefore seems worthwhile to explore whether an analogous institution might be feasible
to implement air pollution abatement schemes.

Briefly, the proposal is that air pollution control authorities be
created with responsibility to evaluate a variety of abatement
schemes, to estimate benefits and costs, to render technical assistance, to levy charges for the discharge of effluents, and to adopt
other means of abatement.

Serious problems of air pollution are found mostly in urban areas
of substantial size. Within an urban area, air pollution is no re-
specter of political boundaries, and an authority's jurisdiction should
be defined by the boundaries of a metropolitan air shed. Although
difficult to identify precisely, such air sheds would roughly coincide
with Standard Metropolitan Statistical Areas. Except in a few cases,
such as the Chicago-Gary and the New York-Northern New Jersey
areas, jurisdiction could be confined to a single metropolitan area. In
a number of instances, the authority would have to be interstate. In
many large metropolitan areas, the authority would have to be the
joint creation of several local governments. There would presumably
be participation by state governments and by the Federal Government at least to the extent of encouragement and financial support.

Each authority would have broad responsibility for dealing with air pollution in its metropolitan air shed. It would institute discharge fees and would be mainly financed by such fees. It would have the responsibility of estimating benefits and costs of air-pollution abatement, and of setting fees accordingly. It would have to identify major pollutants in its area and set fees appropriate to each significant pollutant. The authority could also provide technical advice and help concerning methods of abatement.

Although there would be great uncertainty as to the appropriate level of fees at first, this should not prevent their use. They should be set conservatively while study was in progress, and data on the responses of firms to modest fees would be valuable in making benefit-cost calculations. Given present uncertainties, a certain amount of flexible experimentation with fees would be desirable.

Questions will necessarily arise as to just what kinds and sources of pollutants would come under the jurisdiction of the proposed authority. I do not pretend to have answers to all such questions. Presumably, standard charges could be set for all major pollutants, with provision for variation in each metropolitan air shed to meet local conditions. It is clear that provision should be made for the possibility of varying the charge for a particular pollutant from air shed to air shed. The harm done by the discharge of a ton of sulfur dioxide will vary from place to place, depending on meteorological and other factors. It is probably less harmful in Omaha than in Los Angeles. It is important that charges reflect these differences, so that locational decisions will be appropriately affected.

Consideration would also have to be given to the appropriate temporal pattern of charges. In most cities, pollution is much more serious in summer than at other times. Charges that were in effect only during summer months might induce a quite different set of adjustments than charges that were in effect at all times.

No one should pretend that the administration of an effective air pollution control scheme will be simple or cheap. Measurement and monitoring of discharges are necessary under any control scheme and can be expensive and technically difficult. Likewise, whatever the control scheme, finding the optimum degree of abatement requires the calculation of benefits and costs; these calculations are conceptually difficult and demanding.

The point that needs to be emphasized strongly is that the cost of administering a control scheme based on effluent fees will be less than the cost of administering any other scheme of equal effectiveness. An effluent-fee system, like ordinary price systems, is largely self-administering.

This point is important and is worth stating in detail. First, consider an effluent-fee system. Suppose a schedule of fees has been set. Then firms will gradually learn the rate of effluent discharge that is most profitable. Meanwhile, the enforcement agency will need to sample the firm's effluent to insure that the firm is paying the fee for the amount actually discharged. However, once the firm has found the most profitable rate of effluent discharge, and this is known to the enforcing agency, the firm will have no incentive to discharge any amount of effluent other than the one for which it is paying. At this point the system becomes self-administering and the enforcement agency need only collect bills. Second, consider a regulatory scheme under which the permissable discharge is set at the level that actually resulted under the effluent-fee scheme. Then the firm has a continuing incentive because of its advantage on the costside to exceed the permissible discharge rate so as to increase production. Monitoring by the enforcement agency therefore continues to be necessary.

Of course, under either a regulatory or an effluent-fee scheme, a change in conditions will require the search for a new "equilibrium." Neither system can be self-enforcing until the new equilibrium has been found. The point is that the effluent-fee system becomes self-enforcing at that point, whereas the regulatory system does not.

In conclusion, it is necessary to say a special word about automobiles. Many authorities cite the automobile as the single most important source of air pollution.

Except for the matter of administrative costs, the above analysis applies completely. The best way to deal with automobiles would be to sample the discharge of effluents periodically—presumably at the time of annual inspection—and to charge an effluent fee that depended on the effluent discharged per mile (as sampled) multiplied by the number of miles driven in a metropolitan air shed.

Problems arise with automobiles mainly because of their mobility and because of the great disparity between the number of owners and the number of manufacturers. Their mobility makes it difficult and expensive to meter their use within a particular air shed. A second complication results from the fact that although a number of devices have been suggested, there is at present no inexpensive and reliable method of metering automobile effluents that would be suitable for routine use—for example, as part of annual inspection. Furthermore, since there are 70,000,000 cars on the roads, but only a handful of manufacturers, the administrative cost of a scheme that deals with manufacturers is likely to be much less than the cost of a scheme that deals with owners. A fourth complication results from the fact that most of the known ways of substantially reducing effluent discharges from cars—principally blow-by devices, engine modification, and afterburners—require either replacement or major maintenance after one or two years' use if they are to retain their effectiveness.

The above analysis clearly indicates that the best way of dealing with automobile effluents depends on some costs that are not now known with sufficient accuracy. For example, the scheme presented in the next paragraph is undesirable in the absence of cheap, reliable methods of sampling effluents from cars and of metering the use of cars in metropolitan air sheds.

A simple proposal would be to sample the discharge of effluents from automobiles as they are manufactured and to levy on the sale of each car a tax depending on the sampled effluent discharge. Sampling would be relatively cheap, since effluent discharge would vary little among cars of the same make, with the same engine and anti-pollution devices. This proposal seems to be preferable to recent legislation which requires the Secretary of Health, Education, and Welfare to set compulsory standards for effluent discharge from new cars. My proposal and this legislation share the defect that they would have no effect on cars more than one or two years old, since the devices apparently will remain effective no more than one or two years without maintenance. Since old cars naturally tend to discharge more effluent than new cars, and since most cars are more than two years old, it is clear that further steps are needed if control of auto effluents is to be effective.

It seems clear that any further measure, whether involving effluent fees or direct regulation, will require the sampling of effluents at the time of annual inspection. Given the need for sampling at annual inspection, the question is whether to require that the car meet a certain standard or to charge a fee that depends on the outcome of the effluent sampling. It does not seem possible to answer this question without more detailed data than are available. One possibility would be to make the amount of the annual registration fee depend on the result of the effluent sampling, and possibly on whether the car is registered within a metropolitan air shed, just as some states now make the registration fee depend on the adequacy of the car owner's liability insurance.

NOTES

1. The views expressed in this paper are those of the author and in no way reflect policies of the Council of Economic Advisers or any other government agency. The author is indebted to Allen V. Kneese of Resources for the Future, Inc., for a number of the ideas expressed in this paper.

2. Allen V. Kneese, *The Economics of Regional Water Quality Management*, Baltimore, Johns Hopkins Press, 1964, pp. 192–7.

3. Allen V. Kneese, "New Directions in Water Management," *Bulletin of the Atomic Scientists*, Vol. 21 (May, 1965), pp. 2–8. See also his contribution to this volume.

Risks Versus Costs in Environmental Health *

LESLIE A. CHAMBERS
UNIVERSITY OF SOUTHERN CALIFORNIA

Leslie A. Chambers is professor of biology and director of the Allan Hancock Foundation at the University of Southern California. Between 1956 and 1960 he was director of research for the Los Angeles County Air Pollution Control District. Among the subjects of his many publications are air pollution and environmental health.

SELDOM, if ever, is the dollar appropriation by a legislative body for protection of the public health equated with anything approximating the risks the money is intended to ameliorate. This is true for a number of reasons, among them being the jealousy guarded legislative traditions which limit implementation of forward planning to the term spanned by the incumbency of the elected representatives, and the problem-evading tendency to cut the fiscal pie in proportion to a rationing pattern established in earlier years and limited by some a priori selection of a tax rate just within the bounds of public tolerability. There is also the patent tendency of the paying public to demand protective actions *after* threats have become disasters, to build levees *after* a flood, to probe upward *after* a sputnik has appeared in space, to check propagation *after* the exigencies of proximity have made it apparent once again that two bodies cannot occupy the same space, and that finite material resources adequate for support of two hundred million people are not necessarily sufficient for a billion.

One may consider such tardy actions and reluctant attitudes to be shortsighted, illogical, even potentially suicidal. But they are ex-

* From the book, *Proceedings 2nd AMA Congress on Environmental Health Problems,* Copyright American Medical Association 1965, 535 North Dearborn, Chicago, Illinois 60610

pressions of human behavioral properties, as real and as potent in the total environmental complex as are sunshine, oxygen, air, the perception of historical records, microbiological agents of disease, or emotions and psychosomatic interactions. We—members of the human species—have our existence and express it, as transient foci in the course of cosmologic and evolutionary events which have preceded our time and will follow it. Man's sentience, homocentric though it be, reveals that he exists in no sense apart from his environment; that he is part and parcel of it; that he is a system not bounded by anthropometric dimensions. More awesome still is the extrapolation that man is not now what he was an hour ago, and that the interrelating dynamic processes within his cosmologic niche will make of him something different an hour hence.

Now I have no plan to engage in a philosophical polemic on the nature of man, the cosmos, or even the biosphere. But the subject of risks versus costs in environmental health, while practical in its statement, approaches the esoteric in its fullest consideration. The act of imputing values to contemporary life and human welfare implies ethical conflicts.

Some of the risks to which public-health practitioners are currently addressing their efforts have been set forth persuasively elsewhere. Unfortunately, we lack sufficient knowledge to define with precision the magnitudes of environmental changes likely to react adversely on living systems at all morphological, functional, and genetic levels. Couple this with the notable absence of any widely acceptable indices of value other than dollars—with the strangeness of relating "cost" to anything but units of commercial exchange—and we have a problem. Every once in a while, during discussion of the effort to control air pollution, water pollution, radiation, or some other environmental hazard, the cliche "calculated risk" is set forth as an essential in minimizing the impact of regulation on the economy of an industry or a community. The recommendation seems always to recognize that very minimal environmental stresses may be hazardous or fatal to weaker members of a population, but to imply that these relatively unfit persons, in some indefinable number, should be forgotten in the interest of the greater good. As a biologist attempting to maintain a perspective of the good of the species, I can readily accept this deliberate resignation to natural selection. But as a member of a society whose several systems of ethics do not condone sacrifice of individual lives to the common good, I develop a distinct uneasiness. An ethical paradox appears to be involved.

The basic consideration in costing public-health protection is the value to be placed on an individual. But this is much too simple a statement. Value in terms of what? If statistical derivations of average lifetime earning capacity, or of average dollar value of the individual contribution to the economy, had any meaning in reference to any single human life, tags might be suitably marked. However, this kind of consideration involves an assumption of uniformity that simply does not exist. It might be preferable to bankrupt an entire city rather than to sacrifice a premature Einstein or Newton.

Valuation in terms of individual health and happiness must be very largely based on abstract sensation and professional measurement of deviations from rather arbitrary norms. While acceptable to and demanded by the subjects, and representative of ideals professed by the medical and health professions, values in such units are not often salable to budget analysts, or to a profit-motivated economy.

Values in terms of community welfare seem more accessible, and more readily shaped to conformity with dollar indices. It is relatively easy to observe relationships between poor housing and such overt factors as local air pollution, or between high automotive accident rates and inadequate highway-safety provisions. Probably the reason such relationships are more readily made concrete and usable is that the contributing factors can be dealt with as statistical blocks; the system is gross enough, but not too gross, to fall within the limits of the observational capability of one person, or of a legislative body.

But there are other levels of organizational complexity involving man that we cannot observe directly since the response to environmental adjustment may become apparent only after our children's children's children have occupied our niche. Medawar has pointed out that "it is extremely difficult to think of any social habit or act of legislation that has *no* genetic consequences."

We may recall the disputes which have raged around the question of acceptable radiation dosages; they illustrate well the difficulties of evaluating present actions in the context of time lapse. No one has argued that added radiation will produce *no* genetic effect on future generations; rather, the discussion has centered around the quality of the changes to be anticipated, and the amount of genetic alteration the species can tolerate. There has been a choice between present actions ostensibly for the common good and actions deemed

not so clearly for the common good but aimed at avoiding, or preventing, defective genetic manifestations in a small number of our
lineal descendants. The choice has been ours; the real problem may
be theirs.

Certain less headlined examples may be cited, many of which relate current corrective medical practices to future public-health
problems. Retinoblastoma was, until quite recently, an almost certainly fatal manifestation of a dominant genetic defect which per-
sists in the human gene pool. Early death assured selection pressure,
since it prevented further dissemination of the defective gene. Now
surgical intervention is keeping alive, through the reproductive
period, a number of semi- or totally blinded persons whose descendants will exhibit the same defect and will assure an increase in the
pool of defective genes. Accumulation of data on reproduction rates
in these genetic deviants will almost certainly make it possible to
predict the rate at which additional provision will be required for
the training and care of the blind in future generations. In this, as in
dozens of other types of modern medical intervention, the choice between the common good and the good of an individual is being
made.

On the other hand, it is equally apparent that failure to intervene
in the processes of natural selection, where capability for so doing
exists, may also involve risks. We are in the midst of a great transi-
tion from deliberate promotion of unlimited increase in the human
population, for cannon feed or other purposes, through some rear-
guard actions based on mores and dogmas stemming from the previous assumption of a need for larger numbers, and into a realm of
timorous-to-vigorous promotion of population limitation. Effective
techniques have appeared and have become easily available to those
who, by superior educational and economic stratification, have
access to them.

The population problem needs no amplification here beyond
emphasis on the extraordinarily close relationship between population size and the quality and quantity of public-health controls
which must be devised and paid for. No one concerned with the
preservation of health in our metroplexes can have escaped the impact of the exponential increase in costs relative to numbers of
people occupying an area. Regulation of population increase is a
future essential which is being anticipated none too soon.

But the pattern of insistence on reduced numbers without any concomitant selection can have profound consequences for the species. Selection is occurring by reason of failure to be selective even within our present capability, and it may well be occurring in directions which will affect profoundly the future welfare of the whole community. How are we to determine what is happening? How are we to evaluate any pattern of "intelligent" selection? How are we to implement a pattern of artificial selection? Who is to place approval on any pattern of human genetic selection?

Up to this point we have considered some of the broad questions which remain substantially unanswered. As with the problem of values in a wider sense, most of the questions may never be answered except in relation to other questions. But in the absence of answers, both out actions and our inaction are inexorably giving shape to what will be. Is blind acceptance of the consequences of *ad hoc* adjustment to immediate crises the best that man can provide for himself? There have appeared some glimmers of hope that this need not be the case, and that compatible strategies for present well-being and future improvement can be examined.

Undoubtedly, thoughtful people have recognized that man is a participant in and component of his surroundings in time and space. And many have considered the unreasonableness of environmental regulations restricted to a single chemical, physical, or social factor without concurrent consideration of the chains of interactions consequential to the immediate intervention.

In a very simple case, the matter of controlling emissions of lead into the atmosphere, there is an inkling of the problem. Acceptable level for lead in drinking water have long been established, maximal acceptable concentrations for eight-hour exposure of workmen exist, and there are extensive data on normal body burdens, rates of uptake by various tissues, and rates of elimination. In the few years since urban air-pollution control has been an objective of regulatory agencies, enormous efforts have been expended in assaying atmospheric lead in the general air supply. That it has increased in relation to use of antiknock additives in gasoline is well established. It is therefore possibly reasonable for clean-air advocates to recommend restriction on or prohibition of the use of lead additives in automotive fuels.

On the other hand, it is difficult to imagine how an air-quality standard for lead can possibly have meaning in a local situation without simultaneous regulation or definitive knowledge of the total lead intake from water and food, as well as air. In a somewhat different sense, one may also question the consequences of the specific prohibition of antiknock additives in terms of its effect on other constituents of the atmospheric pollution load. Almost certainly, gasoline composition would be changed to offset the loss of antiknock quality. High compression ratios in automobile engines would be reduced, or other actions would be taken which would affect the quality of hydrocarbon emissions, the quantity of oxides of nitrogen, or the efficiency of combustion. Such induced events in the chain set off by the primary regulatory action might be of more consequence than the circumstance which was supposed to be corrected. And the ripple pattern created would have more remote consequences in terms of local and national economic readjustment, emotional disturbances at certain levels, and even political overtones. I am certainly not advocating that control of atmospheric lead be overlooked; rather, I suggest this situation as an elementary illustration of the fact that any intervention in an existing ecological system can have repercussions well beyond the immediate focus of attention.

A study of the effects produced in several species of experimental animals by exposure to smog in Los Angeles serves to illustrate the same theme at a different level of complexity. The investigation was first planned as an intensive search for evidences of pathological, physiological, biochemical, cytological, or other deviations from biological normality. Equal populations of each species (mice, rats, hamsters, guinea pigs, and rabbits) were exposed continuously to the air people breathe in four metropolitan regions, and to air cleaned as effectively as technological resources would permit. It is not my intention to report here the detailed findings; for the present purpose it will be sufficient to state that a series of rather marginal but significant biological effects of smog have been established in terms of alveolar cytology, increase in total airway resistance, variations in selected tissue and serum enzyme levels, and changes in specific urinary steroids. No significant reflection of these observations in terms of gross pathology, longevity, or body weight has been observed. One can only conclude that a pattern of predictable subclinical response to air pollution exists in relation to the levels of oxidants and other pollutants in the Los Angeles air supply.

In 1964 a psychobiological aspect was added to the complex of studies. Speculation on the possible relationship between susceptibility to air pollutants and stresses of the type experienced by freeway drivers and income-tax payers led to experimental coupling of the two types of insults as part of the investigation. The results have been most interesting. In brief, animals stressed by an electrical-shock regimen to a predetermined degree, as measured by psycho-biological tests, *are* more susceptible to smog. Furthermore, the functional and biological syndromes resulting from the two types of stress are additive and quite similar in detail.

One cannot suppress a host of questions elicited by this remark-able association of responses to sensory stress on the one hand, and to chemically induced stress on the other, nor would we wish to do so. If the alarm syndrome of Selye is a major feature of response to both insults, just how specific need our air-pollution concerns be? If rats and guinea pigs—presumably less completely associated with distant crises through news media and other artifacts of human communication, and presumably less introspective and neurologi-cally complex, than their human handlers—exhibit a smog reaction when frustrated and an alarm reaction when fumigated, just how can meaningful air-quality standards be set in relation to a human population subjected to vistas of violence, intra-species conflict, and personal inadequacy?

Recent history and contemporary events provide sufficient evi-dence of the interrelatedness of man and the circumstances which influence him. Transferral of water reserves from the Owens Valley, the Colorado Basin, and the Feather River to supply the needs of southern California for a few decades, has blighted an otherwise usable part of California, has shaped and will continue to shape the social, economic, and agricultural aspects of several states, has cre-ated international disputes, and has made a heyday for lawyers. And one suspects that equal expenditures of effort and public funds could have tapped the nearby sea with entirely different results.

The tremendous effort in which we are now engaged as a nation, an attempt to relate more intimately with the environment beyond our atmosphere, must inevitably affect and be affected by almost all aspects of our existence. One phase alone, the attempt to invade the lunar surface, is utilizing about 5 per cent of the national budget, and is perhaps an even larger factor in the gross national product. Besides the tremendous readjustments of economy, redistributions of people, and alterations in consumption of natural resources di-rectly implied, we have already experienced literal revolutions in educational perspectives and techniques, and indirect effects on communication, on weather prediction, and very probably on fundamental aspects of individual consciousness involving man's personal estimate of his significance and value.

So far we have essayed to consider the risk and costs of public-health practices in terms sufficiently concrete to be of immediate utility, and have wound up in the far reaches of time or of space. The point may have been unduly labored, that we are concerned with deliberate or inadvertent tinkering with a perplexingly complex ecological system, and with prediction of the consequences of change in a concentration, or in a rate, or in some other single constituent of the system, on its other parts.

Recently, during extended discussions among a group of public-health protagonists seeking means of contending with this maze, the suggestion was made that we need to develop a "technology of complexity." It seems probable that long strides toward a capability for analyzing complexities of the types we face have been made. Mobilization of the procedures of systems analysis and computer technology, and the mathematical concepts of "sets," "groups," and symbolic logic, has gone far in the business world and in the development of military strategies, in the solution of problems related to space exploration, and in a variety of other sectors of human activity involving hundreds or thousands of parameters. The hardware and the philosophies exist and are improving rapidly. Game theory—the technique of selection of a specific action and degree of reaction, compatible with a "complete" system—has progressed well beyond the requirements of winning play at Las Vegas. Indeed, the patterns effective in a game of 21 are apparently somewhat facetious extrusions from the methodologies used in much more serious game planning.

Our greatest difficulty in approaching analysis of a homocentric ecological system, to enable a choice of "plays" appropriate to the maintained adjustment of man to his environment, appears to be related to man himself. Scientists, physicians, and engineers in public-health practices are trained in techniques and perspectives geared to narrow categorical limits. Generalists are infrequent, and it is probable that a complete generalist, capable of interrelating conceptually all facets of the system, is an impossibility. To solve other problems of this sort, such as the development of operational choices for intercontinental warfare, it has been fruitful to establish teams of contributing specialists appropriately tuned to the overall objective and adept in the substance of a particular area. Group members tend, by association, to generalize, but their primary function is to provide input to electronic data-processing and computer systems, programmed to derive action choices on the basis of weighted data and logical sequences supplied by dozens of experts. It is depressing to observe such abdication of preeminence to a machine, but we find solace in the thought that man has been able to create devices with certain capabilities in extension of his own, and that he should use the tools his genius has provided.

A committee, with members representative of the major scientific, social, economic, and political aspects of environmental health, was convened in 1961 under the chairmanship of Professor Paul Gross, to review national needs in all aspects of the subject and to make recommendations for action to the Surgeon General of the Public Health Service. One of our most emphatic recommendations was the establishment of an Office of Environmental Health Sciences independent of the continuing national programs in water- and air-pollution control, radiological health, milk and food sanitation, and other traditional components of public-health concern. The functions of the new Office were defined to include the overall survey and analysis of interrelationships within the whole field I have discussed here. Further recommendations involved the development of several academic centers of excellence, in which could be carried out not only research on man's interacting environment, but educational processes designed to focus attention on the whole, and on techniques for its systematic analysis.

Several actions are under way which will implement the suggestions of the Gross committee. An Environmental Health Institute has received congressional blessing and will be established in North Carolina. In March, 1965, I had the privilege of sitting as a member at the first meeting of a committee which is assigned the task of recommending to the National Advisory Council on Environmental Health locations and necessary support levels for development of academic centers of excellence in environmental health sciences. These will be the keys to ultimate success or failure of our attempt to understand broadly, and to regulate rationally, the ecology of man.

New forms of training and new objectives in education will be essential as we proceed from diversity to congruence; from dissection of the specifics to convergence; from a philosophy of competition, blind to all but a single interest, to one of genuinely calculated strategy. For those who are awed into inaction in the face of complexity, there will be no place in this business; for those to whom complexity is a challenge, and the acquisition of exotic knowledge and new skills a stimulant, the immediate future will be filled with adventure.

The Structuring of Atmospheric Pollution Control Systems [1]

THOMAS D. CROCKER
UNIVERSITY OF WISCONSIN—MILWAUKEE

Thomas D. Crocker, on the faculty of the University of Wisconsin—Milwaukee, is in charge of a research project for the Division of Air Pollution of the United States Public Health Service.

THE ATMOSPHERIC-POLLUTION PROBLEM is clearly one of those cases of "market failure" which, though long sensed if not made explicit by noneconomists, have only recently been felt by economists themselves to be deserving of analysis. The forecasts of increasing atmospheric pollution and the warnings about so-called "shortages" of clean air which abound in the mass communications media imply that the present system of controlling atmospheric pollution is not performing as well as would a modified system. In other words, noneconomists and lately even economists feel that the present means of allocating the air resource among various users and uses is not working as it should work, and more important, as it could work. More precisely, the view is that the relevant variables have not been varying as they should and could. One might infer that those asserting the existence of an atmospheric-pollution problem would profess to have a knowledge of the manner in which these variables should vary. However, although there is agreement about the existence of a problem, there is a profound absence of consensus as to what should be done about it.

Since the injection of various types of flotsam and jetsam into the atmosphere is presently costless to most emitters, the view that the existence of atmospheric pollution is a symptom of faculty resource allocation appears to have some grounding in fact. The divorce of emission costs from emission benefits has brought about a situation in which off-site parties or receptors frequently bear all the costs, while all the benefits accrue to emitters. Most people's sense of equity is justifiably offended by this situation. Unfortunately, the mass media have too often attempted to inflate the magnitude of the offense by pounding away at the problem's emotional aspects.[2] Some popular commentaries give one the impression that the atmospheric-pollution problem will be so serious in another decade or two that it will be necessary to pump all air from the caskets that have been and are about to be buried in the ground. Images of people wearing gas masks or warnings of the imminent abandonment of whole cities and sections of countryside serve to arouse the interest of the public. But they contribute little to the objective solution of the air-pollution problem.

Even knowledgeable authorities have made declarations to the effect that something called "pure" air is worth paying for ". . . whatever the cost in time, money, and effort."[3] It is the contention of this writer that such statements are not warranted by the facts of the problem, and more important, that they cause the efforts to find solutions to be misdirected. Too often, any use whatsoever of the air for waste-disposal purposes is considered to be sinful—the corruption of something which has heretofore been virginally pure. The result has been that most proposals for the solution of the air-pollution problem have been negatively biased in that their recommendations have been founded upon gross rather than net damage.[4] Emitters are usually considered to be the villains of the piece, while receptors are the unfortunates evicted from their spotless environment into the dirty world.

In spite of the extremes to which the pure-air advocates tend to go, there is little doubt they are correct in asserting that today the difference between the cost-savings accruing to parties able to rid themselves of their wastes by emitting these wastes into the air and the damage costs imposed upon receptors by these same waste emissions is not being maximized. However, the criteria of economic efficiency and welfare maximization require that we do not simply reverse the present situation, heave a sigh of relief, and then congratulate ourselves upon the cleanliness of our atmospheric environment. We are no more justified in making the would-be emitter endure all the costs of "pure" air while the would-be receptor receives all the benefits than we are in burdening the receptor with all the costs of "dirty" air while the emitter collects all the benefits. The power of the air to support life and property and its capacity to dispose of wastes are economic assets which both common sense and the criteria of economic efficiency indicate should not be wasted. Considerable grounds exist for arguing that air pollution control programs as presently practiced and espoused have caused, and are likely to cause, a state of affairs in which *waste* of the air resource, in the economic sense of the word, can be expected to take place.

The onus for this state of affairs obviously does not attach to the receptors. But neither does it attach to the emitters. Instead the responsibility lies with a political and socio-economic system which has not yet discovered a means of making the relevant variables vary in the way in which, it seems to me, they should.

The Air as an Economic Resource

The air, or rather the collection of gases and materials which make up the air, as distinguished from airspace, is a flow resource: it is renewable. Pollutants, whether of natural origin or man-made, collect in the air constantly. But winds disperse and dilute these pollutants, so if no more pollutants are emitted, the air overlying a particular land space will ultimately be cleansed of all foreign gases and materials. However, these winds are unlike other renewable resources, such as water and timber, in that man is physically incapable to any important degree of storing or transporting them, or of changing their elemental nature. Since he is physically unable to perform these functions, he is also economically powerless to do so. Thus the problem that man faces with respect to the winds is, for him, a rather uncommon one. With most resources, whether renewable or nonrenewable, he is potentially able to modify to some degree their elemental and/or locational characteristics in order to suit his economic needs.[5] But with the air, man's actions, institutions, and artifacts must be modified. He is unable to adjust the winds to any appreciable extent; therefore he must adjust himself to the whims and vagaries of the air currents. His inability to face up to this fact appears to be the root cause of the atmospheric-pollution problem.

To the best of this writer's knowledge, no one has ever estimated the volume of air likely to be available in the United States to man and his property over any one interval of time. In addition to the relatively simple task of determining the number of cubic miles of "standard" air, there would be the problem of calculating the probable values of a number of meteorological parameters. Until such time as the total volume of air is established, the spread of stories, even though true, which tell of over 400,000 tons of air pollutants [6] being released daily by man throughout the nation must continue to bear a very close resemblance to "scare" tactics. When several hundred thousand tons are balanced against an unknown number, the impact of the tons is likely to be several times what it would be in the true relationship: the value which the unknown assumes in the minds of most people is likely to be much closer to an immutable zero than to a highly variable large number. When this lack of knowledge is combined with the attitude that one should not place an economic value upon the air, the result is too many proposals for the control of atmospheric pollution which are based upon concepts of physical rather than economic scarcity and upon nonrenewable rather than renewable resources. If carried to their logical conclusions, such views mean that our economic welfare will be determined by a "pure"-air theory of value—a theory which is even less desirable than the labor theory of value. Even if economic analysis can offer nothing else (I happen to think that it can) it can serve to correct these misconceptions about the atmospheric-pollution problem. This in itself is a positive contribution.

The air has two key economic dimensions: a life- and property-supporting capacity and a waste-disposal capacity. The unresolved conflict between receptors and emitters of pollutants exists because both of these dimensions are considered by the individual receptor or emitter to be free goods. To emitters, both of these dimensions have a positive value; but to receptors, only the first is of positive value, while the latter is of negative value in the same sense that the housewife—or her husband, if he is the one who has to take out the garbage—considers garbage to have a negative value. A negative value of any good is possible only if its disposal requires the use of a good which has a positive value. Removing the garbage from the premises takes the husband away from his newspaper and his nightly bottle of beer. Allowing the emitter to release his wastes into the air means that the receptor must do without cleaner air. But just as the housewife considers her husband's function in removing the garbage to have a positive value, the emitter of wastes considers the function of air as a waste-disposal unit to have a positive value. Or, just as a reduction in the number of garbage-removal trips has a positive value to the husband, a reduction in the volume of air devoted to waste-disposal purposes has a positive value to receptors. Thus it is worthwhile for receptors to have the volume of air used for waste-disposal purposes reduced, but it is worthwhile for emitters to have this same volume increased.

In the present state of affairs, the receptor receives free a volume of air upon which he places a positive value. Simultaneously, the emitter is given a good which has a positive value for him, but a negative value for the receptor. Neither party possesses a way at present of resolving this conflict to his satisfaction—other than the extremely tedious, time-consuming, and socially costly method of attempting to convince the public and its designated authorities of the dire consequences of reducing or not increasing the availability of that dimension of the air which to him is the most valuable. That is, the present state of affairs makes it worthwhile for emitters to complain about "nonproductive" investment in abatement and control equipment. At the same time, it is worthwhile for receptors to bewail the lack of cleaner air.

But the fact that society provides the air's two value dimensions freely to and without discrimination between receptors and emitters in no way explains why society has done so. Since an increase in the volume of air provided for one of the two dimensions necessitates a reduction in the volume available for the other dimension, that condition of scarcity so necessary to the economist's usefulness and continued employment is clearly present. One would therefore expect the market to allocate the air's two value dimensions according to the criteria of economic efficiency. Receptors and emitters could be expected to exchange rights to the life- and property-supporting dimension and the waste-disposal dimension until such time as the difference between total cost-savings to emitters and total damage costs to receptors was maximized.

However, so far society has generally been unable to define property rights in air and to establish well-structured atmospheric pollution control programs. In most cases, at present, individual users of one value dimension have no way to compensate users of the other value dimension so that it is worthwhile for the latter to make available the volume of that dimension which the former regard as most valuable. That is, the individual receptor can't dig up enough money on his own to make it worthwhile for the emitter to reduce his emissions, and vice versa. Furthermore, even if the individual user is able to pay enough to cause the volume of that dimension which he regards as most valuable to be available, he has no way of preventing the benefits of a transaction in the air resource from accruing to fellow users who do not participate in the transaction. Thus, under present conditions, the ideal outcome described in the preceding paragraph is not likely to occur. What at first glance appears to be a simple problem of causing the production processes of receptors and emitters to be physically independent rather than interdependent is really a problem of finding a means for properly allocating between and among receptors and emitters a jointly used, presently indivisible input—an input the value of which is not intrinsic, but which is instead derived from the net returns air-related receptor and emitter inputs are expected to earn in production. Because of the presently existing absolute indivisibility of the air resource, only the inputs which use either or both of the air's two value dimensions are scarce to individual receptors and emitters. Although the air resource in each of its two value dimensions is a scarce good to society as a whole, it is a free good to the individual receptor or emitter.

The present state of affairs leaves both the individual and the society in a Pareto-worse situation: a situation where everybody is likely to go up the stack together, landing only where the capriciousness of the winds of (ill) luck dictate. Opportunity for either private or public means of allocating over time the two value dimensions of the air in accordance with the criteria of economic efficiency is lacking. The only method yet employed to any extent has been fixed standards, "those artifacts of professional organizations." [7] Unless some alternative means are found which will cause the relative value of each dimension to be reflected in the joint production decisions of receptors and emitters, the present conflicts about atmospheric pollution are destined to continue unabated.

Steps in the Solution of Atmospheric-Pollution Problems

Any attempt to suggest and establish a means whereby the air's two value dimensions will be efficiently allocated over time must proceed through three sequential steps. First, the variables that are not considered to be functioning properly must be specified. Second, at least the nature and preferably the magnitude of the changes which must take place in these variables if a modified control system is to function properly must be confirmed. Third, an evaluation of the various alternative means of achieving this modification must be carried out.

My purpose in the remainder of this paper will be to proceed in a general way through each of these three steps in the hope of identifying some of the features which are common to all atmospheric pollution control problems and which are therefore some of the features which must be considered in all attempts to modify any such problem. Assumptions are made that receptors and emitters are not the same individuals and that all emission sources are stationary.[8] The main points to be developed are that the structuring of individual atmospheric pollution control programs will differ according to the changes which must be wrought in those variables not considered to be functioning properly, according to the degree of knowledge possessed by receptors, emiters, and control authorities about the functioning of these variables, and according to the degree of "privateness" which can be established in at least one of the air's two value dimensions. No attempt will be made to discuss the possible effects of changes in the relationships between and among all possible sets of these variables. Nor will an attempt be made to outline precisely the degree of knowledge and "privateness" necessary for the efficient operation of any one type of control-program structure. Nevertheless, the analysis should help to point the way toward the possibilities that are involved.

The Variables and the Nature of Their Necessary Changes

An atmospheric pollution control program which intends to allocate optimally over time the air's two value dimensions must necessarily take meteorological variables into consideration. Given a specific volume of emissions over any one interval of time, the actions of the atmosphere govern the length of time and the frequency with which all receptors will be exposed to given concentrations of pollutants. But since these meteorological variables act impartially toward neither receptors nor emitters, maximization over time of the difference between emitter cost-savings and receptor damage costs requires that the values which each relevant meteorological variable is likely to assume through time be known for every possible emitter and receptor site.

As previously noted, man is presently unable to exercise any real control over these meteorological variables. Thus, although the variable nature of these meteorological factors will make the emission characteristics which are optimal for any one set of meteorogical conditions inappropriate for another set, they are only given data within whose constraints a control system must operate. For each set of meteorological conditions and for each receptor site and emitter site, the optimal values for each of the variables which can be controlled by man must be calculated. For any one site over any one interval of time, a certain probability value will be assigned to the liklihood of occurrence of any one set of meteorological conditions. In addition, there will be a certain configuration of emission characteristics which will determine the cost-savings functions for emitters and the damage-cost functions for receptors. In theory, therefore, optimal allocation over time of the air's two value dimensions necessitates the calculation, for all possible assumptions as to meteorological conditions over every emitter and receptor site of the associated set of cost-savings and damage-cost functions. By calculating the arithmetic or geometric mean [9] of these functions for all sites a given distance from a specific geographical point or set of points and then summing over all sites, one could determine the mathematical expectation of the difference between cost-savings and damage costs for any one set of emission characteristics.

In this paper, I will assume that an air pollution control authority is able to determine the likelihood that any one set of meteorological conditions will occur over any one receptor or emitter site. The problem of determining the optimal expected cost-savings and damage-cost functions for each receptor and emitter site under each possible set of meteorological conditions can be left to the control authority. We are interested in the variables which a control authority is capable of controlling and the ways in which it can control them.

Apart from the restrictions which an air pollution control authority might place upon the location decisions of emitters and/or receptors, there are four basic variables which are within the power of man and which are therefore within the potential power of a control authority to adjust: (1) the total expected volume of pollutant emissions; (2) the length of the time interval over which pollutant emissions will take place; (3) the rate of pollutant emissions over any one interval of time; and (4) the point in time at which the first pollutant emission associated with any one production program of emitters will occur.

From the above, we see that for emitters

$$C_s = f (Q, k, a, B),$$

where C_s is cost-savings, Q is the expected volume of emissions, k is the length of the time interval over which emissions are to take place, a is the rate of emission, and B is the point in time at which the first emission will occur.

Similarly, for receptors

$$C_d = f (Q, k, a, B),$$

where C_d is *damage costs.*

Everything else being equal, cost-savings for emitters will become greater as Q and a are allowed to assume greater values.

$$\frac{FCs}{FV} > 0, \text{ and } \frac{FCs}{Fa(t)} > 0.$$

These same emitter cost-savings, again assuming everything else to be equal, will become greater as k becomes longer and B moves closer to the present.

$$\frac{FCs}{Fk} > 0, \text{ and } \frac{FCs}{FB} > 0.$$

For receptors, damage costs will become smaller as the values which the control authority allows Q and a to assume decrease and B moves further from the present. As for k, it is difficult if not impossible to generalize about this variable for receptors. Given a specific volume of pollutant emissions, it is not impossible to find cases where less damage is done to receptors if the time interval over which emissions are to take place is shortened. For example, experiments provide some evidence that cattle, because of their partial ability to rid themselves of fluorides through their gastrointestinal tracts, are less affected by relatively large quantities of fluoride over shorter periods of time than by relatively small quantities of fluoride over somewhat longer periods of time.[10] On the other hand, studies with alfalfa indicate that the plant will experience greater damage if exposed to relatively large quantities of sulfur dioxide over shorter periods of time.[11] Thus, since the sign for optimal changes in the receptor or damage cost k will differ according to the type of receptor and the type of pollutant, its determination is likely to be the most difficult measurement problem faced by a control authority— particularly in a problematic situation where there are several types of pollutants and/or several types of receptors.

Nevertheless, all atmospheric-pollution problems occur because one or more of the four aforementioned variables are not varying properly. Therefore, all atmospheric-pollution problems can be solved by causing one or more of these four variables to vary properly.[12] By adjusting each one, and various possible combinations, of these four variables, a control authority can, given knowledge of the expected damage cost and cost-savings functions for every receptor and emitter site, derive a value for each variable which will be optimal at a given point in time.

As we previously stated, the life- and property-supporting capacity and the waste-disposal capacity of the air do not have any intrinsic value. Their value is instead derived from the net returns that the air-related inputs of emitters and receptors are expected to earn in production. Thus the value of the air's life- and property-supporting capacity to the receptors is a direct function of the economic life of their air-related inputs. Similarly, the value of the air's waste-disposal capacity to the emitters is a direct function of the economic life of their plant and equipment. The longer the economic life of receptor and emitter capital facilities, and the greater the expected net returns of these capital facilities, the greater the values that will be placed upon the air's two value dimensions.[13] Any changes in the expected net returns and/or the economic life of these capital facilities will be reflected in their values, and therefore in the values of the air's two value dimensions.

A change in any one of the four key variables which a control authority is capable of adjusting can bring about any one of three types of change or conversion in the use of receptor and emitter capital facilities within the area affected by atmospheric pollution. First, there may be changes in the intensity with which any one capital facility is used. Second, the mix of capital facilities which individual receptors and emitters employ may be converted; and third, capital facilities may be converted from receptor to emitter uses or vice versa. Essentially, the extent of change or conversion in the uses of receptor and emitter capital facilities resulting from a change in one or more of our four key variables is directly related to the extent to which that intensity or use which formerly would generate the highest expected net returns conforms to that intensity or use which presently will generate the highest potential net returns.

The basis of the value of a capital facility is the stream of net returns expected to be forthcoming from that facility. If a capital facility is being used for a particular purpose and will continue to be used for that same purpose, its present value is the discounted value of the expected future net returns to the facility when used for that purpose. That is, its discounted value and therefore its present value is

$$V_p = \sum_{t=1}^{n} \frac{St}{(1+r)^t},$$

where S is the net returns to the facility if it remains in its present use, n is the last year the facility will be kept in this use, and r is the discount rate. S takes account of changes in the intensity of any one use, since it represents expected net returns in any one year or period t.

If a change in one of the four key variables causes another use or mix of uses to be of a higher order than that use or mix which was formerly the highest and best use or mix, the value of the capital facility will be

$$CV_p = \left(\sum_{t=1}^{n} \frac{St}{(1+r)^t} \right) + \left(\sum_{T=n+1}^{m} \frac{S^*t}{(1+r)^t} \right)$$

where CV_p is the present "conversion" value, S^* is the expected net returns to the capital facility in its new highest and best use, and m is the last year the capital facility will be kept in its new highest and best use. Note that CV_p must necessarily lie somewhere between the present value of that use which is first in time and that use which is or will be last in time. In general, the smaller and the less immediate the impact of the change in any one of the four key variables, the more nearly equal will the present conversion value be to the present value of that use which is first in time. However, as t approaches T, the effect upon value of that use which is first in time will be minimal. In any case, the present value of that use which is last in time will be greater at some point in time than the present value of that use which is first in time, for a capital facility would not have another use if the former use continued to be of a higher order.

The concepts outlined in the preceding paragraphs apply to situations where changes in intensity and conversions in the uses of receptor and emitter capital facilities are brought about by general market forces as well as by changes in our four key variables. But, assuming that the general market forces which may differentially affect individual receptors and emitters can be specified, these concepts do provide a basis for determining the differential impact of changes in one or more of the four key variables. Since they provide this basis for individual receptors and emitters, they also provide it for the collection of receptors and emitters. Furthermore, they provide a basis for comparing changes in intensity and conversions in the uses of capital facilities for an area where there is no atmospheric pollution with one where such a problem does exist.

Let us suppose, for example, that we are faced with finding a solution to an atmospheric-pollution problem in an area where fertilizer manufacturers are emitters of pollutants while citrus growers are the receptors. We will assume that during the manufacturing process the fertilizer plants emit gaseous fluorides which settle on the leaves of the citrus trees, causing a collapse of these leaves' cellular structure and a consequent inhibition of the trees' photosynthesis. Let us further suppose that the citrus growers and the fertilizer manufacturers have and will continue to employ, given the expected magnitudes of the four key variables, that quantity of variable inputs which serves to maximize for each individual the present values of the expected net returns obtainable from his capital facilities. What happens to the present values of individual receptor and emitter capital facilities if a control authority allows the magnitude of one of more of the four key variables to increase?

If we assume that rates of emission and the points in time at which the initial emissions are to be allowed to occur are unchanged, the control authority by increasing the allowable volume of emissions will, in effect, stretch the length of time over which the fertilizer manufacturers can emit gaseous fluorides. This simply means that the point in time at which they will have to undertake the installation of more costly control equipment and/or production processes that do not result in the emission of such large quantities of gaseous fluorides is pushed farther into the future. Thus the expected net returns of the fertilizer manufacturers are increased;

therefore the present values of their existing air-related capital facilities are increased. Of course, the closer n (the last year that the existing capital facilities of the fertilizer manufacturers would be used) is to the present before the increase in the allowable volume of emissions, the greater the relative increase in the present values of the existing capital facilities. In essence, the increase in the volume of allowable gaseous flouride emissions has lengthened the economic life of existing fertilizer-manufacturer capital facilities. By increasing the expected net returns of these facilities, the control authority has stretched the time interval over which they will continue to be the highest and best use of each fertilizer manufacturer's site.

From the point of view of the citrus growers, the impact of the increase in the volume of emissions is the opposite of that for the fertilizer manufacturers: the expected net returns of their groves have been reduced and therefore the groves' economic life has been shortened. The citrus growers can follow any one of three courses in response to the new situation. The course which they follow will be that which serves to maximize their expected net returns given the new volume of emissions. First, they can reduce the intensity with which they use their land and groves by reducing the quantity of variable inputs which they employ. For example, they may reduce the number of times during any one growing season that they irrigate their groves or spray their groves against diseases. If this course of action is optimal for the citrus growers and if the new intensity of use actually causes expected net returns to be lower than before, the increase in the volume of emissions has had the effect of reducing the present values of the groves and the sites upon which they are located. Since the increase in the volume of emissions has lowered present values, the point in time when a conversion in use will occur is moved closer to the present.

Second, the increase in the volume of emissions may necessitate an immediate conversion in the mix of the citrus growers' operations. The present value of expected net returns from the present use may be lower than the present value of expected net returns from an alternative use that was formerly of a lower order. For example, some citrus growers may have to cut down their groves and use the sites for the production of watermelons. In this case, $t = T$. That use which was of the highest order before the increase in the volume of emissions contributes nothing whatsoever to the present value of the sites.

Third, the increase in the volume of gaseous fluorides to be emitted may make imperative the cessation of any and all agricultural operations. Nonagricultural uses of the sites—mining, for example—may conceivably outweigh any and all possible agricultural uses. If the ore underlying the sites formerly used for citrus production is used by the fertilizer manufacturers in their production processes, it is evident that the increase in the allowable volume of gaseous fluoride emissions has been a handy device by means of which the fertilizer manufacturers have been able to drive down the prices at which they can purchase mining land.

For citrus growers in each of the above cases, the dollar magnitude of the damage costs attributable to the increase in the allowable volume of gaseous fluoride emissions is equivalent to the present value of the expected foregone net returns from the citrus groves. The damage costs are thus the present value of the expected foregone net returns in $n - n'$, where n' is the last year that the groves will be allowed to remain standing with the increase in gaseous fluoride emission volumes, plus the expected reductions in present values of S_t taking place over the new and shorter economic life of the groves. Similarly, the dollar magnitude of the cost-savings accruing to the fertilizer manufacturers due to the increase in the allowable volume of gaseous fluoride emissions is equivalent to the present value of the expected net returns resulting from the increase in the economic life of their capital facilities, plus the present values of any increases in S_t taking place over the old economic life of these capital facilities.

The preceding manner of looking at the damage costs and cost-savings resulting from an increase in the allowable volume of emissions means, in effect, that any estimation procedure based only upon contemporary damage costs and cost-savings or upon the present values of damage costs and cost-savings over the old economic life of receptor and emitter capital facilities must seriously underestimate the absolute levels of both these magnitudes. If only contemporary damage costs and cost-savings are recognized, the reasons why underestimation will occur are obvious. Although discounting future cost-savings and damage costs over the old economic life of emitter and receptor capital facilities will lead to better estimates than will the contemporary approach, underestimation of both magnitudes will occur because changes in the economic life of these capital facilities are not being accounted for. From the receptors' point of view, damage costs are not simply reductions in present values of S_t over the old economic life of their capital facilities, but these reductions and the present value of the differences between S_t and S^*_t in $n - n'$. For emitters, cost-savings are not simply the present values of the increases in S_t taking place over the old economic life of their capital facilities, but, in addition, the present value of the differences between S_t and S^*_t in $n'' - n$, where n'' is the last year that the emitter capital facilities will be used for their present purposes.

With an increase in the allowable volume of gaseous fluoride emissions, both the contemporary approach and the approach which discounts cost-savings and damage costs over the previous economic life of emitter and receptor capital facilities must overestimate the difference between these cost-savings and damage costs. That is, since the present value of a sum closer to the present is greater than the present value of that same sum farther in the future, the relative magnitude of damage costs to cost-savings is greater than it would be if the contraction of the economic life of receptor capital facilities and the expansion of the economic life of emitter capital facilities are emphasized. If we were to talk in terms of reduction in emission volumes, we would of course be concerned with expansions in the economic life of receptor capital facilities and contractions in the economic life of emitter capital facilities. In this latter case, failure to consider changes in the economic life of emitter and receptor capital facilities would result in underestimation of the difference between the present values of cost-savings and damage costs.

The essential point here is that the objective of atmospheric pollution control programs should be to maximize the present value of the difference between emitter cost-savings and receptor damage, costs. Thinking solely in terms of damage costs, as do many empirical studies, will tend to underestimate greatly the value of the air's waste-disposal dimension—this estimation procedure will in fact mean that a zero value has been attached to this dimension. On the other hand, estimation procedures based on contemporary cost-savings and damage costs, or procedures which fail to consider changes in the economic life of emitter and receptor capital facilities, will either over- or underestimate the value of the air's life- and property-supporting dimension. If one or more of the four key variables is to increase, these approaches will tend to underestimate the life- and property-supporting dimension's value, and therefore, much to the horror of the pure-air advocates, overestimate the waste-disposal dimension's value. Conversely, the use of either of these two approaches to determine the relative values of the air's two value dimensions when a reduction in one or more of the four key variables is being contemplated will overestimate the life- and property-supporting dimension's value and underestimate the waste-disposal dimension's value. The only truly correct estimation procedure is that procedure which takes into account the present values of the expected net returns accruing to or foregone by emitters and receptors over both the old and the new economic life of their capital facilities.

Alternative Means of Modifying Atmospheric-Pollution Problems

We have seen that the central problem facing an atmospheric pollution control authority attempting to allocate optimally over time the air's two value dimensions between and among different uses and users is the determination of the present values of the damage costs and cost-savings which accrue to or are foregone by emitters and receptors when one or more of our four so-called key variables change. As we have implied, the relevant question for a control authority to ask about a contemplated change in one or more of the four key variables is whether or not the change will cause the difference between the present values of cost-savings and damage costs to be increased. If so, the contemplated change is economically justified; if not, the contemplated change is economically unjustified.

One might well question the necessity of all the effort that has gone into arriving at this seemingly simple statement. It all seems rather apparent—once one understands it. Yet this writer has been unable to find any evidence in the applied atmospheric-pollution literature of any attention being given to these matters. No mention is ever made in the writings dealing with actual atmospheric pollution control programs of the time-structure of damage costs and cost-savings, even though ignoring them can be done only at the risk of imposing unnecessarily great losses upon emitters, receptors, and society. One tends to suspect that many of the engineers who have been given the responsibility of administering atmospheric pollution control programs are more interested in optimizing their subjective work loads than in maximizing over time the net social returns obtainable from the air resource. This possibility would tend to account at least partially for the affection with which standards or rules of thumb are regarded in pollution-control programs.[14]

However, the measurement of damage cost and cost-savings discounted values is a job that will arouse envy only in those who prefer extremely difficult undertakings. Obviously, taking all the factors into account which may affect the present values of the two types of costs constitutes a formidable task. Increasing and decreasing returns to the scale of capital facilities, forthcoming changes in the prices of factors of production because of shifts in the factor supply and demand functions, changes in the relative prices of emitter and receptor outputs—all of these things and many more affect the present values of emitter and receptor capital facilities. They will therefore have to be adequately dealt with in the determination of damage cost and cost-savings discounted values. Even if the assumption that all the relevant functions are linear in form is not too gross a deviation from reality, a control authority will still have to have some means of determining, at least over the immediate future, the likely shifts in these functions. Even though the externalities formerly caused by the lack of coordination between and among many interdependent receptors and emitters may have now been made internal by the formation of an atmospheric pollution control authority, the basic physical conditions which originally brought about the atmospheric-pollution problem still exist. Even though control over the air resource has been allocated on a scale sufficient to relate in an optimal manner the receptors and emitters to each other and therefore to the atmospheric-pollution problem, all that the formation of the control authority has done is to change the form in which the necessary allocation decisions must be made. Even though the control program administrators have a thorough understanding of the theoretical niceties of optimal economic allocation of the air's two value dimensions, the practical problem of discovering the actual optimal allocation over any one interval of time must still be wrestled with, and a means for carrying out this allocation must still be evolved.

Nevertheless, let us assume that the atmospheric pollution control authority is fortunate enough to possess perfect foresight. More specifically, let us assume that the control authority can, but at a cost, obtain all the information that it needs to achieve something closely approximating perfect foresight—at least in the sense that the information available to it enables it to carry out its allocative decisions within the context of risk rather than uncertainty.

If we suppose that the cost of gathering more detailed information increases with the accumulated knowledge of the control authority, information gathering should continue until such time as the additional costs of gathering additional information are equal to the present value of the additional social net returns flowing from the increase in the likelihood that over time the control authority will make optimal allocative decisions. But even though we have made the strong assumption that the control authority is able to obtain sufficient information to enable it to deal solely within the context of risk, we have, by stating the entirely reasonable hypothesis that the control authority will have to spend somebody's money in order to accumulate information, reintroduced into the problem that cloud which corrupts so many of the clean and clear creations of planners —uncertainty. In other words, the formal allocation problem has now been recast into a much more complex problem in which the costs of achieving optimal allocation must now be included.

If we no longer take it on faith that all the information which the control authority gathers is completely accurate, the uncertainty problem which the control authority faces is even greater. Even in highly technical meteorological and biochemical information-gathering and interpretation activities—areas in which the control authority will supposedly excel individual receptors and emitters—the contribution of the control authority to the reduction of uncertainty is often apparently not very great. There is no lack of litigation in which the plaintiff supposedly damaged by atmospheric pollution has been armed with extensive technical data, but has not proved to the satisfaction of the court that he has been damaged. If the accuracy of the information which the control authority gathers is uncertain and if it is to base its allocative decisions upon this uncertain information, then the risks of not achieving optimal allocation are of course greatly increased. Conceivably, the use of this inaccurate information for allocation decisions could over time, because of the quasi-irreversible nature of receptor and emitter investment in sunk capital made on the basis of the control authority's allocative decisions, cause the allocation to deviate further and further from the true optimum.

Rather than going to all the trouble of estimating the damage-cost and cost-savings functions by measuring physical and biological variables and forecasting likely future market prices for the factor inputs and outputs of receptors and emitters, the control authority can simply periodically request that these parties state the value that they are likely to place upon various qualities of air at alternative future dates. This so-called interview procedure appears to be becoming more and more of a favorite in the social sciences. Except for the costs associated with gathering data on pollutant concentrations, the cost of this procedure is likely to be nominal compared to alternative means of measurement. But it is difficult to imagine receptors and emitters not being reluctant to disclose information which may result in their having to relinquish that quality of air which they actually desire. The pattern of supposed values which the control authority will have to work with will undoubtedly closely conform to that expressed by receptors and emitters when they can consider either or both of the air's two value dimensions to be free goods. Whether the control authority employs taxes and/or subsidies or whether it attempts to simulate market processes on computers so as to achieve optimal allocation, the measurement difficulties which it faces will be great and probably insurmountable.

Given the uncertain quality of available physical, biological, and economic information, and the potentially high costs associated with the gathering of additional information [15] about atmospheric-pollution problems, the control authority, in order to impress receptors and emitters with the necessity of regarding the air's two value dimensions as scarce economic resources, appears to be justified in setting minimal standards. The standards imposed upon emitters are generally direct or indirect forms of emission or locational standards, or combinations of both, while those, if any, imposed upon receptors are generally locational in form. If the control authority imposes standards upon emitters alone, it has in fact placed a minimum but no maximum economic value upon the air's life- and property-supporting capacity. At the same time, it has placed a maximum but no minimum value upon the air's waste-disposal capacity.[16] Similarly, the imposition of standards upon receptors alone amounts to placing a minimum but no maximum value upon the waste-disposal dimension, and a maximum but no minimum value upon the life- and property-supporting dimension. Thus the effect of placing standards upon *both* receptors and emitters is not to call for the performance of specific acts by receptors and emitters. Instead, the effect of these standards is merely to restrict individual receptor and emitter initiative in air uses to certain predetermined channels.

Given sufficient legislative authorization, the control authority can establish a set of standards which will apply to just about every conceivable air-related activity. If, in addition, it allows each activity to which particular standards apply to vary only within a relatively narrow range, it can do away with nearly all the uncertainties involved in measurement. The authority can then simulate market processes or employ taxes and/or subsidies in order to achieve an optimal allocation within the constraints imposed by the standards. The greater the costs of gathering information, the more restrictive will the standards have to be in order to minimize the impact of the lack of that information which the control authority has not been able to gather for making its allocation decisions. That is, the greater the uncertainty of the control authority about how receptors and emitters will react to changes in the four key variables, the narrower must be the range in which the control authority can allow individual receptor and emitter air-use decisions to be operative. Otherwise, the control authority may unknowingly be pursuing contradictory and inconsistent objectives.

The central problem involved in the preceding paragraphs is the question of the extent to which it will be necessary to substitute for the individual preference functions of receptors and emitters the preference function of the control authority for various qualities of air at differing locations. The less the information the control authority has about the individual preference functions of receptors and emitters, the greater the extent to which it will have to substitute its own preference function. Even if we accept the idea that the control authority will generally be superior to individual receptors and emitters when it comes to physical and biochemical information gathering and interpretation, it is a bit difficult to see how the control authority will be any better than receptors and emitters at determining their individual preference functions. It need not follow from the obvious necessity for public and therefore centralized ownership of the air resource that all decisions as to how the two dimensions of the resource will be intertemporally and interspatially allocated should be centralized. That is, completely centralized decision-making is not a necessary condition for centralized ownership. Just as a public utility may supply water at a charge varying with quantity, time, and location to a variety of competing uses and users, an air pollution control authority can supply rights to the use of the air's waste-disposal dimension at a charge varying with quantity, time, and location to competing receptors and emitters. The objective of this charge or set of charges should be, as we argued earlier, to maximize the difference between the present value of cost-savings to emitters and the present value of damage costs to receptors.

I would like to suggest that a market pricing system which defines emission rights in terms of our four key variables [17] according to meteorological conditions and location, and which is open to both emitters and receptors on a periodic competitive basis offers as yet unexploited possibilities of drastically increasing the likelihood of achieving optimal intertemporal and interspatial allocation of the air's two value dimensions. By the same token, the informational requirements necessary for the control authority to insure something approximately optimal intertemporal and interspatial allocation will be greatly reduced under such a system. Although the atmospheric pollution control authority's responsibilities will continue to be a good deal broader than the basic governmental function of providing legal and tenure certainty in property rights, its necessary work will not have to include all the guesswork involved in attempting to estimate individual emitter and receptor preference functions.

All in all, there is little doubt that the signaling potential of a price system has not yet been given its due in most atmospheric pollution problems. Regardless of the ability of an uninhibited market pricing system to bring about a closer approximation to optimal intertemporal and interspatial allocation of the air's two value dimensions, an atmospheric pollution control authority cannot, unless it wishes to carry out its allocations without regard to the preferences of individual receptors and emitters, neglect the information-providing potential of a price system. It is one of the advantages of a price system that in order for it to work efficiently, the only person who needs to know about how any given user will use the right he has purchased is the user himself. He has to decide how much to offer for a certain right. Whether or not he will obtain it depends on what others are willing to offer. If, for some reason, the market doesn't conform to his ideas about his future needs, then he doesn't have to participate in the market. The decisions that he and all other users of the air resource make with respect to the purchase of emission rights thus reveal to the control authority the real economic values of the air's two value dimensions.

Given the difficulties implicit in the estimation of individual receptor and emitter preference functions by means of interviews or direct calculation of damage-cost and cost-savings functions, some provision for the purchase of emission rights by receptors and by emitters is necessary. While providing a means of verifying receptor and emitter preferences, such a provision also produces objectively quantifiable information for purposes of setting and checking standards. One might argue that a system based on taxes and/or subsidies can accomplish the same ends, but it is a bit difficult to imagine the control authority varying its taxes and subsidies over relatively short periods of time and then observing the reactions of receptors and emitters to these variations. Although the theoretical results of varying taxes and/or subsidies and of observing actual market-determined prices may be similar, the practical ease of carrying out the two alternatives differs greatly. Unless the control authority is willing to vary its taxes and subsidies over rather wide ranges for each receptor and emitter site and for each time period being considered, it will be posed with the technically impossible problem of estimating ranges of preference functions for which it has no information.

As we have previously noted, the essence of the atmospheric-pollution problem is the almost total absence between receptors and emitters of linkages which will cause their joint production decisions to reflect adequately the relative values of the air's two value dimensions. The value of the air's waste-disposal dimension to emitters is in no way related to the numbers and types of receptors harmed, and the value of the air's life- and property-supporting dimension is in no way related to the numbers and types of emitters who desire to use the waste-disposal dimension. Part, though by no means all, of the problem stems from the currently employed concepts of property rights in air which, in essence, fail to distinguish sufficiently between the rights of the underlying landowner in the air and in the airspace over him. The resemblance between the problems caused by this failure and the problems caused by the old absolute-ownership doctrine of groundwater law is obvious. The latter doctrine defines the groundwater user's rights in terms of reservoir space, but fails to define his rights relative to the rights of other groundwater users in the water that percolates through that space; existing property law in air defines the air user's rights in terms of airspace, but fails to define clearly his rights relative to the rights of other air users in the air that flows through that space. In both cases, the result is that the owner of the space uses the resource within the space until such time as for him and him alone the present value of its marginal-value product is zero.

The general failure of most modern property law in air to distinguish between air and airspace is harmless enough when the air's two value dimensions are plentiful and therefore free. No harm is done by relating the user only to the resource itself rather than to other users. But when the resource is no longer plentiful, property and tenure relations, if the necessary coordination between and among users is to take place, must be defined in terms of man and men rather than man and air. That is, property rights in air must link users to each other as well as to the air. The rights of any one user of the air resource relative to any other user of the air resource must be clearly defined. Until such time as property rights in at least the air's waste-disposal dimension are defined in terms of our four key variables and according to meteorological conditions and location, the efforts of atmospheric pollution control authorities will continue to be reminiscent of the often unsuccessful efforts of the United States Government in the last half of the nineteenth century to evict squatters from public lands that had never been legally acquired from the sovereign power which supposedly owned them.

However, simply introducing a precisely defined system of emission rights which can be purchased and traded by both emitters and receptors will neither enable a market or pricing system to operate effectively nor provide the degree of collectivization necessary for something approximating optimal allocation of the air's two value dimensions between and among receptors and emitters. Even though the emission rights which cause the technological externalities are now set forth in a form amenable to selling and trading, a means or organization which will enable such selling to occur has not yet been provided. It is still necessary to find a means to achieve cooperation among receptors to whose advantage it is *not* to cooperate with each other. That is, it is worth the while of the individual receptor not to purchase an emission right, in the hope that his neighbor will purchase one, and vice versa: the emission rights are to some degree lumpy. Since the individual who purchases an emission right is unable to appropriate all its benefits for himself, he is willing to sit back and let his fellow receptors spill some benefits onto him. Any one receptor's needs cannot be satisfied to the complete exclusion of other receptors' needs. Thus there apparently exists a need for additional collective action. Since we have already presupposed the existence of a control authority among whose functions it is to sell emission rights, this additional collective action must mean some form of centralized decision-making. The range in which private receptor and emitter choice is operative narrows, and the range for collective or centralized choice broadens.

If a market pricing system is to have any applicability in atmospheric-pollution problems, it is necessary to work with groups of receptors encompassing land areas large enough to make possible the purchase of emission rights in discrete and homogeneous units. Ideally, each group of receptors should be of that size which will enable it to appropriate all the benefits from its purchase of an emission right. Furthermore, some means of sharing the cost of purchasing the emission right among members of the group must be formulated.[18] Decision-making and some estimation of individual-receptor preference functions and damage-cost functions by the control authority will be necessary for the determination of the boundaries of each receptor group and for cost-sharing arrangements within any one receptor group. The manner in which the control authority might go about arriving at the best attainable boundary constraints among groups and cost-sharing arrangements within groups cannot be dealt with here, since the writer has not yet worked out the implications of the various alternatives. Nevertheless, it is apparent that neither completely centralized decision-making by the control authority nor uninhibited market processes, even if emission rights are precisely defined, can bring about optimal intertemporal and interspatial allocation of the air's two value dimensions. That structuring of atmospheric pollution control programs most likely to approximate an optimal allocation of the air's two value dimensions will be a mix of standards, taxes and/or subsidies, some of which of necessity will be arbitrary, and market processes. Even though there may be no great difference theoretically in the rationality of centralized decision-making and uninhibited market processes, any control authority which does not take advantage of the ability of the market to provide information for the structuring of forthcoming authority decisions and the correction of past authority errors must have a serious misconception of its responsibilities to society.

In summary, the basic question in atmospheric-pollution control is not of an either/or nature, a choice between completely centralized control and individual receptor and emitter control or lack of control. It is a question instead of what the proportions will be in which private and collective decision-making elements are combined. The proportion of each element employed must be dependent on the extent to which it can reduce uncertainty and enhance communication. The choice is not between two systems of control, one perfect and the other imperfect, but between two imperfect systems, each with its own set of errors. It is thus necessary to do more than simply test the two alternative decision-making systems against what are considered to be optimum results, and reject them if they don't conform. It is instead necessary in each problematic situation to test each possible mix of the two alternatives against optimum results and to accept the best of these mixes. If we look upon the control authority as being the owner of a donkey with a split personality, divided between receptors and emitters, we can say that the authority will not get the donkey to move at an adequate pace by using the stick of standards and taxes and/or subsidies. Neither will the donkey move in the correct manner if the authority has to stand in front of his nose offering him the carrot of market prices. Only if the rider sits upon the donkey's back holding the stick with the carrot attached to its end will the donkey take it upon himself to move correctly. The question is the proper length and thickness of the stick and the proper size of the carrot.

NOTES

1. This paper is part of a larger project dealing with the economics of air pollution and financed by U. S. Public Health Service Grant No. AP00389-01.

2. For example, a recent advertisement for a book dealing with air-pollution problems screams in large block letters: "With every breath you take you bring poisons into your body." Such statements, even though true, remind me of the character in the comic strip *Morty Meekle* who worries unceasingly about the dangers associated with the millions of germs to be found on the head of a pin.

3. Leslie A. Chambers, "Classification and Extent of Air Pollution Problems," in Arthur C. Stern, ed., *Air Pollution*, Vol. I, New York, Academic Press, New York, 1962, p. 21.

4. One currently popular figure of $10,000,000,000 in annual national damages is clearly a gross estimate.

5. For an interesting presentation of the implications of this modification ability for the economics of natural-resource use, see M. Mason Gaffney, "Soil Depletion and Land Rent," *Natural Resources Journal*, Vol. 2 (January, 1965), pp. 537–57.

6. Kimmis Hendrick and Robert C. Cowen, "Cities Designed for Breathing,"

The Christian Science Monitor (March 31, 1965), p. 9.

7. Although the writer wishes that he could claim this phrase for his own, he must acknowledge that its creator is Professor Gordon Maskew Fair of Harvard University.

8. One effect of these assumptions is to rule out one of the most important sources of atmospheric pollution—the automobile. Nevertheless, most of the concepts presented here are also applicable to atmospheric-pollution problems caused by the automobile.

9. If the underlying relationships which determine these functions are nonlinear, rather than linear, a geometric mean would have to be employed. I am indebted to Professor Gladstone Bonnick for pointing this out.

10. P. H. Phillips, "The Effects of Air Pollutants on Farm Animals," in Paul L. Magill and others, eds., *Air Pollution Handbook*, New York, McGraw-Hill, 1956.

11. P. J. O'Gara, "Sulfur Dioxide and Fume Problems and Their Solutions," *Industrial Engineering Chemistry*, Vol. 14 (1922), p. 744.

12. A problem could of course be solved by holding the four variables constant for emitters and varying the land space devoted to any one receptor or emitter use. However, for any one receptor site, the effect of such a move would still be to cause one or more of these four variables to change.

13. The term "capital facilities" as employed here refers to any input potentially capable of producing an output over time. Thus the reference is to land as well as to capital in the usual sense: an input which has been created by man and is capable of producing an output over time.

14. The reasons for the dominant use of physical standards for purposes of control are by no means always attributable to the engineers usually directly responsible for the practical administration of air pollution control programs. Too many of the scientific experiments which are carried out, particularly with respect to physical receptor damages, are not set forth in terms amenable to the determination of the time-structure of damage costs and cost-savings.

15. The potentially high costs associated with the gathering of additional information are not limited to the simple costs of accumulating it. There may also be costs implicit in failing to take immediate action while hoping that more and better information will be available at a later date.

16. Over time, these minimum and maximum values will of course vary.

17. Actually, as long as the point in time which the first emission can occur is included in the right, the right will be clearly and precisely defined if any two of the other three variables are included. For example, defining the right in terms of the allowable volume of emissions and the interval of time over which emissions can take place means that emissions must occur at a certain rate per unit of time.

18. The writer does not pretend to have worked out the conditions for the optimum size of such a group. Neither has he yet tried to determine an optimal means of cost-sharing within such a group. With respect to the first matter, some valuable suggesting and hypotheses can be found in O. A. Davis and A. S. Whinston, "The Economics of Complex Systems—The Case of Municipal Zoning," *Kyklos*, Vol. 17 (1964), pp. 419–46.

Strategies for Measuring the Cost of Air Pollution [1]

RONALD G. RIDKER
SYRACUSE UNIVERSITY AND THE BROOKINGS INSTITUTION

Ronald G. Ridker is on leave from Syracuse University, where he is an associate professor of economics. He is a visiting professor of research at the Brookings Institution, Washington, D. C.

I TAKE IT that what we are concerned to measure are the net social benefits of different levels and types of air-pollution controls. In effect, we wish to perform a series of conceptual experiments in which we alter the level of controls and then observe their effects on welfare. On the basis of such information we would then advise that controls be set at the point at which net social benefits are maximum. Since I have been engaged in a project whose goal is to develop and test out methods to measure the economic costs of air-pollution damage, most of my comments and examples will pertain to this aspect of the total measurement problem.[2] Accordingly, this paper focuses primarily on the methods and problems of estimating what might be called the cost-of-pollution schedule or curve, a curve that relates changes in ambient air quality to the economic costs that these changes entail.

Now this is hardly an easy task. It takes only a brief consideration of the problems to discover that we are faced not with just one, but with almost an infinite variety of tasks. Air pollution is a multidimensional phenomenon. It comes from a wide variety of sources, affects a multitude of objects, and can result in a wide variety of changes in behavior. These effects are not always immediate, but tend to be spread over time in different ways depending on the object affected. And to add to the problems, data are poor, the relevant functions are stochastic in nature, and the "independent variables" of any given analysis tend to be highly intercorrelated. In this situation, one cannot expect a priori to find proxies that can be used to represent broad categories of pollutants or of effects. There is no alternative except to undertake a series of studies on a fairly detailed, disaggregated level. After the fact, one may be able to make useful generalizations, but there is no way to know this without undertaking a wide variety of specialized studies.

This brief paper cannot discuss all these problems; indeed, some of them are quite mundane and tedious to recount. It is more interesting and fruitful to consider a number of alternative strategies that can be used in measuring the costs of pollution damage. The problems encountered in using these approaches will become clear enough from illustrations included to explain each approach.

To begin, let us cut the overall problem down to manageable size by making a number of assumptions. First, assume that factors having the same consequences as air pollution, as well as our knowledge about ways to adjust to these consequences, are held constant. This assumption means that, for example, we ignore changes in non-pollution causes of diseases and improvements in our ability to prevent diseases. This is not a particularly unrealistic assumption, given available samples of observations. Many of these variables change through time rather than through space (within this country), and since measurements on air pollution do not go back far enough in time to permit substantial use of time-series data, we are in any case forced to rely upon cross-section data. Second, we assume that intervening variables such as topological and meteorological conditions can be ignored. A corrosive pollutant, for example, will cause more damage in warm, humid weather than in a cold, dry climate. But such variables typically behave in irregular and unpredictable ways, and changes in the effects of air pollution as they change are not fully understood. All that can be done here is to take care in our choice of measurement studies that such factors are, in fact, constant. This consideration, for example, would throw some doubts on the usefulness of cross-section interurban studies but would not affect intraurban studies, for within a city (at one point in time) weather conditions can be assumed to be more or less constant. Third, we must assume that adequate air-pollution measurements are available and—equally important—that we know how to use them. That is, we must know a sufficient amount about the way pollution works to know whether a measure of the average level of intensity or of peak intensities would be most appropriate. These last assumptions are obviously unrealistic in many instances, but unless they are made, there is no sense in starting the process of measuring the economic costs of air-pollution damage.

Finally, we ignore the effects that changes in air-pollution levels can have on such economic variables as employment and income distribution. If the level of air pollution were reduced, window washers, paint manufacturers, and possibly even doctors would do less business; but the controls that brought about this reduction would stimulate employment in the manufacture of control devices. In effect, we assume that such shifts in employment occur relatively easily and that their net effect is negligible. The same assumption must be made about effects on technology, though a study of controls would have to take certain kinds of technological changes into account.

Now let us assume that ambient air quality as measured on a particular scale—say, annual geometric mean sulfation rates—rises in a particular locality. Three different levels or stages of effects can be distinguished. First, the pollution has certain direct and immediate effects. It may damage paint, cause throat irritation, result in a discoloration of the leaves of plants, and raise certain age-specific mortality and morbidity rates. Second, these effects give rise to certain adjustments which individuals and firms make so as to reduce the direct impact of the pollutant on them. An asthmatic may adjust by moving from the area, a spinach grower by shifting to another crop, a homeowner by painting more often, and so forth. These adjustments serve to reduce the cost of the direct effects of the increased pollution, but can be quite costly in their own right. Third, these adjustments involve actions that affect others. When spinach production shifts from one location to another, the price of spinach is likely to be affected, some jobs created and others destroyed. Such social-interaction effects can also be quite important consequences of the initial rise in pollution.

Each of these different levels of effects suggests a different strategy for measuring the economic costs of air pollution. Only the last strategy, which takes into account social interactions as well as direct effects and adjustments, is adequate from a theoretical point of view. But because of data limitations, clues must be obtained wherever they can be found. Furthermore, each level of analysis can contribute to our understanding of the whole situation.

The Cost of Air-Pollution Damage in the Absence of Adjustments

If we are willing to ignore the adjustments that an individual can make to reduce the impact of air pollution on himself, as well as the social interactions that result from these adjustments, the following information will suffice to obtain the desired cost figure.

First, we must have a description of the damage per unit of each object affected as a function of the intensity of air pollution, all other factors that could cause such damage being held constant. If we assume for the moment that there is a determinate relationship between each damage and the particular pollutant concerned, then the relationships can be represented thus:

$$D_i = f_i(S), \qquad i = (1, \ldots, n)$$

where D_i is a measure of the ith type of damage per unit of object affected by the pollution and S is a measure of pollution (in our example, annual geometric mean sulfation rate). In this notation each different damage to each different object must be identified separately. Second, a monetary weight (a price or a cost per unit) appropriate to measure the importance of the particular effect must be obtained. And third, an indication of the number of units of the objects affected is necessary.

On the assumption that the monetary weights and the number of units affected stay constant as the level of pollution varies, the total cost for this pollutant can be obtained by multiplying the damage function by the appropriate cost per unit damage, C_i, and the number of units affected, Q_i, and then summing over all types of damage. In symbols, the total cost function is:

$$\sum_{i=1}^{n} C_i Q_i f_i(S),$$

and its derivative with respect to S is the marginal cost.[3]

A few words about each of the three types of information required by this approach is in order. The specification of the damage function is the responsibility of the technical expert in the field concerned—the metallurgist if we are talking about metal corrosion, the epidemiologist or physiologist if we are concerned with damage to human beings. But if the experts' studies are to be useful as inputs into benefit-cost analyses, the damage function must be specified in terms relevant to loss in economic functions. Indications of changes in human respiration rates or in the chlorophyll content in plants are not useful for this purpose. Changes in absenteeism rates or in fruit yields are relevant.

To date, very little is available in a form that is useful for economic analysis. Under these circumstances, the best that an economist can do is to indicate what is required for an economic analysis of a specific pollution problem and then to concentrate on measuring the unit costs and the quantities at risk.

The task of obtaining a figure for the price or cost of a unit of damage varies from the trivial to the highly complex, depending on the type of damage considered. If there is a market for the objects concerned, the price prevailing in that market can serve as a useful first approximation. If there is a simple, direct way to eliminate the damage—for example, the repainting of objects subject to corrosion —the minimum cost of such maintenance or repair can be used as a conservative estimate of the loss due to the damage.[4] If there is no market for the affected objects, it may still be possible to construct a useful cost figure from market data. This is the case, for example, with some categories of effects on human beings. A minimal but still useful estimate of the mortality cost of a particular disease can be obtained from figures indicating loss of earnings, and market costs of treatment and of burial, if they are judiciously combined with a wide variety of assumptions about life expectancy, employment rates, discount rates, and the like.

But finally, there will be some categories of loss where no market reflections whatsoever are present. The most important and difficult example in this category is what might be called "psychic costs." This category includes everything from the anguish of death to the disappointment felt when one's view of the mountains is obscured by smog. Economists have generally ignored this category on the grounds that it cannot be accurately measured, and that in many cases its inclusion would not alter the decision that a benefit-cost analysis which is adequate in other respects leads to. The difficulty when considering air pollution is that there are important cases where this category *would* make a difference in the policy decision if it were included. Indeed, I suspect that the increased demand for clean air over the last fifty years or so comes mainly from a desire for a more beautiful environment and only secondarily from an increased knowledge of the detrimental effects of pollution.

Within the framework of this first approach to measurement, there is only one way that such psychic costs can be measured; people must be directly asked how much they would be willing to pay to obtain the more pleasant environment. It may be that direct-interview attempts to obtain such indications are bound to fail and that the only adequate way is to face people with actual choices on which they have to vote. But ultimately, this question can only be answered on the basis of empirical evidence. In a small way, we are attempting to provide such evidence by including a number of willingness-to-pay questions in a household survey being undertaken for the project cited in footnote 2.

The problems of measuring the number of objects vulnerable to air-pollution damage are fewer. In some cases the data are already gathered, as for example, information on the number of persons, automobiles, and houses exposed to urban environments. In other cases, sample survey methods can be used to make the necessary estimates. This is not to say that such a survey would always be easy. It would be quite costly, for example, to obtain a reasonable estimate of the extent of exposed surfaces such as unprotected metals that could be damaged by air pollution. But in principle, such a task certainly could be accomplished.

As an example of this approach, our attempts to measure the economic costs of a number of diseases thought to be associated with air pollution can be mentioned.[5] Cost estimates of treatment, absenteeism, and premature death, where relevant, were made for cancer of the respiratory system, chronic bronchitis, acute bronchitis, pneumonia, emphysema, asthma, and the common cold. Unfortunately, there is unsufficient information available to go beyond providing such unit-cost figures. In particular, we cannot estimate the proportion of total cases that may be attributable to air pollution. By obtaining cost estimates, however, at least the first step toward gathering the necessary materials has been accomplished.

Since this approach to measuring the costs of air-pollution damage leaves out adjustments and social-interaction effects, its conclusions will be biased. If all the direct costs have been measured, the bias is likely to be on the side of overstating the costs of air-pollution damage, for the net effect of the adjustments must be to reduce the associated costs—otherwise, the adjustments would not have been undertaken.[6] This is unfortunate, for it means that, in contrast to many benefit-cost analyses in the public-health and human-resource fields, we cannot stop at this level of analysis and be sure that we have conservatively assessed the damages.

Individual Adjustments

It is difficult to think of cases in which there are no possibilities available to an individual for adjusting to a detrimental change in his environment. In the worst cases, the possibilities may not be very significant; but something, if only sublimation, can always be done to reduce the impact of a change.

Consider an individual who suddenly finds his asthma getting worse as a consequence of increasing levels of air pollution. There are several logically possible courses of action open to him. On the most general level of classification, he may do nothing, simply suffering the additional discomfort involved; or he may do something he would not otherwise have done. A change in his behavior may take three different forms. First, the individual may change the amount of time he spends in the affected area, by taking longer vacations outside the area of his residence, for example, by moving his place of residence, or by changing jobs. Second, without changing the amount of time spent in the affected area, the individual may try to offset the detrimental effects by taking some remedial action—for example, staying indoors and filtering air coming from outside, or taking additional medications. Third, without changing his location, the individual may try to obtain the removal of the added levels of pollution from his environment. Perhaps the most obvious example here is political action to force factories to control emissions. Such actions have as their goal the elimination of the pollution, as compared to the other actions, which try in different ways to eliminate the negative consequences of the pollution. The second category can be further subdivided according to whether the activities are undertaken by the affected individual or purchased in the market.

If we accept the normal assumptions about human behavior made in microeconomic theory, several implications for measurement follow. First, no matter what the individual does, a loss in utility is involved. If he does nothing, he suffers a direct psychic loss; if he adjusts in any way, he transfers at least some of the loss to other categories, where it appears in a different form. In so doing, he may reduce the total impact of the loss, but he cannot completely eliminate it. Second, the individual will generally find he can cut his losses by spreading them among a number of categories—by letting his car remain a little dirtier *and* by washing it a little more often. Third, there is no a priori reason to assume that some categories of behavior will be so small, relative to others, that the losses resulting from them can be ignored.

These points raise serious problems for measurement. They mean that we must search far and wide to discover the effects of pollution damage, that we cannot concentrate on one particular category of loss and hope thereby to obtain a reasonable approximation for the others. After the fact we may discover that certain categories of adjustments are unimportant and can be ignored, but there is no way to know this until the measurements have been made.

In contrast to studies utilizing the first approach to measurement, in which only direct costs are considered, attempts to measure the costs of various categories of adjustments to the effects of air pollution cannot rely upon a damage function provided by the pollution expert. Any relation between air pollution and the cost of adjustments to it must be based upon data specifically gathered for this purpose. In principle, the procedure is straightforward. First, each logically possible and mutually exclusive category of adjustment that can be used to minimize the effects of a particular pollutant on a particular object must be identified, and behavior falling into these categories measured. Second, all important variables that could also explain this behavior must be identified and measured. These measurements must be made in such a way that variations in the variables over time and in space can be associated with similar variations in the pollutant. Finally, for each category of behavior, statistical analysis must be applied to separate out the effects of the pollutant from the other factors that could also explain the behavior involved. The result will be the equivalent of a damage function that must then be combined with estimates of unit costs and quantities at risk and aggregated over different categories of behavior to obtain a cost-of-pollution function.

To illustrate this approach, reference can be made to a sample survey we conducted which, among other things, attempted to determine the extent to which maintenance and cleaning costs in the home are related to air pollution. This study was undertaken in Philadelphia in three neighborhoods that appear reasonably comparable in all respects except levels of pollution. Since the study is essentially exploratory, having as its goal the identification of differences in cleaning activities and the major factors that cause them, the questionnaire is quite long and covers a range of material that may eventually prove to be unnecessary. For example, the observed differences in the cost of keeping interior walls clean may appear in monetary form, in terms of a difference in frequency with which the task is performed, in terms of time spent performing the task, in terms of energy expended on the task, or in terms of "psychic loss" (i.e., letting the walls get dirtier). Until it is determined that some of these forms of behavior are of trivial importance, we must continue asking about each. Furthermore, since at best air pollution is likely to explain only a small proportion of the variations observed in this set of variables, we must go much further than the normal consumer-expenditure study in asking for information that can help separate out other—and probably more important—causes for the variation. Thus, in addition to income, education, ethnic background and the like, we have asked about the shade of paint used, whether pets live in the house, what kind of heating plant is used, how many members of the family smoke, and so on. Preliminary results of depth interviews suggest that some of these seemingly trivial factors are actually quite important. They also suggest that we may have a situation in which, after eliminating other reasons for the observed variations, we will be able to show that air pollution is really a significant variable.

Market Effects

In the previous section we considered the fact that individuals make adjustments to the direct effects of pollution in order to minimize their impact. For practical reasons it may not be possible to go beyond this level in making measurements. But the only completely adequate way to measure the social losses involved in additional levels of pollution is to take into account social interactions, the effect of one person's actions upon another. Perhaps the most important category of interactions for our purposes is that of the effects that occur because people are linked together by their purchases and sales in different markets. Even though you are not affected by the pollution, you may be greatly affected by the fact that I, who am affected, alter my market behavior.

To a large extent such market effects represent transfers of benefits or costs between economic units rather than an additional set of consequences not taken into account (in principle, at least) by the second measurement strategy. For example, initially spinach and orchid growers bore the brunt of the costs involved in not being able to produce in the Los Angeles area; but to the extent that their prices rose as a consequence, some of these losses were transferred from the producers to the consumers. Similarly, in the housing market, a rise in pollution in one sector of the market will result in some offsetting fall in property values and rents in that sector and some rise in the unaffected area.[7] In this fashion, the market tends to spread the consequences of pollution among individuals.

From a measurement point of view, this spreading of effects is unfortunate. First, it means that estimates of the costs of pollution based on the second strategy of measurement in all probability understate the true costs. This method includes only the costs of the affected individual's adjustments and of necessity must utilize market data that already incorporate such spreading effects; it does not include the costs that have been transferred to those who were not initially affected by the pollution. Only if the pollution effects cannot be transferred will the second strategy yield correct results. Second, as explained below, such spreading effects seriously complicate both the measurement problem and the problem of interpreting the meaning of any estimates based upon market data.

The proper way to measure such effects is to estimate the difference between the consumer plus producer surpluses in each market affected before and after the change in pollution, and to sum these surpluses over the markets affected. Since air pollution is so small an effect that spending on it is hardly likely to alter the marginal utility of income, these surpluses can be adequately estimated by changes in the areas between the aggregate demand and supply curves to the left of the equilibrium point in each market.

Now, if this prescription were to be followed exactly, estimates of the demand and supply curves for each important market would have to be made; and for each, all other factors that could explain shifts in the curves would have to be controlled so that any remaining variations could be explained by air pollution. This is virtually an impossible task. However, so far as air pollution is concerned, there is one market that is more likely than any other to reflect the majority of effects. This is the land, or real-estate, market. If the land market were to work perfectly, the price of a plot of land would equal the sum of the present discounted streams of benefits and costs derivable from it. If some of its costs rose (*e.g.*, if additional maintenance and cleaning costs were required) or some of its benefits fell (*e.g.*, one could not see the mountains from the terrace) the property would be discounted in the market to reflect people's evaluation of these changes. Since air pollution is specific to locations and the supply of locations is fixed, there is less likelihood than in most instances that the negative effects of pollution can be significantly shifted onto other markets. We should therefore expect to find the majority of effects reflected in this market, where we can measure them by observing associated changes in property values.

There are a number of points that can be made against this strategy of measurement. First, there are several difficulties of the kind that most statistical studies of economic phenomena have in common: the fact that the markets do not work perfectly, the fact that at any one point in time we cannot be sure we are measuring equilibrium values, the problems of setting up an adequate statistical model that can separate out all factors other than air pollution which can also explain the observed variations in the dependent variable, including especially the problems raised by the presence of multicollinearity. There is nothing unique about these problems; the only issue is whether they are so severe in our case that the attempt to use this method should not be made. Unfortunately, I know of no way to answer this question except to try, and to decide afterward.

Second, there is a question of just what is being discounted in the property values. In order for a particular consequence of air pollution to have an observable effect on property values in different parts of the city, buyers and sellers must know that these consequences vary in different parts of the city. They need not know that air pollution causes these effects, but only that, for example, repainting is less necessary in some areas than in others. This issue is of some importance in aggregation estimates of costs of air pollution based upon different measurement methods, for the problem of double counting is a very real one at this point. While it would take a detailed, separate study to find out just what negative consequences of pollution are being discounted, it is likely that the answer will depend strongly upon the particular class of buyers and sellers involved. To minimize this problem, as well as to reduce the complexity of developing a statistical model that can explain other reasons for variations in property values, it is best to undertake separate property-value studies for residential, commercial, and industrial land. It is for these reasons that the property-value studies included in our project are restricted to the residential segment of the whole market.

Third, quite apart from the issue of aggregation, there is a problem of interpreting the numerical results obtained. For reasons stated at the outset of this chapter, it is necessary to rely upon cross-section rather than time-series data. In addition to the normal problems of interpreting cross-section results, consider the following. Suppose there is a completely homogeneous region and that one-half of this region suffers an increase in air pollution. Property values will go down in the polluted area and up in the clean area, though there will be a net decline in total values in the whole region.[8] It is this change in total values that we want to measure.

However, from cross-section data all we can measure is the difference between property values in the clean and in the polluted area. Can we infer from this differential anything about the contrast in values before and after pollution?

Unfortunately, our conclusion must be very circumscribed. We can say that the presence of such a differential clearly indicates that economic costs have been incurred. We can also say that this differential represents the amount that one individual must pay if he wishes to live in the clean rather than in the polluted area. But if we multiplied this cost difference by the number of houses in the polluted area to obtain an estimate of the costs of pollution associated with households, we would be overstating these costs. Again this is due to market adjustments: if the pollution were to be eliminated, homes in the previously clean area would not be in as great demand and their prices would fall; the prices in the polluted area therefore would not rise by as much as the differential implies. Until time-series data become available, there is little that can be done except to present such an estimate and to use it as an upper bound to the possible costs that pollution can have on property values.

As an example of this approach a cross-section property-value study of data from St. Louis can be mentioned. In addition to the normal variables on median number of rooms, income, and the like, we have included information on school quality, crime rates, lot size, and accessibility to shopping and industrial areas, in the hope of explaining a portion of the variance so large that the remainder can reasonably be attributed to air pollution. In addition we are trying several procedures we hope will take care of the multicollinearity problem, which appears to be quite severe. After many false starts, we have at last obtained some interesting results. Property values appear to be linearly related to annual geometric mean sulfation rates, and dividing sulfation levels into eight equal zones, they appear to decline by about, $245 per zone, other things remaining constant. Our model of the housing market explains 90 per cent of the variance in property values.

Conclusion

In conclusion two additional points can be raised. First, although the last of the three measurement methods is the most appropriate for estimating the cost-of-pollution curve, data problems and other practical difficulties make it impossible to rely exclusively on this method. But when the other two methods are used in conjunction with this one in order to obtain an overall assessment of the costs of air pollution, the possibility of double counting arises. There are ways to guard against this and similar aggregation problems, but special studies (e.g., to determine just what is being discounted in property values) appear to be necessary for this purpose.

Finally, while this paper avoids treating problems of data collection directly, it should be evident that this is probably the single largest measurement problem involved. Air-pollution data are sparse; published data on expenditures and other variables that can explain these expenditures are generally too aggregated over categories and over geographic regions to be of much use; virtually no data are available on nonmarket behavior; and most important, information on the direct effects of air pollution, especially in a form usable by economists, is extremely scarce. An obvious note on which to conclude this paper, therefore, is to plead for more data collected specifically for the purpose of air-pollution research. Data collected for other purposes will not solve these problems.

But I should like to raise a question about this obvious conclusion. Data collection is a very expensive process. In effect what is required to justify this expenditure is a benefit-cost analysis of the research activities themselves. Given the payoff probabilities and costs involved, it is not at all certain that such an effort is warranted.

Let me put the matter somewhat differently. Once I had a conversation about this point with a public administrator in the British air-pollution program. In effect he said, "You Americans behave as if you have sufficient time and money to investigate a problem to death before you decide to act. In Britain we take note of a problem we do not like, take some action to correct the problem, and then do research after the fact to determine whether we were right." There is something to this. Under the best of circumstances we may never obtain an accurate measure of what I have called psychic costs. Yet this category may well be the most important, and sufficiently large to warrant increased control measures. Should we therefore wait until all evidence on damages is in before acting, or should we perhaps use an incremental approach in which we try out alternative controls and simply observe whether the electorate appears to be satisfied with them or not? I do not pretend to have an answer to this question, but I submit it as worth considering before any significant increase in funds for data collection is contemplated.

NOTES

1. The research underlying this paper was supported by a contract from the U. S. Public Health Service.

2. See Ronald G. Ridker, *Economic Costs of Air Pollution, Studies in Measurement*, in preparation.

3. Care must be taken in aggregating to avoid including costs of adjustments or market effects (unless these are used as proxies for the direct effects). For example, crop damage should be included, but not changes in land values that result. Otherwise there is a danger of double counting.

4. Implicitly this approach assumes that people will not spend more to eliminate the damage than they estimate the loss to be. This approach puts a considerable burden on the specification of the damage function. It must be able, for example, to indicate the need for repainting of a house solely because of air pollution—that is, independent of the desire to change its color and of all other motives that may be involved. If it is purified of other causal factors in this respect, then the above assumption is likely to be justifiable.

5. Professor Alphonse Holtmann of Wayne State University was responsible for the research leading to these estimates. See Ridker, *op. cit.*, Chapter 3.

6. In the case of the costs of diseases associated with air pollution, all the costs could *not* be measured, and therefore our estimates may have been understated.

7. In this case, from the point of view of renters, the costs of pollution

are spread among them. From the point of view of owners (rent receivers), there is an arbitrary redistribution which, in the aggregate, we assume cancels out.

8. The decline in total values should occur because affected locations yield less utility than previously whereas there is no offsetting increase in utility in the unaffected area.

The Use of Government Statistics in Air-Pollution Control [1]

EDWARD T. CROWDER
UNITED STATES BUREAU OF THE BUDGET

Edward T. Crowder is a senior official of the United States Bureau of the Budget. He is an assistant chief of the Office of Statistical Standards and has a wide background in the planning and coordination of government statistics.

THE RELATIONSHIP OF specific bodies of data to public-policy formulation and to the administration of government programs is a matter of constant concern to me and my colleagues in the Office of Statistical Standards. This concern is a two-sided one. On the one hand there is a responsibility for the adequacy of the Federal statistical system for the various purposes which it is expected to serve; and on the other hand there is a responsibility for preventing waste and duplication and unwarranted burdens on those who supply the data. It is necessary to ask, day in and day out, with respect to the flow of new or revised statistical and administrative data-collection plans, What purpose will this serve? How important is this purpose? Are these precisely the data needed for this purpose, or are the requirements greater or smaller or different? Is every part of the plan essential, or can it be shortened or simplified? Are the statistical techniques proposed adequate to produce valid data? How accurate must the data be? How frequent? How prompt? If the plan were not adopted, how well could we make out with data already available in the files of the sponsoring agency or some other agency?

Two recent developments have brought into unusually sharp focus the problem of evaluating government statistics in terms of the need for the data. In 1964 President Johnson issued an instruction to all agencies of the Executive Branch to examine all of their existing reporting requirements and weed out anything not essential. At about the same time a subcommittee of the House Post Office and Civil Service Committee was holding hearings on the problem of reports required by the Federal Government, and it has subsequently issued an extensive report of findings and recommendations.

It would be pleasant to inform you that the experience in dealing with problems involving the use of government data for policy formulation has led to publication of a hundred-page pamphlet, available for seventy-five cents at the Government Printing Office, entitled *Using Government Statistics for Economic Policy Formulation*, with an appendix on air-pollution control.

There is no such pamphlet. There is not even a five-page mimeographed statement of "Guidelines," and I am forced to improvise on the basis of what I can glean from my experience that seems relevant or seems likely to be relevant as this subject grows in importance.

I shall first sketch the broad outlines for the Federal statistical system, as a basis for thinking about what Federal statistics are contributing or can be made to contribute to the problem of air-pollution control. Second, I shall review rapidly what appear to me to be the points of contact which have already developed between those responsible for the study of air pollution and the Federal statistical resources—a review based on a rather rapid survey on my own part which has been far from exhaustive. Then, on the basis of this survey, and some speculation of my own, I shall discuss several issues bearing on the ways in which needs for Federal data for air-pollution analysis can be met and are most likely to be met; and the degree to which these needs are likely to be satisfied.

The existence of a central coordinating agency for Federal statistics is a reflection of what must be regarded as one of the distinctive features of the United States statistical program, namely decentralization. Programs for the collection, processing the publication of statistics have grown up within the Federal Government in a great number of places as a result of a natural tendency for an agency with a particular sphere of influence to develop some sort of a statistical program about its own activities and about the people, businesses, or phenomena with which it is concerned. This distinguishes our system from that found in many foreign countries where a much greater degree of centralization prevails. Here, although there is some concentration of statistical activity in, for example, the Bureau of the Census, a full description of Federal programs involves a surprisingly long and varied list. One of the first things the novice research worker interested in Federal data finds he must learn is where to go, and the answer is not always obvious.

This dispersion of statistical activity has been defended as desirable. It leads to the performance of statistical work in agencies which are interested in and expert in the subject matter and are likely to keep the statistics technically sound and abreast of current problems. On the other hand it calls for a great deal of interagency cooperation and coordination. Agencies that produce data must be mindful of the needs of users other than themselves. A very significant part of our statistics comes from data collected for administrative reasons. Examples are the statistics of income, based on income-tax returns; statistics of imports, based on Customs entry forms; and some of our employment data, based on Social Security reports. Some statistics reflect the cooperation of a number of agencies. Thus the balance-of payments statistics involve contributions not only from the main compiling agency, the Office of Business Economics, but also from the Census Bureau, the Customs Bureau, the Immigration and Naturalization Service, the Office of International Affairs at Treasury, the Federal Reserve System, and the Maritime Administration.

In discussions of the Federal statistical organization it is customary to point out that the agencies which participate fall into three broad classes. There are "general-purpose statistical agencies," which collect and publish statistics in specific fields for general use. Then there are "analytical and research agencies," which make analytical use of the statistics collected by other agencies, and to some extent synthesize them into more complex bodies of data such as the national income and product accounts. Finally there are a great many administrative and regulatory agencies whose statistical activities are primarily a by-product of their administrative operations.

A bird's-eye view of the Federal statistical system would reveal certain general outlines which I have time to sketch only in very broad strokes. (There is indeed a Government Printing Office pamphlet, by the Office of Statistical Standards, which does this in more detail. It describes *The Statistical Services of the United States Government.* It is 136 pages long and tells a great deal about the kinds of statistics available and the contributions of the various agencies. It does not, however, tell how to use the data.)

Looking first at the general-purpose statistical agencies, we see the Bureau of the Census, with its periodic censuses of population, housing, agriculture, manufactures, mineral industries, business, and governments; and its programs of current statistics in most of these and in related fields. We see the Bureau of Labor Statistics, with its well-known measures of employment and of prices, and related statistical series. Also in this group is the Statistical Reporting Service of the Department of Agriculture, with an extensive program concerned with agricultural production, prices, employment, and related agricultural subjects. And finally the National Center for Health Statistics, the source of vital statistics and statistics on health and morbidity.

The agencies classified as analytical and research agencies include the Council of Economic Advisers, the Economic Research Service of the Department of Agriculture, the Office of Business Economics in Commerce, the Board of Governors of the Federal Reserve System, the Bureau of Mines, and several others.

Finally, the list of administrative, regulatory, and defense agencies includes a great number of bureaus in the several major departments, and nearly twenty independent offices. In this group is the Public Health Service, with its extensive program. The programs of other agencies range widely over many subject-matter fields—from passports to prisons, wages to wildlife, electric power to education, and from corporate securities to social security.

What are the important points of contact between the problem of controlling air pollution and this vast system for the collection and processing of statistical data? A review of the data requirements for air-pollution control leads to a quick impression that they are remarkably varied. A comprehensive listing would be what we call a "laundry list" of miscellaneous statistical items. I have looked for a systematic point of departure for describing them. Actually, I have taken two points of departure. First, I quote from a handbook describing the programs of the Department of Health, Education, and Welfare, and specifically of the Division of Air Pollution of the Public Health Service. The program objective of the Division is described as directed toward determining, through research, the effects of air pollution, and developing and improving methods for the characterization and abatement of air pollution. With respect to the present program of the Division, the handbook states, "Research emphasizes effects on health, agriculture, and materials; identification of specific pollutants; the role of meteorology; uses of specialized instrumentation; and criteria for effective abatement. The program involves direct intramural laboratory research and epidemiologic field studies; direct contrasts; and support of research in other Federal agencies, States, communities, universities, and private research agencies."

My second and simultaneous point of departure is a survey sponsored by the Public Health Service to determine what kinds of information people in this field need, or think they need. Here are the main topics in the list of types of information: pollution-measurement methods—specifically, pollution effects on human health, materials, plants, animals, and visibility; standards relative to ambient air and emission; economic losses; atmospheric reactions and applied meteorology; radioactivity; legal aspects; planning and zoning.

These listings indicate, I repeat, a remarkably wide variety of types of data being brought to bear on one basic problem. I have tried to familiarize myself with actual examples of what is being done in these various fields by searching the records, talking with my colleagues who deal with the agencies involved, and holding selective consultations with people in those agencies. An enumeration of all the examples I have found of statistical activity directed toward air-pollution problems, would indeed be a "laundry list," but here, for illustrative purposes, are a few of the items:

the development by the Bureau of the Census of an index of industrialization for specified areas;

research on damage to crops by air pollution, carried on by or with the cooperation of the Department of Agriculture;

studies in the economics of fuel and fuel consumption by the Bureau of Mines;

measurement of the level of pollution by the network of stations sponsored by the Public Health Service;

an impressive array of medical studies on the relation of pollution to health;

an equally impressive array of laboratory and of engineering studies concerned with measurement and control;

a large program of meteorological research.

In addition to such examples of what has been going on, there is an intriguing list of fields in which research has been contemplated and perhaps some initial steps have been taken. These include opinion surveys on public awareness of the pollution problem; the study of the extra-economic effects of air pollution, such as effects on the incentives and initiative populations; extension of consumer-expenditure statistics to cover air-pollution problems more specifically; the study of effects on the design of industrial products (as on the color of clothes); the study of effects on tourism; the more precise analysis of mortality statistics in terms of the timing of deaths in relation to pollution; the analysis of police records for the relationship of pollution to accidents; and transportation studies.[2]

Looking further for evidence of what is being done, I have given some attention to the content of the community surveys which precede or ideally should precede community action on the air-pollution problem. Such surveys cover a range of information about the quality of the air and the sources of pollution. I have turned the pages of a 1963 survey of "Air Pollution in the National Capital Area" to see what goes into such a local study. The main topics are: population growth and density; employment; weather phenomena; fuel consumption; transportation characteristics; waste-disposal methods; emissions of air pollutants by industrial and commercial establishments; plant damage; and measurements of pollution from the network (the national air pollution monitoring network).

Because there seemed to be, superficially at least, a broad analogy between problems of air pollution and problems of water pollution I went further and examined a proposal recently under consideration for a regional study aimed at water-pollution control. I found this to be one of the most ambitious economic studies I have ever examined, involving a solid study of the economic base of the region, and including in its measurements the gross regional product and the development of input-output tables. I see little reason to suppose that air-pollution control will suggest such a comprehensive approach to local economic analysis, but the project I have alluded to is a reminder of the extent to which the analysis of regional and local problems can lead to efforts at extensive refinement of social and economic statistics.

These then, are the kinds of things which workers in the field of air pollution feel that they need to know; which they look for in libraries; which are included in community surveys; and the measurement of which is encouraged and financed by the Public Health Service program. We turn now to the question of how these workers can make use of the Federal statistical system.

To begin with, how does anyone go about making use of Federal statistics and Federal statistical facilities? Or, more precisely, what are the ways in which the Federal statistical system may be made to serve a particular need for data? There are ordinarily several alternatives. If the data one wants are regularly collected and published, one simply buys the appropriate book or bulletin, or, better still, tries to obtain it free. But the problem may be one for which the published data are not quite suitable. It may be that the necessary information has in fact been collected, but has not been tabulated in the desired manner. Here the solution can be simple. Certain Federal agencies are prepared to make special tabulations for users if they are reimbursed for the cost. This has for a long time been an established practice at the Bureau of the Census, and the policy has been given general encouragement by the Bureau of the Budget.

Sometimes the desired data are not being collected. There are occasions, if the needed information is limited and specific and the purpose important, when an appropriate item or items may be added to a questionnaire or report from being used or planned for. other purposes. Such arrangements are not unusual.

It is a further extension of this idea to propose a special survey to meet the precise problem at hand. If a Federal agency desiring such data is not equipped to make its own survey, some other agency with facilities or familiarity with the subject-matter field may be found. Thus at the Census Bureau, the Current Population Survey of a national probability sample of households is used as a vehicle for the collection of data for other agencies through a changing series of supplements to the basic form.

If none of these approaches appears feasible, an agency desiring information may choose to make a contract with an outside research organization, or may seek to insure the development of the desired data through grants. This method has been widely used in the air-pollution field.

This review of the nature of the Federal statistical system and of the data needs for air-pollution control suggests certain generalizations. First, to a very considerable extent air-pollution control has been conceived as a local problem involving the use of data not on a national scale, but for small areas. A great emphasis is therefore placed on the city, the county, the metropolitan area, as the statistical universe. To be sure, air does move about and respects no political boundaries, and we have all read of the time when tons of dust from North Africa were dumped on the British Isles. But I read also that polluted air is rapidly diluted as it moves from its source. At any event, there can be no question about the heavy emphasis on local data in the literature of community action. This fact has important implications with respect to the use of Federal statistical data.

There is a corollary to the point that control of air pollution lays heavy emphasis on local data, namely that it involves an important role for state and local governments. This too has significant implications with respect to the role of the Federal Government.

Furthermore, many of the data needs which I have enumerated involve information different in nature from the well-known bodies of social and economic statistics. I refer to meteorological data and to the results of medical, engineering, and chemical research. In a broad sense, of course, any data based on statistical methods are statistical; but it may be useful to distinguish the results of scientific testing, laboratory research, medical studies, and the like from the familiar activities of agencies such as the Census Bureau with which the term "government statistics" is popularly associated.

These three characteristics of the data problem in the field of air pollution have, I suggest, important implications with respect to the role of the Federal Government. Let us look first at the implications of the first two generalizations—that much of the data is desired on a local basis, and that this entails an important role for state and local governments.

It is obvious that the statistical programs of the Federal Government have traditionally met more readily the needs for analysis of problems on a national scale than for analysis of local or regional problems. Censuses do of course provide data in great geographic detail; but the information available through censuses is limited and infrequent. Similar information for periods between censuses or on other subjects is not necessarily available on a local basis. Such data are expensive. A sample large enough, for example, to measure unemployment for the nation will be far too small to give also a measure of unemployment for metropolitan Washington.

There is of course a demand for, and a recognition of the need for, more and more data on a local basis. Thus in testimony in 1962, the head of the Office of Statistical Standards proposed a program for expanding the statistics available on a local basis, including annual population estimates for the two hundred largest metropolitan areas and for other areas and counties in which there is special interest. The strengthening of local statistics has been an important feature of recent budget planning. Thus the President's budget request for fiscal year 1966 provided for an expanded program of population estimates for local areas between decennial censuses. This program began in 1964 and by the end of 1965 is expected to cover thirty-eight Standard Metropolitan Statistical Areas. The funds requested for 1966 would permit extension to thirty more SMSA's. There is also provision of funds for consultation and advice to local groups and individuals on appropriate techniques for estimating the population of areas not covered. The program of the Census Bureau already contains funds for annual estimates of state populations and for periodic projections of the states' future population changes.

In March of 1965 a spokesman for the Federal Statistics Users Conference appeared before the Joint Economic Committee and emphasized the fact that recent legislation has created a great demand for local data. He pointed specifically to the Federal-Aid Highway Act of 1962, which requires systematic urban-transportation planning as a condition for Federal highway aid; this planning is to involve information on "a wide variety of subjects, including population, employment by industry, per capita income, and income-consumption patterns." Similar demands for local data, he pointed out, arise from the Economic Opportunity Act and other legislation.

I cite still another evidence of growing interest in and demand for statistics for smaller geographic areas. Quite recently, the Office of Business Economics of the Department of Commerce established a new division concerned with making regional income estimates and related problems.

Much of the interest in local data for air-pollution analysis will, I anticipate, stress the so-called Standard Metropolitan Statistical Areas as the unit of analysis, and it may be helpful parenthetically to say a word about this statistical concept. Standard Metropolitan Statistical Areas are geographic areas of contiguous counties delineated by the Bureau of the Budget for use by the various agencies publishing economic and social statistics, to insure the comparability of the small-area data available from different programs. Another contributor to this volume has suggested that the proper geographic unit for effective action on air pollution might be something comparable to the SMSA. As currently defined, each SMSA must include at least one city with a population of 50,000 or more, or two contiguous cities which together meet roughly the same size standard. Certain other criteria of metropolitan character are applied: per cent of the population in the nonagricultural labor force, population density, integration of adjoining counties. The Washington SMSA, for example, includes the District of Columbia, Montgomery and Prince Georges counties in Maryland, and Arlington and Fairfax counties and the cities of Alexandria and Falls Church in Virginia. A considerable amount of economic and social data concerning SMSA's, published by the Federal Government, is already available.

To the extent that the Federal Government stops short of providing data on small areas as a regular service, what role can or should it play with respect to the provision of needed local data? Several alternatives suggest themselves. Federal Government subsidies to the states and localities is one possibility. Joint Federal-state sponsorship is another. Federal technical guidance for localities making their own surveys is still another. All of these approaches have precedents. To the extent that there is need for uniformity from locality to locality in concepts and methods involved in statistics collected outside the direct authority of the Federal Government, we may anticipate an important coordination problem.

Let me turn now to a third generalization about the collection of data for air-pollution control. By reason of its nature, as noted above, much of this research is of a type which, if sponsored by the Federal Government at all, may well be carried on under contracts or grants rather than as part of the regular activities of an established statistical agency.

As is well known, the financing of research to be carried on outside the Federal Government has reached substantial proportions. It appears to offer an attractive flexibility to an agency which is not staffed to undertake the kind of research it needs. It also occurs in fields in which the objective is not so much to purchase information as to encourage research.

To what extent is data collection carried on under such an arrangement to be reviewed and coordinated by the Federal Government in the same manner as though it were being carried on through a regular agency? The Federal Reports Act has been interpreted to cover not only the collection of data directly but the "sponsorship" of data collection through contracts or grants. There are those who feel that such review is at best impracticable or at worst an interference with freedom of research. And yet it is clear that the government has a stake in and a responsibility for what goes on under its sponsorship and that, at the very least, there are possibilities of duplication in uncoordinated contract and grant research. I refrain from commenting on this issue, and am in no position to predict how it will come out, but I may point out that it is being given serious attention.

I have emphasized the fact that air-pollution research is to a considerable extent carried out on a local basis and is often financed through grants and contracts. I can repeat, also, that much of it—for example medical research and weather research—is outside the area normally thought of as "government statistics." I ask now, are there really important tie-ins between this air-pollution problem and the more familiar programs designed to collect social and economic data?

I think there are. In spite of the emphasis on local data, the basic statistics on population and industry as provided by Federal programs are sure to play a role in broad projections of the air-pollution problem and appropriate actions. We have already noted a tendency for the Federal programs to reach further down into localities. We have seen examples of actual or potential uses of the kinds of data collected by the Bureau of the Census, the Bureau of Mines, the Bureau of Labor Statistics. I can foresee, for example, future interest in systematic data on the use of pollution-control devices and on the production of such devices. I foresee further interest in collection through established statistical channels of health and related household data bearing on air pollution. If the problem is attacked through national regulation or tax policy, obvious fields of study suggest themselves in relation to the financial impact on affected industries. The Federal statistical system must expect to be faced with demands reflecting such lines of inquiry.

In conclusion, I want to make certain observations which have no peculiar relationship to the problem of air pollution but bear on the use of statistics for any policy-making purposes. As a long-time member of the crew who watch over the Federal statistical system in the interests of preventing duplications, avoiding waste, and protecting the public from unnecessary data requests, I have had occasion to observe the natural human tendency to wish to make a survey as a sort of reflex action when faced with a difficult problem. This is a common experience when a new program is set up or a new problem confronted. In the absence of a clear basis for action, it is natural to want to make a survey, and once a survey has been decided on it is equally natural to want to put into it whatever seems interesting. One thing leads to another.

It is well to remind oneself constantly that not all problems are data problems, and the answer is not always or necessarily more or better data. It is rewarding for an administrator planning the collection of new data to ask himself precisely what it is he needs; to visualize, not a questionnaire, but a final tabulation based on the data the questionnaire would produce; to imagine different possible numbers in the cells, and to ask how his actions in policy-making or day-to-day administration would differ if he found this number instead of that number in a particular cell.

This leads to the very important question—if a survey is to be made at all—of how accurate the data must be. Error, of course, is unavoidable, and there has been some conspicuous attention given lately to the inaccuracy of economic data. But the practical problem is to find out how much accuracy is actually appropriate, and to assess the costs of attaining such accuracy. Widely different degrees of accuracy may be called for under different circumstances. The policy maker must ask to what extent the statistics actually affect his decision. Does he require a figure accurate within 5 per cent, or essentially only an indicator of a general magnitude or of a direction of change? An honest answer will be invaluable in planning the statistical program.

This about exhausts what I feel can appropriately be said about the use of data for air-pollution analysis by one who is not a specialist in air pollution. The problem is one which at many points lends itself to more precise measurement than many of the problems with which I normally deal; it is one which presents an intriguing variety of data inputs—including weather recordings, the household laundry costs, and the economics of the automobile and electric-power industries—and one which by reason of its importance presents an exciting challenge to all of us who are concerned with the use of data to solve social problems.

NOTES

1. The views expressed are those of the author and not necessarily those of the Office of Statistical Standards.

2. For much of what I have learned of these potential fields I am indebted to Dr. Emanuel Landau, of the Public Health Service, who has been good enough to tell me of the directions in which he and others are thinking.

The Use of Consumer-Expenditure Data in Air-Pollution Control

HELEN H. LAMALE

UNITED STATES BUREAU OF LABOR STATISTICS

*Helen H. Lamale is an internationally recognized author-
ity on family budgets and consumer-expenditure surveys.
At the Bureau of Labor Statistics of the United States Department of Labor she is chief of the Division of Living
Conditions Studies and also a research director.*

ANY MEANINGFUL DISCUSSION OF the use of consumer-expenditure
data for measuring costs and effects of air pollution must start with
a somewhat detailed description of the nature and source of the expenditure data, and the general uses and limitations of such data
with respect to analyses of special problems, such as air pollution.

Bureau of Labor Statistics

The Bureau of Labor Statistics surveys of consumer expenditures
form the only comprehensive volume of data drawn from household
surveys on family income, expenditures, and changes in assets and
liabilities. These studies, dating back to 1888, were among the first
undertaken by the Bureau of Labor Statistics. There were nationwide *urban* studies in 1901, in 1917–19, and in 1934–36. The first
large-scale national study was made in 1935–36. A small-scale
national study was made in 1941; a small-scale urban study in 1944;
a large-scale urban study in 1950; and a large-scale national study
covering the years 1960–61 has recently been completed. There is a
fairly extensive compilation of the statistics from the studies in
Chapter G of the Census Bureau publication *Historical Statistics of
the United States, Colonial Times to 1957* and a recent supplement to

this publication. After the 1950 study, I prepared a monograph, *Methodology of the Survey of Consumer Expeditures in 1950*, which was published in 1959 by the University of Pennsylvania in the series *Study of Consumer Expenditures, Incomes, and Savings*. Appendix sections in this monograph deal with the historical studies, giving reprints of some of the old questionnaires and references to publications.

The studies preceding the 1935–36 Consumer Purchases Study were quite limited, covering only wage- and clerical-worker families of two or more persons in urban areas. The 1935–36 study was the first comprehensive study in terms of the total United States population, including the rural farm and nonfarm population, and also including all occupational groups. It wasn't coincidental that the survey coverage was extended in 1935–36. Throughout the 1920's there was a growing awareness of the importance of the consumer in the total economy and of the need for comprehensive data on patterns of spending, on the relationships of expenditures to income, and on changes in assets and liabilities. When the national income and product accounts were developed in the Department of Commerce in the late 1930's, much of the bench-mark data in the household sector was drawn from the 1935–36 Consumer Purchases Study.

Individual-City Data

Except for the small-scale studies in 1941 and 1944, each survey has provided individual-city data; in other words, in each of the large-scale surveys, the individual city, or standard metropolitan area, has been the primary sampling unit. However, very few of the city samples are large enough to permit intracity analysis of detailed item-expenditure data, except perhaps on the basis of a dichotomy of central-city versus suburban-area data for groups of homogeneous cities. There are several possibilities of this kind. It is also relevant to note that several of the very large metropolitan areas have been included in each major survey since 1901, *e.g.*, Pittsburgh, Boston, St. Louis, Philadelphia, New York, and Chicago. Thus, historical data have been accumulated for a sizable number of metropolitan areas, but there are problems of noncomparability because of the limited occupational coverage in the earlier surveys.

The urban studies in 1950 and in 1960–61 have a central-city identification code, *i.e.*, each family reported upon is identified as living in the central city or in a suburban area. For broad regional levels—three regional levels in 1950 and four in 1960–61—the data have been summarized by location within metropolitan areas and by size of place. The Bureau of Labor Statistics conducted the 1960–61 survey in cooperation with the Department of Agriculture, and the survey includes rural farm and nonfarm families. This is the first time since 1941 that there has been a complete coverage of all United States consumer units, rural and urban.

The urban portion of the 1960–61 survey had as its primary sampling unit the Standard Metropolitan Statistical Area (SMSA). The sample included thirty-four SMSA's and thirty-two urban places outside metropolitan areas. In addition, Cincinnati was surveyed as a pilot city, with data for 1959, and five SMSA's were surveyed for 1963. These additional SMSA's all have populations of over a million, so when the findings of this survey are combined with our data for the twelve standard metropolitan areas in the 1960–61 study which have populations of over a million, we have recent expenditure data for all standard metropolitan areas with over a million people in 1960. A summary of the basic reports that have already been published, a description of our general-purpose tabulation program, and a list of the SMSA's in the sample are available. In the very large standard metropolitan areas, half of the families in the sample were surveyed in each year; in the smaller metropolitan areas and cities, half of the cities in the sample were surveyed in each year. However, the sample for each year was a representative cross section of the United States urban population. All of the rural families were surveyed in 1961.

Status of General-Purpose Tabulations and Publication

In the years prior to the 1960–61 survey, the Bureau of Labor Statistics had relatively limited funds for general-purpose tabulations and publication of its expenditure data. The surveys in the 1930's were tabulated quite extensively through a Works Progress Administration grant. The 1935–36 Consumer Purchases Study was analyzed quite extensively by the National Resources Committee in cooperation with the Central Statistical Board. The 1941 and 1944 surveys were wartime studies to be used for policy determination and for answering questions on the many wartime problems involving savings, rationing, and the like. They were not very extensively tabulated for use in general economic research. Furthermore, the sample sizes were too small to permit very much disaggregation in the statistical summaries. Like its predecessors in 1917–19 and 1934–36, the 1950 urban survey was intended primarily to supply a basis for revision of the weights in the Consumer Price Index (CPI). The funds granted to the Bureau covered the cost of the tabulations associated with the index revision, but there were no funds provided for any other tabulations. Thus, in 1953, having revised the CPI, the Bureau had a great mass of data, and no funds to tabulate or to make them available to anybody. In 1954, the Ford Foundation made a grant to the Wharton School of the University of Pennsylvania, through which the Bureau prepared the detailed statistical summaries published by the University in 1956–57 [1] in an eighteen-volume series. The 1950 survey sample covered ninety-one urbanized areas (as defined for the 1950 Census) and smaller urban places. Most of the statistical summaries are for nine classes of cities: large cities (central cities and other cities with populations of over 50,000), suburbs, and small cities, in North, South, and West. The grant from the Ford Foundation to the University made possible a monographic series, the first of which was the methodology monograph, previously referred to. There was also a series of papers prepared for a conference held at the Wharton School in March, 1959, and published by the University of Pennsylvania in *Consumption and Savings*, Volumes I and II. These papers illustrate the wide variety of statistical techniques that can be used in analyzing consumer-expenditure data, particularly variance analyses and multiple-regression analyses. Although none of these papers deals with air-pollution analysis, they give an analyst who is contemplated the use of expenditure-survey data for such a special purpose some idea of how he might go about it.

Content of the Expenditure Survey of 1960–65

The 1960–61 survey consists of a complete recording for each sample family of one year's income, expenditures, and changes in assets and liabilities, accompanied by an extensive list of the socio-economic characteristics of the consumer unit. The data for these expenditure surveys are collected by personal interviews. These are "depth" interviews; the actual interview time, *i.e.*, the time spent with a family, averaged, in 1950, about eight hours spread over several visits. In 1960–61, we think we reduced it a little. To improve our efficiency we spent more time in training interviewers and editing questionnaires, so about seven hours, on the average, were spent with the family. The family is encouraged to refer to receipts and other records. There are worksheets that can be left with the family if the respondent does not have at hand certain parts of the information and wishes to consult other family members. The reporting form contains a great deal of item detail at the data-collection level, because the Bureau has found that including the item detail helps the family recall expenditures, and results in more complete reporting for the total category. Thus, much of the item-expenditure data included in the schedule is intended not to yield a precise statistic for individual items, but to improve the reporting for the category.

Not only is the interview conducted in depth, with detailed rather than global questions, but the expenditures are recorded on a "structured" schedule. For example, expenditures for food are obtained in conjunction with expenditures for other items bought in grocery stores and other retail outlets, e.g., drugstores. Thus, the interview is tailored to parallel usual shopping patterns. We found our 1950 expenditure estimates for food so reported were very much closer to the aggregates than had been the earlier comparisons, using an "unstructured" interview. We haven't had a test of the aggregates for 1960–61 food expenditures, but we have reason to believe they are quite good, because the distributions of expenditures from the survey compare favorably with the distributions in the aggregate data. It is important to remember, however, that the primary purpose of this survey is not to build up estimates of aggregates. The primary purpose of this survey is to obtain average family expenditures, and more important, the distribution of expenditures—the relationships among them—as needed to determine the relative importance of expenditures for different goods and services in the revision of the CPI weights.

The other important use of the consumer-survey data is to obtain the distribution of expenditures as associated with various socioeconomic characteristics of the families—size, ages of members, number of earners, and so on. The 1960–61 study includes about forty pre-coded family characteristics of this kind. In order to define the family on an economic basis, i.e., as a consumer unit (as distinct from the Census definition of a related family), the Bureau of Labor

Statistics establishes the financial relationship of the people living in a household: the family consists of those who pool income and share expenses. In the Census definition, the family includes all related persons in the household; this is referred to as a demographic family. Of course, for most households, the families are the same whether defined on a demographic or on an economic basis. In some instances, however, the Bureau places in a single group people in a household that Census would set apart, or we consider separately people that would be regarded by Census as belonging to the same family.

The Bureau of Labor Statistics also "reconstructs" the family. Our aim is to get expenditures for the family as it lived during the survey year. So we may have some part-year members, resulting, for example, in a 3.5-person family. This may mean three full-year family members and a baby born in June; or may indicate that one member married in June and left the family, thus having half-year family membership. The family size is based on full-year equivalent family membership, in contrast to the Census method of counting the persons in the family at the time of the interview. This has a significant effect on the level and distribution of income as reported to the Bureau, compared to Census income reports. Average income in the Bureau reports tends to be consistently higher than the Census income averages, and Bureau reports show fewer families at the lower end of the income distribution because of these definitional and procedural differences.

My purpose in describing these details of the expenditure survey is to emphasize that it is a survey designed to obtain general family statistics. It is not designed to obtain aggregate-cost estimates, such as the national accounts. As I mentioned earlier, the data can be reconciled with the household sector of the national accounts, and the average expenditures per family, when multiplied by an appropriate estimate of total consumer units, should give a fairly good aggregate cost, or expenditure, for most items, but these aggregate estimates will be derived data, and do not reflect the primary focus of the study.

The major categories of expenditures used in most of the statistical summaries for individual cities are illustrated in Bureau of Labor Statistics Reports, *Consumer Expenditures and Income*.[2] These include household-operation expenses as a total. Supplement 3 to these reports by region and for the total United States urban includes substantially greater item detail. For example, for the household-operation category, which is of most interest to air-pollution analysts, Supplement 3 by region and the United States includes a breakdown of household operations as follows: laundry supplies, cleaning supplies, household-paper supplies, laundry and cleaning sent out, domestic service, day nursery, telephone, and so on. The data at the major group level (e.g., total household operation) have been tabulated by ten variables: income, family size, age of family head, occupation of head, education of head, race of head, family type, housing tenure, number of earners, and size and location of place of residence.

In the classification by place of residence metropolitan areas (SMSA) are separated from non metropolitan areas. Then within metropolitan areas, separate tabulations are made for central cities; other cities of 50,000 population or more; places of under 50,000, inside the urbanized area of the central city; and places from 2,500 to 50,000, outside the urbanized area, but still in the metropolitan area.[3] Outside SMSA's the place of residence is coded as urban, rural nonfarm, or rural farm.

Each family report has been thus coded by place of residence. These residence codes appear on the machine-tabulation cards and tapes. The actual address of the family within the particular community appears on the schedule, but it would be a major job to go back to these schedules to reclassify families to specific communities within SMSA's. The cost of going back to the schedules is generally prohibitive, except for major products which are well financed. Doing so is, of course, much cheaper than conducting another survey.

In 1960–61, much of the editing and coding of the schedules was done by machine. As a result, we have many listings on file which contain a schedule-number reference to the original report. If a proposed investigation deals with a very small group of families, which can be identified on these listings, the task of going back to the schedule may be considerably easier. In some cases, the desired data may be found on the intermediate listings of the individual-family reports. Of course, after the data are published, the intermediate work tapes and cards can be retained for only a limited time. After the 1950 data were tabulated and published in the eighteen volumes by the Wharton School, the basic cards were destroyed. There are a few listings which give some individual-city data, or individual-family data, and new cards could be punched from these listings, but it is very difficult to obtain anything from the 1950 study which was not included in the published tables. We hope this will not happen to the 1960–61 data. Despite the rather extensive general-purpose tabulation and publication program, the Bureau has received numerous requests for special tabulations. In cases where these requests could be met from existing unpublished data, we have provided copies at cost. We have been unable, however, to undertake special tabulations, even on a reimbursable basis. Since many of the requests have been from other Federal agencies which have data-processing equipment, we have made the basic data tapes available to them, on a rental basis. For other users who have access to data-processing equipment, we are proposing to prepare a "general-purpose family tape" which could be bought on a restrictive contract basis which would comply with our nondisclosure regulations. A description of this proposed tape is available upon request. The proposed general-purpose family tape is not at the level of item detail that would be appropriate for a special-purpose project, such as air-pollution cost analysis.

Expenditures Affected by Air Pollution

Theoretically, expenditures in almost every category can be affected *indirectly* by air pollution, and maybe sometime, well in the future, these remote air-pollution effects will be traced back through the expenditure pattern.

Practically speaking, analysts will have to start by identifying expenditure items on which air pollution would have a *direct* effect, *i.e.*, an effect measurable by annual-expenditure data. Professor Ridker [4] has listed the following:

> Repairs and Replacements on Owned Homes—Lodging out of Home City—Laundry Supplies—Cleaning Supplies—Household Paper Supplies—Laundry and Cleaning Sent Out—Domestic Service—Household Textiles, Total—Eye Care, Including Glasses —Waves, Shampoos, Tinting—Toilet Soap—Face Powder, Creams, and the Like—Recreation out of Home City

> Three of these "items"—Repairs and Replacements on Owned Homes, Lodging out of Home City, and Recreation out of Home

City—are really subcategories of expenditures, and include many important expenditures probably not directly affected by air pollution. For example, Lodging out of Home City includes room expenses for children away at school, and Repairs and Replacements includes replacing a furnace, broken windows, and so on. The other items listed are likely to be affected directly. In addition, expenditures for water would seem to be a likely candidate for investigation in this respect. I understand that medical expenditures have also been suggested for analysis, but that medical advisers discourage the idea that medical expenses can be broken down in a manner that is meaningful in relation to air-pollution effects. Even if the survey information revealed the nature of the illness associated with the expense, the initial association with air pollution could not be distinguished from other causes, such as epidemics. Furthermore, there is the problem that family members are variously affected by air pollution in connection with differences in their place of work, as compared with place of residence.

The total expenditures for the items, as selected by Professor Ridker, by families of two or more in urban places in 1960–61 averaged about $456. This was about 6 to 7 per cent of their after-tax income, and about 7 to 8 per cent of total expenditures for current consumption. In analysis of this type, more stable relationships are apparent if expenditures for selected groups or items are related to total expenditures for current consumption rather than to income, thus avoiding the problems caused by differential savings rates. These estimates set the upper limit of possible costs for this list of items. Obviously, only some fraction of the $456 can be attributed to air pollution. This is not a very large share of total spending or income. However, this is a question of relativity. Even a small share multiplied by millions can add up to a fairly large aggregate cost.

Other Considerations

There are other unanswered questions in the analysis of air pollution. Are such costs too broad to tie to a particular expenditure? For example, what are the costs of not having as much sunlight as one would like to have? How can such satisfaction costs be measured? Can the consumer, through his spending pattern, do much to combat his dissatisfactions? It seems clear that the information needed to answer such questions cannot be obtained from a general-purpose survey such as the Survey of Consumer Expenditures in 1960–61.

Purpose of Air-Pollution Cost Analyses

Before undertaking any empirical research, the analyst should question the purpose for which a figure on the cost of air pollution is needed. What kind of precision is implied by the use that is to be made of this figure? If it is required only for a global purpose, to describe the general dimensions of the problem, then something derived from a hypothetical situation may be all that is needed. From the 1960–61 data cited above, we might say the average cost per family cannot be more than x dollars, and multiplied by x consumer units, the total cost cannot be more than so much; or we can say that it falls within such-and-such a range. A precision instrument is not needed to measure something in miles! If the purpose for which the estimate is being made is general, the analyst ought to give serious consideration to making cost estimates of the hypothetical kind. This does not mean, however, that analyses of consumer-expenditure data have no place in the air-pollution cost problem. Stating the purpose provides the basis for determining just how the data can and should be used and for evaluating the limitations of these data with respect to the end product.

Uses of the Consumer-Expenditure Data

The survey data cover receipts and disbursements without regard to the reason for the consumer's action. Generalizations can be made by relating such data to socio-economic facts, e.g., income, family size, region, and the like, but air pollution, per se, is not a particular factor directly associated with such expenditure data. It is necessary, therefore, to separate the effects of variations in air pollution on consumer expenditures from the effects of other factors—income, climate, family size and type, customs, region, manner of living, and so on. Taken as a whole, the "other factors" are no doubt of much stronger influence on consumer expenditures than is air pollution. The effects could be measured by means of multiple regression and/or variance analyses.

Major Types of Analyses

There are two types of analysis of consumer-expenditure data which might contribute to an understanding of the air-pollution cost problem. Changes over time in expenditures for items affected by air pollution might be correlated with the changing degree of air pollution in specific localities to identify and establish the nature of the relationships of expenditures to air-pollution costs. The other type of analysis would involve a comparison of consumer expenditures in places with varying degrees of air-pollution density. This would involve a pooling of data for high-density areas both within and across cities and a comparison of expenditures for affected items in such places with expenditures in localities of lower air-pollution densities. It should be recognized at the outset that such analyses are microeconomic in nature and will involve the putting together of many pieces of disaggregated data. The usefulness of both of these types of analysis would be highly dependent upon whether the air-pollution data were accurate enough to serve as a discriminant variable—a question the air-pollution-data specialist would have to answer. The value of this kind of analysis is that it would identify the expenditures most significantly affected by air pollution and give clues to the areas where attention should be concentrated.

A Consumption Framework

Probably the most valuable use of the consumer-expenditure data is that they provide, both currently and historically, the consumption framework for specific areas as related to the socio-economic characteristics of the areas. This gives the analyst a framework within which to consider the effects of air pollution and their impact upon consumption expenditures. The data provide the basis for deciding where information is needed, and the kinds of information needed to build the bridges between the expenditure data and air-pollution effects.

The consumer-expenditure survey can also provide the air-pollution analyst with guidelines for designing special "air-pollution" surveys in specific areas, either on a broad scale or with a case-study approach, insuring that supplemental questions are developed in such a manner that the special-study finding can be related to the general consumer-expenditure survey bench-mark data.

In conclusion, it should be clearly understood that the producers of general-purpose survey data, such as the Bureau of Labor Statistics consumer-expenditure data, cannot recommend their use for such special purposes as air-pollution cost analyses. It is the producer's function to point out their potentialities. It is the responsibility of the air-pollution analyst to explore their research potentials and to make the final decisions as to their use. In so doing, he should recognize the need for a thorough investigation and a careful evaluation of the costs involved in utilizing available data, as compared with the costly job of collecting data in household surveys.

NOTES

1. *Study of Consumer Expenditures, Incomes, and Savings, Statistical Tables, Urban U. S.—1950*, Vols. I–XVIII, Philadelphia, University of Pennsylvania Press, 1956–57.

2. U. S. Department of Labor, Bureau of Labor Statistics Reports, Series No. 237, *Consumer Expenditures and Income*, November, 1962– .

3. Table 10 in Bureau of Labor Statistics Report No. 237–93, "Total United States, Urban and Rural," 1960–61, *Ibid.*, pp. 6, 11, 16.

4. Unpublished correspondence with Professor Ronald G. Ridker.

Air-Pollution Control in the Metropolitan Boston Area: A Case Study in Public-Policy Formation

LESTER GOLDNER
DIVISION OF AIR POLLUTION, PUBLIC HEALTH SERVICE,
UNITED STATES DEPARTMENT OF HEALTH, EDUCATION,
AND WELFARE

Lester Goldner is chief of the Legal, Economic, and Social Unit of the Division of Air Pollution of the United States Public Health Service. He is a graduate of the Graduate School of Public Administration of Harvard University.

AIR POLLUTION, a product of increasing industrialization and concentration of population, is a problem which in the last few decades has assumed increasing significance in the United States and other technologically advanced countries. Statutes attempting to deal with the problem were enacted as early as the twelfth century in England. But it is only recently that public concern in many areas of the country has mounted rapidly in response to dramatic acute air-pollution episodes, and to recent research which suggests that exposure to low levels of contaminants, such as are found in many of our urban areas, may be associated with the incidence of heart disease, lung cancer, and other respiratory diseases.

There is general agreement that our air ought to be kept as clean as possible. There is often disagreement about what is "possible" or "desirable." An effective program for the control of air pollution requires varying degrees of regulation of the location and operation of sources causing air pollution, and the expenditure of considerable funds for the construction, installation, and maintenance of air pollution control equipment and procedures. Other types of regulations impinge upon such habitual and time-honored activities of the average citizen as the backyard burning of rubbish and leaves. Consequently, there are in any community numerous individuals, groups, and special interests which, either as sufferers of or contributors to air pollution, are directly affected by the nature and extent of public action concerning the problem.

In the Boston area, concern over air pollution resulted in the adoption in 1959 of a resolution by the Massachusetts legislature ordering a study by the Legislative Research Council of air pollution in the metropolitan Boston area. In May, 1960, a large area of South Boston was covered by a downpour of a black, oily substance. The 1959 study and this dramatic episode led to the enactment of a comprehensive air pollution control law in 1960, which replaced a rather weak and limited statute of 1910. Subsequent to the enactment of this legislation, air pollution control rules and regulations were promulgated, effective August 1, 1961.

Our study is primarily interested in identifying specific interest groups involved in the air-pollution problem in the Boston area and assessing the nature and effect of their participation in the development and enactment of the legislation, as well as their influence on the subsequent appropriations for and administration of the act. But first some generalizations can be made about the problem of control in urban areas.

Factors Affecting Metropolitan-Area Air Pollution

In examining the air-pollution problem in terms of the process of formulating public policy, certain general considerations stand out.

1. There are tremendous differences in air-pollution problems among the various communities and areas of the country. The significance of a single pollutant or group of pollutants in a particular locale will depend upon such factors as the topography and meteorology of the area, the number and types of sources involved, the quantities of pollutants emitted, the density of the population, and where it is located relative to the sources. The variety of sources creating air-pollution problems is almost as great as the variety of activities characteristic of modern life. Some examples of such sources, most of which were identified as existing in the metropolitan Boston area are: (1) industrial sources—steam power plants, industrial heating and refuse burning, construction operations, metallurgical operations, junkyards and scrap-metal recovery plants,

the paint and lacquer industry, petroleum-processing plants, chemical industries, paper mills, food-processing plants, tanneries, rubber-goods plants, textile mills, and other general manufacturing operations; (2) domestic sources—backyard burning of rubbish, home heating, household and apartment incinerators; (3) municipal sources—refuse burning at open dumps, municipal incinerators, sewers and sewage-treatment plants, road dusts, and construction operations; (4) transportation sources—automobiles, trucks, railroads, airplanes, ships.[1] Each community presents a specialized problem, and the sources and pollutants which may be of concern to one geographical area will not necessarily be a problem to another.[2]

2. There are two general types of air-pollution problems: community-wide and localized.[3] Although the two are often interrelated, recognition of this distinction helps in analyzing a particular problem and determining the type of control effort required; this distinction is particularly relevant in public-policy formulation.

A localized problem is one which exists in a limited area, usually immediately downwind from a specific source of pollution (although because of such factors as meteorology, topography, and the height of stacks emitting pollutants, a localized problem area may center at a considerable distance from the source). As one moves farther and farther downwind from the source, natural processes in the atmosphere may dilute and disperse the offending substance until it no longer constitutes a problem. In addition, the "receptors" (people, vegetation, domestic animals, homes, industrial plants or other property) located close to the source but outside of the localized air current, may substantially or completely escape the effects of the pollution.

Community-wide pollution by definition affects a large area, although not necessarily to the same degree as localized pollution. A significant characteristic of a truly community-wide problem is the complex mixing of pollutants which occurs in the atmosphere to the point where it is frequently impossible to distinguish one pollutant from another or to identify the source of each. Further, interactions occurring in the atmosphere may produce secondary pollutants differing from the original agents emitted.

In many cases, localized pollution contributes to the community-wide corruption of the air we breathe. Not only can motor-vehicle emissions cause a temporary localized problem within a radius of a few feet, but these exhaust gases may contribute to a chronic

community-wide pollution, lingering long after the localized problem has disappeared. Weather patterns also have their effect.
Emissions from a factory stack may be confined to the area immediately downwind as long as a steady wind blows. However, if the
wind dies down, such emissions may accumulate in the air over the
city and contribute to a community-wide problem.

The existence of these two general types of problems has important implications for air-pollution control at the community level.
Because localized air-pollution problems, though they may be quite
severe, affect persons and property located in limited segments of a
community, they may be a matter of relative indifference to the
areas of the city escaping them. Therefore, even though a serious
problem may exist for many groups and areas in the community, an
abatement program may not elicit the broad-based public support
required to cope with it. In contrast, in dealing with the community-
wide problem, originating in a myriad of sources of varying intensities and aggravated by secondary contaminants created in the
atmosphere by chemical interactions, it is difficult, if not impossible,
to identify specific culprits. A solution requires, therefore, comprehensive and pervasive control measures regulating the "normal"
activities of homeowners, industries, government, and the general
population. A high degree of public understanding, acceptance, and
support for such a comprehensive program must be mobilized for
truly effective action. If an air pollution control program has a limited budget (as most such programs normally do), it can only deal
with limited aspects of the difficulty (most desirably, as part of a
long-range plan to effect the general amelioration of the problem).
Consequently, it may be faced with outraged cries of "Why pick on
me?" from those selected for initial action. Also, such a piecemeal
program is frequently established during the height of one of the
periodic public waves of concern over pollution. It may face the
danger of subsequent public apathy or outright opposition as the
concern recedes, unless noticeable improvement in the overall situation is effected immediately.

Although the distinction between localized and community-wide
air pollution may be important to the air-pollution specialist in
understanding the nature and effects of the problem, such a distinction is not nearly so important to the persons affected by the pollution. Those who live immediately downwind from a particular
source of pollution are not comforted by the fact that their problem

does not bother the rest of the community. Certainly, their claim to relief regardless of the extent to which the problem may affect others in the community cannot, in good conscience or in good politics, be ignored.

Some differences are expressed by authorities in the field as to the character of metropolitan-area air-pollution problems. The Boston metropolitan-area problem is a good example. Thus one authority in the Boston area, from the Harvard School of Public Health, told me that he considered the air-pollution situation in this vicinity to be primarily one of a series of localized problems rather than a community-wide problem. He held that the likelihood of a community-wide problem developing was slight for the following reasons: the meteorology and topography of the area provided for unobstructed ventilation of the atmosphere by the winds; the trend in the Boston area was toward the replacement of heavy industries normally causing air pollution by less culpable industries, such as electronics and research and development operations; and the tendency of industry generally was to locate on the perimeter of the area, along Route 128. This position contrasted with the characterization of the problem by another eminent authority in the field: ". . . Metropolitan Boston is in the first stages of what could become a severe air pollution condition arising from the multiplicity of diverse and dispersed sources." [4]

3. A factor affecting the intensity of pressure and support for an air-pollution-control program is the considerable variation among individuals, groups, and geographic areas with respect to their sensitivity to and tolerance of the effects of air pollution. The reaction of people to odors, murkiness, and generally reduced visibility in the atmosphere, grimy clothing and buildings, and physiological effects, such as low-level eye and throat irritation, is highly subjective. What some people consider a nuisance or an irritant may be completely acceptable to others. This appears to depend on factors such as the history and traditions of communities and people as well as their socio-economic status. This is particularly striking in many of the coal and steel towns of Western Pennsylvania and the Ohio Valley, where the visitor from less polluted areas is appalled at the odors and general griminess. The residents of these areas, in contrast, appear to be completely indifferent or resigned to such conditions. Even such aspects as the toxic effects of air contaminants, while superficially amenable to quantitative description, involve a subjec-

tive consideration because even the slightest concentration of contaminants may be injurious to small fractions of the population, such as the very old or persons with some debilitating condition.

Indifference of some groups in the Boston metropolitan area to situations which would be quite disturbing to others was undoubtedly for many years a factor in the apathy toward air-pollution control even where the situation was "obviously" bad. An attorney involved in the investigation of the 1960 Boston sootfall incident and the drafting of subsequent legislation stated that he grew up in the South Boston area, a heavily industrialized "workingman's" district. He stated that even as a boy he could recall the terrible dirt and soot in the area. His mother complained of the curtains on the windows becoming black after a few hours, of the layers of dust and dirt which would accumulate on the windowsills and the exterior and interior walls of their house. However, according to him, this condition was accepted and tolerated by the people in the area as one of the "givens" of city life; when they complained or grumbled about it from time to time, it was always among themselves and it never became a matter to take to the local politicians. This acceptance of the grosser and more visible manifestations of the problem, coupled with the difficulty of comprehending the adverse effects of invisible contaminants, accounted, in his opinion, for the ease with which the General Court continued to fail to provide sufficient appropriations for air-pollution control. This indifference to what the experts would define as a real problem, although particularly striking in a "workingman's" area, is probably an operative factor in any urban dweller regardless of the socio-economic class of the area in which he resides. Dirt in the city's air and streets is accepted by many as an inherent part of city life, and by a process of desensitization, it may escape notice completely.

4. Air-pollution controls and regulations often run afoul of both public and private interests or industries, so that opposing objectives must be reconciled. One example is the matter of refuse disposal in the community. In many areas publicly supported refuse-collection systems are quite rudimentary and the disposal of refuse is left in large part to the homeowners and commercial establishments, who have the option of either contracting with a private garbage collector or disposing of their rubbish by backyard burning, with resultant air pollution. In other areas a refuse-collection system is maintained by the muncipality, but the disposal system may involve

hauling the collected refuse to a dump area, where the refuse is burned. A more expensive method for disposing of refuse is the sanitary land fill: refuse taken to an appropriate land-fill area is promptly covered with clean fill; because the refuse is not burned, no air pollution results. However, this method may not be either acceptable or feasible for some areas since, in addition to requiring the proper equipment and capable operators, it is also contingent upon the availability of properly located vacant lands. The most expensive method of refuse disposal is by incineration, a method involving heavy expenditures for construction, maintenance, and operation of the incinerator plant, and frequently, heated opposition by residents of the area in which the plant is to be located. Many jurisdictions are understandably quite loath to adopt this method.

Another example of conflict between air pollution control interests and other governmental agencies is the problem of the disposal of demolition debris. With the growing number and scope of urban-renewal and highway-construction projects, this is becoming an increasingly serious problem. To the redevelopment and highway agencies responsible for such projects, the least expensive and most convenient method for disposing of lumber and other debris from rights of way and demolished buildings is to burn it on the site. But this creates severe air-pollution problems; therefore, in many areas throughout the country such agencies, as well as private construction projects are under increasing pressure to discontinue the practice of on-site open burning and to shoulder the heavy expenses involved in transporting such material to a proper disposal site or in instituting improved on-site disposal methods and procedures.

When the air pollution control agency and the other agencies involved in these issues are all within the same governmental structure, the conflicts between them are ultimately resolved within that structure and are therefore rarely apparent to the public. However, when, as in the Boston area, the air pollution agency operates apart from and at another governmental level than the other agencies, such conflicts are not only likely to become public, but tend to be aggravated.

It should further be noted that the conflicts may involve not only the government versus industry, and the various governmental agencies which disagree among themselves, but also in many areas organized labor, which will frequently align itself with the industry being threatened by controls against the air-pollution agency.

Where an industry threatens to leave the area if subject to "unreasonable" controls, and the issue is perceived as one of Clean Air versus Jobs, organized labor will almost invariably opt for the latter.

5. A final consideration with respect to the general problem is that research has not yet provided definitive answers regarding many aspects of air pollution. There is considerable statistical and other circumstantial evidence giving rise to concern about the effect upon health of polluted air. At the present time, however, the issue cannot be stated as clearly as the proposition that x number of people will die or become ill if certain actions are not taken. This situation is of course not a new one in the history of public health. The case for action, even though all the answers are not in, was made by the Surgeon General of the Public Health Service as follows: "A few minutes ago, referring to the circumstantial evidence relating cancer to atmospheric pollution, I remarked that the case has not yet been proved. This legal metaphor is frequently used. I submit to you that it is misleading. In law, the suspect is innocent until his guilt has been proved beyond reasonable doubt. In the protection of human health, such absolute proof often comes too late. To wait for it is to invite disaster, or at least to suffer unnecessarily through long periods of time. Many years ago, before anyone had seen a germ or positively identified a single causative agent of epidemic diseases, far-sighted leaders observed the association between epidemics and filth. Wherever they had sufficient foresight to act on this circumstantial evidence, they made striking progress. Cleaning up the city filth resulted in better health. Years later they found out why." [5]

However, although in the past observations of "far-sighted leaders" have led to public-health action, air-pollution and other environmental health problems differ significantly, with respect to required actions, from the communicable-disease problems referred to by the Surgeon General. The difference lies in the fact that necessary control actions often are directed against the interests of powerful economic groups, and in the absence of conclusive, demonstrated, and documented evidence, such groups are in a very strong position to block what they call, "hasty and unreasonable" action. To cite an example, the position of the Boston Edison Company, as expressed by one of its vice presidents, is that it has never opposed any "reasonable" requirements to abate air pollution and that its major effort with respect to the state legislature and administrative agencies is to prevent the imposition of unreasonable controls pushed by impractical purists. In this case, he stated that if Boston Edison were able to control 98 per cent of its air-pollution emissions there would always be someone pushing for the expenditure of millions of more dollars to make it 99 per cent.

The difficulties which this type of situation presents to the air-pollution-control agency are clearly underlined by the following explanation, given by the state Department of Public Health, of the reasons for the admittedly minimal nature of the rules and regulations which were promulgated: "The department felt that the need for these regulations was self-evident and required no extensive documentation beyond that already available. . . . It would probably be unwise to adopt more stringent regulations without some means of relating the regulatory effect to present and also to expected or desired future air quality. A considerable increase in survey effort, both atmospheric monitoring and source evaluation, seems desirable, if a further regulatory program is to be developed in an equitable manner and based on demonstrated need." [6]

Air Pollution Control Efforts in the Boston Area

The first law [7] pertaining to air pollution in the metropolitan Boston area was enacted largely at the urging of the Boston Chamber of Commerce in 1910. It was amended several times subsequently, and provided the basic jurisdictional framework for the present Metropolitan Air Pollution Control District. The 1910 act gave to the State Board of Gas and Electric Light Commissioners the responsibility for smoke inspection and abatement in Boston, Brookline, Cambridge, Somerville, Everett, and Chelsea. The authority of the Board was limited to policing the emission of visible smoke from chimneys and other types of smokestacks, including those of locomotives. The law did not empower the Board to adopt rules for the enforcement of smoke control; instead, the legislation established the permissible degree of emissions for all types and classes of stacks, set forth the method of observation and enforcement, and prescribed penalties. The Board was given the power, after serving notice and conducting a hearing, to order any person or corporation to stop or abate the emission of smoke observed to be in violation of the act. This order was enforceable in the Superior Court. To finance the smoke-control activities, the law provided that funds were to be made available initially by annual appropriation of the General Court and that the funds actually expended for the program were to be reimbursed by the cities and towns involved in proportion to their annual taxable valuation.

The legislation was at the time, and remains to this day, a unique arrangement in the field of air-pollution control. It is remarkable for the method of creating the District by state fiat; for the lodging of the control of operations in a regular department of the state government; and especially for the method of financing, under which the cities and towns incorporated in the District were, without any direct representation in its control, required to finance its operations. The San Francisco Bay Area Air Pollution Control District, created in 1955, was also established directly, by the California State Legislature, without requiring the concurrence of the counties involved. However, the Board governing the Bay Area district, which is empowered to adopt the policies and set the budget of the district, consists of representatives from each county board of supervisors and from the cities in the area. Furthermore, the law sets a limit to the budget of the district. In contrast, the Boston district is established and run by the state with no statutory limit on its budget and is financed by the cities and towns concerned without any direct voice in the matter.

Enactment of the 1910 law was largely in response to complaints by the Boston Chamber of Commerce and other groups who were suffering economic loss resulting from smoke damage to merchandise and buildings. Responsibility for administration of the law was placed in the agency concerned with the regulation of public utilities because the railroad and power companies at that time were the principal offenders.[8]

Unfortunately, a detailed legislative history of the act of 1910 which might have documented the background and politics involved is not available. Discussions with various persons in the state government have suggested some of the factors which may have been involved. The district affected by the original air-pollution law consisted of old, heavily industrialized, highly congested areas; the proximity of the cities and towns to one another certainly must have suggested the necessity for controls which would encompass a territory larger than any one of the existing jurisdictions. Further, the period in which the 1910 act was passed was one in which the "Yankees" in the area had pretty much abandoned all hope of gaining control of Boston and were transferring to the state or to special districts a number of powers and authorities that would normally have been vested in local governments. Thus, the choice of a state-run smoke-abatement program was seen as a means of getting the necessary action to control smoke while avoiding any entanglements with the Boston city government. In the election of 1910, Boston had been placed firmly under the control of Mayor "Honey Fitz" Fitzgerald. The industries which were to be affected by the law viewed with great misgiving the allocation of further power to the Boston city government, and saw a state-run program as the lesser of two evils. Although the intensity of feeling on this issue has probably subsided, this viewpoint seems to be operative today and may account for the negligible "home rule" outcry against the Metropolitan Air Pollution Control District, which constitutes a gross violation of home-rule principles. However, it should be noted that a knowledgeable observer of the situation feels that "home rule" is very much a part of the politics of air-pollution control in the Boston area. He attributes the lack of financial support by the state legislature to the sensitivity of the legislators to the political power of the towns and cities. While the local areas have gone along with the idea of the District (perhaps out of inertia, since the form of the District was established in 1910), they have done so only because just a small amount of money is involved. However, if significantly increased funds were to be appropriated to the state agency, it is felt that there would be considerable outcry and opposition from the municipalities which would be subject to increased assessments.

Since 1910, the law has been amended several times. In 1928,[9] twenty-two more communities were added to the District; subsequently three more jurisdictions were added. In 1954,[10] the Division of Smoke Inspection, which had been responsible for administering the smoke-control law, was transferred from the Department of Public Utilities (the successor agency to the old Board) to the Department of Public Health. The transfer of this function to the Department of Public Health was in conformance with the national pattern which had emerged in which air pollution control authority at the state level has been vested in the health departments. Furthermore, the Department of Public Utilities interposed no objection to this transfer; on the contrary, it was quite willing to be rid of a function which was minuscule in size, somewhat tangential to its major functions and interests, and generally viewed as an unrewarding stepchild of the department.[11]

Thus, by 1954, after a period of forty-four years, the original smoke-abatement program, which had had jurisdiction over six municipalities, was enlarged to cover thirty-one cities and towns in the metropolitan Boston area. Responsibility for the program was transferred from the Department of Public Utilities, which had viewed air pollution primarily as a problem of nuisance abatement, to the Department of Public Health, which, with its sensitivity to air pollution as a health problem, viewed air pollution as including invisible contaminants as well as visible smoke. However, the authority of the Department was still limited to the enforcement of a smoke-control law, which had been rendered obsolete in the forty-four years intervening since its enactment by great changes in the nature and understanding of the problem and the available technical administrative methods of meeting it.

The Legislative Struggle to Modernize Air-Pollution Control in Metropolitan Boston

Perennial efforts by the Department of Public Health to broaden its authority to meet the problem were unsuccessful until 1959, when the General Court directed the Legislative Research Council, an agency of the General Court, to make an investigation and study relative to the problem of air pollution in the metropolitan Boston area.[12] None of the persons interviewed has been able to throw any light on why, after successive failures, this first concrete manifestation of legislative interest in air pollution occurred. Senator Powers, president of the Senate, who later came to play a leading role in the enactment of air-pollution legislation, has stated that one of the big reasons for the small amount of air-pollution activity in the legislature prior to 1959 is that the Senate had always been controlled by the Republicans; it was not until 1959 that the Democrats gained control of both houses of the General Court. At this time Powers became the first Democratic president of the Senate in the history of the General Court. He claims that the Republicans were to a great extent under the influence of the large industries which oppose regulation of air pollution, and that with the general lack of interest in the problem it was easy for them to kill off any measures they wished. In saying this, Senator Powers has insisted that he is not indulging in mere political oratory, but that this is a realistic characterization of the system in the legislature. However one may evaluate Senator Powers' statement, it is a fact that after years of inaction, the legislature did take action in 1959; there was no discernible change in the objective situation except the one Senator Powers suggests.

Senator Powers' viewpoint differs from that of Representative Tynan, a Democrat from the same district. In response to my question as to whether there are any party issues in the legislature, he said particularly that the party system is nonexistent in the legislature, and that each legislator decides his own positions on the basis of the specific political pressures which are operating upon him. The Representative said that although air pollution is not now a significant issue, it will become one when attempts are made to get the big industries in the area to install expensive air pollution control equipment. At that time, he believed, big business will probably make its opposition to air pollution enforcement measures felt.

The study report authorized by the legislature in 1959 was prepared by Dr. Rolf Eliassen, Professor of Sanitary Engineering of the Massachusetts Institute of Technology, with the assistance of Dr. James L. Whittenburger, Assistant Dean of the Harvard School of Public Health; it was submitted to the legislature on February 5, 1960.[13] The report noted the changes in the character of the problem as follows:

> The pall that hangs over much of metropolitan Boston on many mornings, sometimes persisting throughout the day, is evidence that in one respect present pollution control systems are not adequate. Air pollution today is more than stacks belching their blackness against the sky. Coal has nearly disappeared from the cellars of private homes, and has been completely abandoned by the railroads. This discontinuance of the extensive use of coal . . . is partially . . . offset by the tremendous growth of large power generating stations which use coal as fuel, at least in part. . . .
>
> . . . But overbalancing the decrease is the fantastic increase in the general use of petroleum in its several forms, and the number and complexities of raw materials used and the waste products which are released by the industrial community.

Air pollution has "changed its stripes, but has not sheathed its claws." The invisible gasses and the tiny particles that now pollute our environment are less felt, but are more to be feared, than the layers of soot that once infiltrated Boston's homes. Metropolitan Boston is in the first stages of what could become a very severe air pollution condition arising from a multiplicity of diverse dispersed sources.[14]

With respect to the legal authority available to meet this growing problem, the report stated: "The Division of Smoke Inspection labors with 1910 statutory regulations which were adopted when the railroads burned coal and the automobile was more curious than commonplace. This law was farsighted for its time and for many years enabled the control of smoke stacks to the point where Boston was considered a 'clean' city. To date, however, the scope of Chapter 651 of the Acts of 1910 is not wide enough to cover adequately new sources of atmospheric pollution." [15]

The report identified a tremendous variety of sources of air pollution in the metropolitan Boston area.[16] In summarizing the existing situation, the report stated: "Area-wide air pollution increases largely uncontrolled. It arises from thousands or even millions of sources, since vehicles and home heating units contribute about half the present amount. Little is being done to meet this situation in the area of metropolitan Boston, except for action against an occasional stack from which excessive smoke is detected. Apart from voluntary efforts by some public relations conscious industries, and occasional cleanups by individual plants after action by health agencies, area-wide atmospheric pollution control is negligible in the metropolitan region." [17]

Under the rules of the General Court, reports of studies and investigations carried out by the Legislative Research Council may not include legislative recommendations. Operating under this limitation, it is clear that the authors of the report came as close as they possibly could to the forbidden area and at times, indeed, appear to have crossed the line. The clear implications of the report were that an area-wide or district approach, cutting across the numerous cities and towns in the Boston metropolitan area, was necessary; that such a district should have broad authority to prescribe and enforce rules and regulations governing all sources and forms of air pollution, whether visible or invisible; that the state should play a leading role in the district's operations; and that, as a minimum, there should be a fourfold increase in funds for air-pollution control in the metropolitan Boston area.

In line with many of the concepts expressed in the report (in the preparation of which the Department of Public Health played an active part), the Department submitted a recommendation and bill to the legislature designed to replace the existing Division of Smoke Inspection with "an agency which can efficiently and economically effect the proper control of all air contaminants throughout the metropolitan Boston area." In a summary of its recommendations, the Department stated that the "statutory limitations of the present law permit control by the Division of Smoke Inspection only of black smoke from stacks, whereas the need is for a uniform means of control of all types of air pollution over the entire affected area. Further, the present statute . . . does not provide for any representation by the communities of the smoke control district over the expenditure of funds which they provide, or over the degree of control exercised. The proposed act would remedy these defects. It would replace the Division of Smoke Inspection with a Metropolitan Air Pollution Control Commission in the Department of Public Health, and the Commission would be empowered to adopt and enforce suitable air pollution control regulations, with the Division of Sanitary Engineering providing all necessary services, including manpower, equipment and laboratory services." [18]

The Department's bill as introduced [19] provided for a commission consisting of the commissioner of the Department of Public Health and six registered voters of the municipalities of the district, appointed by the governor with the advice and consent of the Council for overlapping terms of three years; one of the appointees had to be a physician, another a registered professional engineer, and a third a representative of industry. This recommendation was made in the hope that such a commission would generate broader support particularly from among those concerned with "home rule" and "state interference." [20]

Because the legislature had, in the previous session, authorized an air-pollution study, and with the impetus given by the report by the Legislative Research Council, the Department was relatively hopeful its bill would be passed. However, by May it appeared as if the bill would be killed. In the General Court, the parliamentary device used effectively to kill a bill without anyone having to go on record to do so, is to refer it to the Ways and Means Committee, which serves as a recess study committee for any bills having to do with the expenditure of funds, without attaching any date for a report to be made. In May, 1960, this was the disposition in store for the bill, and all hopes for its passage were gone. However, almost providentially for the Department, there was a dramatically severe downpour of a black, oily substance over a large portion of South Boston on Friday, May 13. Also providentially, this area is represented in the General Court by Senator Powers, the president of the Senate. The downpour galvanized him to take an intense interest in air-pollution legislation. Further, a prominent member of the House, Representative John Tynan, from the same South Boston district, happened to have been on the street in the area at the time of the downpour. With a swiftness amazing to veteran observers of the General Court, an order establishing a special Senate committee to investigate the episode was passed on the following Monday, May 16, with Senator Powers as chairman. By May 19, the special committee had been organized; William F. Coyne, a local attorney, was appointed to serve as counsel to the committee; an engineering firm was engaged to serve as consultants, and after due notice, the committee commenced public hearings. The report of the special committee [21] was submitted in July, 1960. Relevant portions of the report include the following passages:

> On Friday, May 13, 1960, between 8:30 A.M. and 9:30 A.M. a portion of the South Boston District of the City of Boston was covered by a black oil-base type substance. The area subjected to this debris . . . covered approximately one square mile wherein reside over 10,000 people.

> .   .   .   .

> Description of the fallout by observers likened it to a "black snowstorm," which completely covered the clothing of the people who were in the streets. The pedestrians sought escape from the fallout by going into stores and doorways. Automobiles, sidewalks and streets in the affected area were similarly covered. . . .

> An inspection employee in the Division of Smoke Abatement testified that ". . . it was the worst (situa-

tion) I had ever encountered in my thirty-one years of
state service. . . ."

. . . .

It cannot be overemphasized that the visual deposit
in South Boston on May 13 was caused by precipitation of contaminants generally existing at all times in
the air and which people breathe throughout the year.
The atmospheric conditions were such that, on this
particular day, the material was forced to settle out in
a concentrated area.

Air pollution, however, unlike the tragic incident
in South Boston is not an intermittent or accidental
occurrence but, rather, a constantly increasing men-
ace. By our very ignorance of conditions existing, and
neglecting proper control of the sources, we are allowing the air we breathe to turn into a deadly combination of materials which may cause irreparable damage
to public health.

The law governing smoke control in the Metropolitan District permits only the control of visible smoke
discharged from stacks to the extent specified by
statute. State Smoke Inspectors do not possess authority to enter private property in performing their duties. . . . Since the power of state inspectors is
limited, it is then necessary for them, when the situation warrants, to seek the aid of local health inspectors
to assist in investigations.

Since the inspectors in the Smoke Inspection Division have control only of visible smoke, the weather
conditions of Friday, May 13, 1960 presented a most
peculiar problem for . . . the low ceiling obscured
the tops of the stacks of the two largest plants in the
contaminated area from view. This situation raised a
technical problem as to jurisdiction for purposes of action, i.e., state authority re smoke emission or local
authority re abating a nuisance via the health department.[22]

With respect to the specific causes of the episode, the committee
found "that certain natural phenomena and mechanical failures of

indicating equipment at the Metropolitan Transit Authority station . . . combined to result in the South Boston sootfall incident and to, jointly, be the cause thereof." [23] However, the report noted, "none of the above-listed sources can be eliminated from the overall problem of air pollution in the metropolitan area. . . ." [24]

There was considerable controversy over the finding of the committee that the MTA plant was the specific cause of the episode, and doubts as to the correctness of the committee's finding appear to linger in the minds of many to this day. Representative Tynan, who is a close political ally of Senator Powers', stated at the hearings that on the basis of his personal observations of the situation, he was certain the downpour emanated from the stacks of the Boston Edison power plant located in the area. Two years later, when I interviewed him, he continued to insist that Boston Edison was the culprit. He felt that Senator Powers had been misled by the technical report submitted by the state Department of Public Health and that, ultimately, the power of the Boston Edison Company lay behind the committee's finding. In later discussions concerning this point, staff members of the Department of Public Health insisted that their investigation and report was completely objective and was based upon sound technical judgment. It was pointed out that primarily because the issue had been raised by Representative Tynan, the report was later reviewed by an independent engineering consultant, who concurred in the Department's findings. They pointed out that although Representative Tynan may have been perfectly honest and sincere in his statements, his conclusion was not one that a lay person could competently make.

Two significant issues are involved in the findings as to the cause of the episode. They are: (1) the political mileage that can be derived from an issue involving the protection of the well-being of the people against an overbearing utility (this point was also, of course, emphasized by the vice president of Boston Edison); and (2) the question of who would be liable for damages in the many lawsuits which were expected to be filed by persons affected by the episode. In a discussion with me about Boston Edison's influence on the legislature, Representative Tynan knowingly referred to the fact that it is one of the most powerful industries in the area and presumably exercises a pervasive influence in various ways. He did not specify what this influence was. As for any pressures upon him with respect to legislation, he stated that his district is mainly a "working-class" one, and if there is any powerful pressure on him it comes from organized labor; such groups as Boston Edison don't even bother to make representations to him since they know he will give them short shrift.

The Senate committee appended to its report a draft of recommended legislation,[25] based to a great extent on the nearly killed Department of Public Health bill. It included a strong statement urging enactment of the bill as follows:

> It appears that the Department of Public Health and the local communities are not sufficiently equipped to meet and overcome this general problem of air pollution; further, the extent to which it has become a problem and the damage it may and can do is not fully comprehended either by officials or by the public. The public must be educated to the inherent dangers. The agencies who can meet, control and overcome the challenge need funds and skilled employees.
>
> • • • • • • • • • • •
>
> The only certain method of preventing trouble is to reduce air pollution as much as possible before we are faced with a catastrophe. The agency needs more money to do its work. Public safety demands immediate positive action.[26]

A slightly amended version of the Senate committee's bill was finally enacted in October.[27] The new law, which presently governs the operations of the district, establishes a Metropolitan Air Pollution Control District (MAPCD), consisting of Boston and twenty-nine cities and towns covering the area generally within the circumferential Route 128. It also provides that additional contiguous cities or towns may be admitted to the District upon application, subject to approval by the Department of Public Health. The Department is given broad powers to control the pollution of the atmosphere within the District without qualification as to whether the pollution is visible or invisible or as to the sources of such pollution. The Department is empowered, after a public hearing, to prescribe, amend, or repeal rules and regulations "to prevent pollution or undue contamination of the atmosphere within said district." With the impetus of the South Boston sootfall episode and the strong interest of Senator Powers, the commission feature of the original health department bill was dropped as unnecessary in order to accomplish its passage.[28]

Under the act, the personnel of the Department are authorized to enter and inspect any property, premise, or place, and to stop and detain for inspection any motor vehicle. The Department is empowered to order any person, corporation, or political subdivision to stop or abate violation of any of the rules and regulations adopted by it; violations of its orders are subject to fines of from $50 to $100 for the first offense and from $200 to $500 for each succeeding offense, with each day or part thereof of violation constituting a separate and succeeding offense. In addition, the court, on petition of the Department, is empowered to restrain, through injunction, violations of any rules and regulations. The Department is authorized to maintain and operate air-sampling stations and devices, to make or perform routine and special examinations and inspections, observations, determinations, laboratory analyses, and surveys, to maintain records, and to perform such other acts as it deems necessary to carry out the program. The costs of the District, to be reimbursed by the cities and towns in it, are to be assessed against them, not only in proportion to their assessed valuations, as provided in the 1910 act and in the original health department bill, but in proportion to population as well. The act also authorizes the establishment in other parts of the state of air pollution control districts similar to the Boston district upon joint application of the cities and towns desiring to form such a district and approval of the Department.

As noted above, in discussing the circumstances surrounding the enactment of the bill, Senator Powers cited the favorable legislative climate for air-pollution legislation resulting from the assumption of control of both houses of the General Court by the Democrats in 1959. However, when I reminded him that even after the Legislative Research Council report, the Department's bill was, in May, 1960, on its way to being killed, Senator Powers conceded that no action would have been taken had it not been for the sootfall episode. He stated that when it did occur in his district he became personally involved, and because of his power as president of the Senate, he was able to push through the special order for the Senate-committee study and the final legislation, which was enacted before the opposition lobbyists really knew what was happening. Further, by that time, because of the sootfall incident, no one was really in a position to oppose the bill. He felt that the lobbyists probably made no representations to him against the bill because they knew there was nothing they could do about it and because in such a situation they take a practical point of view and do not fight a sure thing; instead, they save their fire for a later time when something can actually be done to achieve their goals.

I asked Senator Powers why—despite the fact that the Department of Public Health's air-pollution duties were considerably enlarged, and in light of the strong statement in the Senate committee's report concerning the need for additional funds, and statements made by Senator Powers at the time which were interpreted by many as his personal promise that additional funds would be forthcoming—to date no increase of funds for the District had been appropriated and it continued to limp along on the incredibly inadequate budget of $55,000. I noted that it is a fairly standard technique of pressure groups, when they are unable to block unwanted legislation, to attempt to gain their ends by preventing the appropriation of adequate funds which would allow the administering agency to carry out the purposes of the legislation. I suggested that perhaps the lobbyists had "saved their fire" for the appropriating process, "where something could be done." At first, Senator Powers responded on a rather general level. He referred to public apathy, but he refused to blame the public for it. Instead, he severely criticized the professional public-health leaders for failing to do more in publicizing the air-pollution problem. With respect to appropriations, Senator Powers said that the big concern of the Democrats has been to institute economies which would avoid the need for higher taxes, and he cited the fact that over the last four years no new taxes had been imposed. In considering appropriations there are always demands for more funds than are available and therefore choices must be made. The big item of spending in Massachusetts recently has been education; air pollution, in the general competition for budget money, has not received sufficient attention to rate any additional funds. Further, he felt it is very difficult to get the legislature to appropriate money for air pollution since there is no political payoff in it, such as there would be in building a bridge to which one could attach a plaque bearing one's name. Senator Powers stated that he even has trouble getting senators to serve on the Public Health Committee of the General Court because there are no big political issues involved. As a result, the people who do serve on the Public Health Committee do so only reluctantly. Thus, the turnover on the Committee is fairly high, and as a result, there is no one legislator who has become an authority in the field and who can be depended upon to push air-pollution legislation or other health matters. The Senator concluded by stating that he felt the way the Department could get additional appropriations was to use the authority and funds it now has, to take action against air-pollution violators. Senator Powers seemed to feel that not too much could be done unless something happened to draw newspaper and public attention to the problem.

Throughout the interview two seemingly conflicting ideas were expressed. On the one hand, on a number of occasions, Senator Powers unabashedly referred to his personal power and influence within the legislature as an indispensable element in securing the enactment of the 1960 legislation. On the other hand, he seemed to say that despite his own personal interest in the problem there is little hope of getting additional appropriations for the air-pollution program unless public apathy toward the problem can be overcome. Presumably another sootfall episode could do it; falling short of that, aggressive and dramatic action by the Department of Public Health which would focus public attention on the problem is necessary.

Senator Powers' own remarks, taken together with the observation by Representative Tynan that party discipline in the General Court is nonexistent and that each legislator acts in terms of the specific pressures impinging upon him, provide the basis for a reconciliation of the Senator's two seemingly conflicting views. He may indeed possess the power and influence he has ascribed to himself, and it is quite possible that, even with the public apathy, he could, if he wished, secure additional funds for the air-pollution program. But, to accomplish this Senator Powers would have to "invest" more of his influence than he is willing to employ. Thus, although throughout the interview I was struck by Senator Powers' knowledgeability about the technical as well as the political aspects of air pollution (I saw him without an appointment, so there was no possibility of his being briefed beforehand), it is also clear that to him as a political figure, air pollution is but one of a number of issues comprising the overall political situation in which he operates, and that he is not prepared to sacrifice all for air-pollution control.

I also discussed the circumstances surrounding the passage of the

1960 act with William Coyne, the Boston attorney who was retained as counsel to Senator Powers' special committee, and who was described by a columnist in one of the Boston newspapers as a key figure in the drafting of the bill which the Senate committee recommended. At the time he was retained, Mr. Coyne was serving as "legislative agent" (the local euphemism for "lobbyist") for the retail stores association. Mr. Coyne too saw public apathy as the dominant political element in the lack of follow-through by the legislature in providing adequate funds for the enforcement and administration of the 1960 act. Thus he said that with the installation of devices by industry to suppress the grosser manifestations of air pollution, and with the general shifting from coal to oil as a fuel, the problem is somewhat less noticeable among the people and is therefore less likely to generate any significant pressures for correction of the situation. (He said he was convinced of the seriousness of the problem on the basis of what he had learned while serving with the Senate committee.)

With respect to his experience in drafting the bill, he stated that he did not recall any specific pressures upon him. He felt that because of the sootfall incident and the active interest of Senator Powers no one could have successfully opposed the measure, and to his knowledge no one actually tried to do so. Mr. Coyne recalled some stirrings on the "home rule" issue, and it was on the basis of anticipated opposition that a proposal to make the air pollution district controls applicable on a statewide basis was dropped. He recalls that there was another proposal to provide for state appropriations to finance part of the District's costs; this, too, was dropped in anticipation of opposition from the areas outside the District to using state funds to support a regional operation. One feature of the bill which was considered to be highly significant was the provision giving the Department of Public Health the right of entry into private property to investigate violations of air-pollution regulations.

With respect to his general approach in drafting the bill, Mr. Coyne said that he relied heavily upon the recommendations of the Department of Public Health, that for the most part, he served in a strictly staff capacity to Senator Powers, and that the only original contributions he made were confined to sharpening up some of the legal phraseology in the bill. He stated that Senator Powers reviewed the drafts which he prepared and that Senator Powers generally went along with such drafts except when, as in the instances noted above, political expediency dictated the necessity for modifications.

The Role of Pressure Groups and "Legislative Agents"

I interviewed Henry Kurth, Vice President for Steam Operations of the Boston Edison Company, concerning the air-pollution situation in the Boston area. Mr. Kurth stated that the Boston Edison Company has been a leader both in engineering research and in the installation of the most advanced air pollution control devices available. He said the company had installed very expensive electrostatic precipitators, costing almost a million dollars each, and that it uses oil instead of coal wherever possible, which tends further to reduce air pollution. Also, the company has experimented with the use of various kinds of oil additives in an effort to decrease air pollution.

Mr. Kurth said philosophically that one can't really get rid of air pollution completely and that a utility is always a handy target for attack because of its large power plants, which necessarily involve some air-pollution emissions. What people fail to understand, he said, is that a utility merely represents one large power-generating operation in lieu of each home having its own power-generating and heating devices. The small quantities of smoke which would be given off by each of the multitudes of homes if they used their own power-generating devices are now consolidated into emissions from a few plants and so become a noticeable target for attack.

Mr. Kurth said that Boston Edison has always had a policy of voluntarily doing whatever is necessary to reduce air pollution from its plants, but he conceded that the effect of the smoke-control program over the years has been to exert pressure on the company to expedite necessary installations.

The big concern of the company, he said, is to prevent "unrealistic" legislation and regulations, such as a requirement to install excessively expensive control equipment when only a very insignificant reduction in air-pollution emissions would result. As noted previously, he felt that there would always be some people who, if air-pollution control were at 98 per cent, would insist upon the installation of millions of dollars' worth of equipment in order to raise the figure to 99 per cent.

He explained that his is a technical office concerned with actual power operations. Dealings with the legislature at a political level are handled by the legislative agent of the Massachusetts Gas and Electric Association, whose function it is to keep watch on legislative developments of concern to the power industry, to keep the companies informed, to appear at hearings and sponsor various kinds of bills, and to maintain contacts with the legislators. He disclaimed any detailed knowledge of the specific methods of operation of the agent, but insisted that insofar as Boston Edison is concerned, it uses open and aboveboard methods. When Mr. Kurth confers with legislators or with the staff of the state health department, his arguments are confined to such technical matters as the reasonableness and feasibility of proposed regulations; when he wins a point it is on that basis alone. To demonstrate that Boston Edison does not always get its way, he said that although the company opposed the elimination of the classification of stacks in accordance with size, the stack classification was deleted from the 1960 act. He said a number of times that this was a very ill-advised action. I asked Mr. Kurth what he felt the motivations of the Public Health Department staff were in failing to accept what he felt was a reasonable approach with respect to stack classification. He felt that the staff was acting under pressure from various legislators who control the Department's appropriations, who in turn are under pressure from discontented constituents who feel that "something must be done" to get rid of the smoke.

As a general method of operation, the Boston Edison Company does not testify at public hearings, but confines itself to informal conferences with the Department of Publc Health. A big company, he stated, will never speak at a public hearing because of the danger of being misquoted by newspapers; it prefers, instead, to work quietly, but if this doesn't work, upon rare occasions it will state its case at a public hearing. In response to my question, he acknowledged that certain companies attempt to pressure the legislature; they may appeal to employees or stockholders to take a stand on legislation. He stated that the Boston Edison has not resorted to these devices with respect to air pollution.

He felt that most of the outcry about air pollution was from a few disgruntled people, most of whom had knowingly moved almost under the stacks of the Boston Edison Company and then started to complain when the smoke became obnoxious. He had little sympathy for them since he felt that they could expect nothing better if they moved so close to a power plant. He mentioned the Edgar plant at Weymouth as a case in point. When it was constructed a few decades ago it was completely isolated, but over the years, homes were built in the area, constantly getting closer to the Edgar plant. Today Boston Edison is faced with a significant problem of complaints by people who live in the area.

A somewhat similar view of the functions of the legislative agent was expressed by Mr. Coyne, who it should be noted, was the legislative agent for the retail stores industry. Mr. Coyne gave the "official" explanation of the duties of the legislative agents and denied that any devious methods are used by them to influence legislators. Their primary function is to review all legislative developments, to inform their clients of these happenings, and to request their guidance or technical advice as to how to proceed. Thus, he said, they serve mainly as channels of communication and information. When I said I had heard that some industries, particularly utilities, make it a practice of filling certain jobs only upon recommendation of friendly legislators, he became indignant and stated that while this practice may occur (insisting at the same time, in good lawyerlike fashion, that he was not conceding that it *does* occur), it would probably be limited to jobs that are actually needed and that unnecessary jobs would not be created for this purpose. He felt that opposition from the stockholders and the supervision of the Department of Public Utilities would tend to prevent such practices.

In contrast to Mr. Kurth and Mr. Coyne, Senator Powers, although steering clear of specifics, said the lobbyists and the industrial groups they represent exercise considerable influence in the legislature; he attributed to them a major role in blocking air-pollution legislation for a number of years. However, he said, because of the almost total lack of public interest in the problem, they really do not need to exert very much influence to gain their ends.

Representative Tynan, also without going into specifics, saw the heavy hand of the Boston Edison Company in what he felt to be the "whitewash" of the South Boston sootfall episode, but he too felt that, in the absence of countervailing pressures on the legislator, very little specific pressure was needed to influence the many legislators with whom the legislative agents maintain cordial relations on a year-round basis.

Only one of my interviews, with a member of the staff of the General Court, produced anything in the nature of specifics with regard to the activities of the legislative agents. He stated that the main opposition to air-pollution legislation came from the Boston Edison Company and a leading chemical company in the area. He thought that the Public Health Committee in the General Court has been generally sympathetic to the Department of Public Health and its programs and has not opposed air-pollution legislation. He said, rather, that the killing of various bills over the years was the result of the behind-the-scenes work of the legislative agents of the power industry, particularly with the Ways and Means Committee, whose jurisdiction encompasses all bills that involve the expenditure of funds. He was unable to cite the precise details with respect to air-pollution legislation, which he had not followed too closely, but in general, he felt that the agents are able to pressure members of the General Court in two ways. First, the power company has large numbers of clerical and other jobs which are filled on recommendation of the legislators; if the legislator is unfriendly the company will not accept his recommendations for such jobs. (Particularly when there is an absence of political issues, the ability to fill jobs becomes a vital matter in the political life of a legislator.) He recalled that one of the people with the power company had stated that over two hundred jobs were filled on recommendation of legislators. The other method of influencing the legislators, he said, is by campaign contributions, which are made in many ways although, legally, political contributions by companies are prohibited.

When I discussed this matter with a staff member of the Department of Public Health, he corroborated Mr. Kurth's description of Boston Edison's methods of operation vis-à-vis the Department of Public Health. He said that he had no knowledge of any "political" pressures being exerted by Boston Edison on the Department and he felt that in general, at the technical level, Boston Edison's cooperation with the Department had been quite good. He told me that when Boston Edison made representations to him on the stack-classification issue, Boston Edison lost completely, and on another issue, the limits on the emission of visible smoke as specified in the new regulations, a compromise was finally arrived at which set the standard midway between the 1910 limitations and those originally proposed by the Department.

For information on appropriations for the air-pollution district, I interviewed the budget examiner for the Department of Public Health in the state Bureau of the Budget, and William Bixby, formerly commissioner of the budget, who was serving as special assistant on budgetary matters to the commissioner on administration and finance, and who was considered to be the governor's principal staff adviser on budgetary matters. The budget examiner stated that Governor Volpe's budgets for fiscal years 1962 and 1963 did not contain any increases for the Metropolitan Air Pollution Control District. As a general budgetary policy of the governor, no increases have been allowed except for very unusual items where prior commitments dictated appropriation increases. The big concern, both of the governor and the General Court, has been to avoid the necessity of increasing or imposing new taxes, and this general situation has created great hardships in all departments of the government. Mr. Bixby confirmed the budget examiner's understanding of the general budgetary policy. Further, with respect to the air-pollution item, he did not feel that an increased appropriation was really justified. He explained that a large part of his job is to serve as a complaint bureau, and to tap various sources of information to learn of any unhappiness on the part of legislators or outside interest groups with respect to budgetary items. The Department's request for an increase for the District had been referred to him, and his survey of the situation revealed no opinion one way or the other as to the adequacy of the current budget. On that basis, he assumed that the current appropriation level was satisfactory.

Current Status of the Program

Under the new law, the Department adopted a set of rules and regulations effective August 1, 1961,[29] which defined an air contaminant as including, but not limited to, "dust, fly ash, fumes, gas, mist, odor, smoke, vapor, pollen, micro-organisms, radioactive material, ionizing radiation, any combination thereof or any decay or reaction product thereof." Atmospheric pollution was defined to mean "the presence in the ambient air space of one or more contaminants or combinations thereof in such quantities and of such duration as to (a) cause a nuisance; (b) be injurious or be, on the basis of current information, potentially injurious to human or animal life, to vegetation, or to property; or (c) unreasonably interfere with the comfortable enjoyment of life and property or the conduct of business." The regulations contained a general prohibition of emissions from air-contamination sources "of such quantities of air contaminants which will cause, by themselves or in conjunction with other air contaminants, a condition of atmospheric pollution."

The regulations banned all open burning, a widespread practice in the Boston area, except as might be approved by the Department. The regulations exempted, however, open fires intended for the reduction of leaves, the backyard burning of rubbish from buildings containing three or less dwelling units, and open fires for cooking purposes. The Department said that the proviso for approval of open burning was temporary, and after a necessary changeover or adjustment period, open burning would generally be prohibited. Another section of the regulations prohibited the use of medium to high volatile bituminous coals in hand-fired furnaces. Further, written approval of the Department was required for design criteria, preliminary and final plans, and specifications in connection with the construction of large power plants and incinerators. The 1910 limitations on emissions of smoke from stacks were continued on a substantially more stringent basis.

The new regulations were considered to be of a minimal nature, particularly when compared to those of other jurisdictions. The Department felt it had gone as far as it could in promulgating regulations based upon available technical data concerning actual conditions in the Boston area, and that it would be unwise, in the absence of strong technical justifications, to adopt more stringent rules and regulations. In order to accomplish this, a considerable increase in survey effort, both atmospheric monitoring and source evaluation, would be necessary before the regulatory program could be developed in an equitable manner, based upon demonstrated need. The entire program hinges on additional appropriations to permit the necessary gathering of technical data.

Because of its limited resources, the Department has had to confine itself to problems it could solve with the least expenditure of staff time and funds. When the new regulations went into effect, the Department concentrated upon the elimination of open burning.

Open burning in the Boston area was done primarily for private and municipal refuse disposal and for the recovery of metals from waste or junk material. The municipal refuse problem involves a disinclination by most people, including public officials, to spend money on refuse disposal. For many municipalities in the Boston area, open burning is the least expensive method of getting rid of rubbish. Further, even assuming a basic willingness to act (which could not at this time be assumed) considerable time is required for the planning, financing, and carrying out of either the sanitary-land-fill method or incineration as substitutes for open burning. Meanwhile, it is impossible to stop even temporarily the flow of refuse, and it is not acceptable to simply let it pile up uncompacted and uncovered. The Department therefore found it necessary in many instances to permit the continuation of open burning of refuse while the community or communities involved sought the best acceptable alternative. The intricacies of this problem are difficult to explain to irate groups that are subject to the obnoxious effects of the dumps, and the Department was faced with continual public pressure to do something about what was an admittedly severe problem in many localities.

In one instance, in 1962, in response to such pressures for action, the Department, after a public hearing, issued an order to the city of Boston to discontinue open burning of refuse (other than demolition lumber) in the Dorchester area. At the public hearing, Senator Powers led the group demanding that the Department take drastic action. When I talked to him about this matter, he pointed out that over the years the Boston city government had refused to do anything about the burning dumps, which had been a long-standing nuisance to the people in his district as well as elsewhere. The explanation, which he had found unacceptable, was that it would cost too much money to build an incinerator. Therefore, it was one of his specific objectives in writing the 1960 legislation to take this power from Boston and transfer it to the state.

Later, a staff member of the Boston City Health Department told me that his department had been concerned for a number of years about the Boston city dump but had been unsuccessful in doing anything about it because of the opposition of the Department of Public Works and the overall city government policy of avoiding the large expense required to discontinue the dump. Although at the public hearing the Health Department officially supported the Boston request for a postponement of any action by the state, it was the general feeling within the Department that the time had finally come when strong action would be needed to get the city to take steps to discontinue the dump. In general, he said, the city Health Department did not oppose the 1960 legislation, even though it meant transferring certain authorities from the city Health Department to the state Department of Public Health. On the contrary, he said, the Health Department was very happy to "get off the hook" since it was now up to the state to crack down on the big offenders, including the city government itself.

An official of the Department of Public Works was quite unhappy about the whole situation. He felt that the state's action had created a tremendous crisis for the Boston Department of Public Works and the city of Boston, which would now have to devise some stopgap method for handling its refuse and was also faced with the problem of financing a multimillion-dollar incineration facility. There was the problem, too, of finding, somewhere in the area, a suitable location for such an incinerator, which no one would want near his home.

At the time of our interview it was still a question whether the state Department of Public Health would be able to gain compliance with its order, which became effective on July 1, 1962.[30]

The state Department of Public Health felt that it was making slow, but definite, progress toward the discontinuance of other problems of open burning of municipal refuse. Contrary to its original expectations, the Department was finding that most of the representations it got from legislators were in the form of encouragement to take more aggressive action toward the nuisances of the dumps rather than any attempt to get the Department to relax its pressures.

With respect to the burning of auto bodies and other junk materials for the recovery of metal, there are three alternatives open to businesses: (1) cease the practice of burning off the nonmetallic materials from the metals and sell the auto bodies, insulated wire, and so on at substantially lower prices; (2) build a suitable incinerator (for most of the small-scale operations in the Boston area, this is considered not to be feasible); or (3) build a large incinerator, financed either by an entrepreneur who would be in a semimonopolistic position or by a number of these businesses joined together on a cooperative basis. In order to allow these businesses time to determine their course of action and develop suitable plans, the department initially approved, in most instances, the continuation of open burning for a limited period. It was intended that if reasonable effort and substantial progress were demonstrated by an operator his permit would be temporarily extended. However, after a few months, the Department observed very little action being taken toward the discontinuance of open burning by these businesses, and it served notice that, unless progress had been demonstrated, it would order the discontinuance of all such burning on July 1, 1962.

It was understood that these businesses were considering sponsoring a bill which would exempt their operations from the air-pollution regulations. It was felt, however, that such a move would not be successful. Although the auto-junk dealers had a trade organization, it was almost completely inactive with respect to developments concerning air pollution. Although the public hearings in connection with the 1960 legislation and the subsequent rules and regulations promulgated in 1961 were widely advertised, the auto-junk dealers' association was not heard from until the Department started to serve notices of violations after the regulations went into effect on August 1, and even after that date its activities were only sporadic.

One of the big complaints of the local junk dealers was that these rules and regulations gave a competitive advantage to businesses operating just outside of the District. Another serious problem was that, as with refuse, it was not possible or desirable to discontinue the metal-recovery operations. It was pointed out that if the margin of profit on scrap metal became too low as a result of air pollution regulation requirements, it was possible that the many automobiles which were destined for the junkyard each day would just be left on the streets because the return to the owner would be so small as to make it not worth the trouble of selling the old car.[31]

Summary and Conclusions

The overall situation with respect to air-pollution control in the Boston area is summarized in a publication of the Department of Public Health as follows: "This article could perhaps have better been entitled 'On the Difficulty of Being Reasonable.' On the one hand we have an irate minority of the populace (in general, justifiably irate), and on the other hand we have businessmen concerned with the increased cost of doing business, municipal officials concerned about instituting a more costly procedure and in many cases unable to immediately effect any change, and the majority of people concerned primarily with their tax rate. In the middle, we find the Department of Public Health, deeply concerned about the health and economic implications of the growing air pollution problem, charged by the legislature with controlling this problem, and beset on both sides by sufferers—those who are aggrieved by effects of some present practices and those who will be aggrieved by any required change in present practices." [32]

Insofar as public-policy formulation is concerned, the dominant theme is widespread public apathy. Apparently there are substantial groups of people throughout the area who are very severely affected by localized air-pollution problems and who vent their extreme unhappiness on the local authorities or occasionally on the state Department of Public Health. However, in the nature of the situation, their complaints would be much more effective if they were brought to bear on the legislature and if their efforts were organized and sustained. Presumably in the operative system of decision-making these people comprise one of the disadvantaged, inarticulate groups which lack both the resources with which to bargain and access to the people who do bargain. In contrast, the groups which tend to oppose effective control action, because their economic interests are at stake, are highly organized and articulate. They have command of substantial material incentives (jobs and money) with which to bargain, and are strategically located and have easy access to the various decision-making institutions and persons.

The striking fact about the situation is that, although the need for taking more aggressive action to control air pollution in the Boston area to avert present and potentially serious hazards is widely recognized by many knowledgeable and "influential" persons, the only significant action which has been taken in decades was largely the result of a fortuitous accident, the sootfall episode in South Boston, rather than the efforts of any one or any combination of these people.[33] If, as it appears, further needed action will require another such sootfall episode, or another Los Angeles, or another Donora, Pennsylvania, in which seventeen persons died, serious questions are raised as to whether modern industrialized and urbanized America can long afford its present system of decision-making.

NOTES

1. Commonwealth of Massachusetts, *Report Submitted by the Legislative Research Council Relative to Air Pollution in the Metropolitan Boston Area* (Senate No. 495, February 5, 1960), pp. 25–6.

2. U. S. Department of Health, Education, and Welfare, Public Health Service, *Proceedings, National Conference on Air Pollution, 1958* (*Public Health Service* Publication No. 654), Washington, D. C., U. S. Government Printing Office, 1959, pp. 34–8.

3. *Ibid.*, pp. 31–2.

4. *Report Submitted by the Legislative Research Council Relative to Air Pollution in the Metropolitan Boston Area, op cit.,* p. 22.

5. *Proceedings, National Conference on Air Pollution, 1958, op. cit.,* pp. 4–5.

6. *Air Pollution Control in Massachusetts,* Boston, Massachusetts Department of Public Health, December, 1961 (Mimeographed.)

7. Commonwealth of Massachusetts, *Acts of 1910,* Chapter 51.

8. John C. Collins and James L. Dallas, "Atmospheric Pollution and Radiological Health," *Commonwealth,* Vol. 5 (March, 1957), Boston, Massachusetts Department of Public Health, p. 5.

9. Commonwealth of Massachusetts, *Acts of 1928,* Chapter 301.

10. Commonwealth of Massachusetts, *Acts of 1954,* Chapter 674.

11. Interviews with staff of the state Department of Public Health.

12. Commonwealth of Massachusetts, Senate Order No. 657 of 1959, cited in *Report Submitted by the Legislative Research Council Relative to Air Pollution in the Metropolitan Boston Area, op cit.,* p. 2.

13. This is the *Report Submitted by the Legislative Research Council Relative to Air Pollution in the Metropolitan Boston Area,* cited in footnote 1.

14. *Ibid.,* p. 22.

15. *Ibid.,* p. 23.

16. These are summarized on pp. 128–29 of this paper.

17. *Ibid.,* p. 23.

18. Commonwealth of Massachusetts, House No. 42 (November 4, 1959), p. 4.

19. Commonwealth of Massachusetts, House No. 45 (1960).

20. Interviews with staff of the state Department of Public Health.

21. Commonwealth of Massachusetts, *Report Submitted by the Special Committee Established for the Purpose of Investigating the Downpour of Smoke, Soot, or Oil over a Portion of the South Boston District of the City of Boston* (Senate No. 647, July, 1960).

22. *Ibid.,* pp. 5–9.

23. *Ibid.,* p. 11.

24. *Ibid.,* p. 10.

25. *Ibid.,* pp. 58–63.

26. *Ibid.,* pp. 56–7.

27. Commonwealth of Massachusetts, *Acts of 1960,* Chapter 676.

28. Interview with staff of the state Department of Public Health.

29. Commonwealth of Massachusetts, Department of Public Health, Metropolitan Air Pollution Control District, *Rules and Regulations to Prevent Pollution or Undue Contamination of the Atmosphere Within the Metropolitan Air Pollution Control District* (undated).

30. It is understood from recent discussions with the Department staff that the dump in question was in fact subsequently closed. The refuse (other than demolition debris) is now being disposed of at two dumps in the metropolitan area, and to a lesser extent, at the city incinerator. Disposal of demolition debris is being accomplished by means of burial within Boston, by burning at sites outside the Metropolitan Air Pollution Control District, and by burning on barges at sea. It is interesting to note that a primary factor which led to this change was not related to air pollution: A refuse truck hit a child while en route to the dump. This event caused a furor in the neighborhood, leading to the passage of an act by the General Court specifically ordering the dump to be closed.

In general, the Department states that except for illegal operations, primarily carried out at night in order ot escape detection, there is no open burning being done in the District.

31. According to the Department staff, open burning of scrap, except for illegal operations carried on at night, has ceased since that time. Three methods are now used for disposal of auto bodies and other scrap: (1) two privately owned auto-body incinerators are in operation, which process substantially less than 50 per cent of the total volume of junked cars in the area; (2) some autos are hand stripped of the combustible materials; (3) a substantial number are taken to nearby areas outside the District for burning. It is noted that as a result of the increased costs of scrap-metal recovery which these methods entail, the problem of abandoned cars on the streets of the area has indeed grown. It is also noted that the increase in burning outside the District has resulted in an enlarged volume of air borne pollutants carried into the District.

32. David Standley, "Air Pollution Control Regulations for Metropolitan Boston," *Sanitalk*, Vol. 9 (Fall, 1961), p. 11.

33. Although, as noted above, some progress has been made with respect to open burning, the District's budget for coping with the total problem in the area, continues to be substantially the same as it was when the report of Senator Powers' committee (see pp. 142–43, 145) stated "that the Department of Public Health and the local communities are not sufficiently equipped to meet and overcome this general problem of air pollution."

Setting Criteria for Public Expenditures
on Air-Pollution Abatement:
Theoretical Foundations and Limitations

HAROLD WOLOZIN
THE AMERICAN UNIVERSITY

Harold Wolozin is an associate professor of economics at The American University. He was for many years an economic adviser to the departments of Commerce, Interior, and Labor, and since 1962 he has been a consultant to the United States Public Health Service in Washington, D. C.

The Problem and Its Setting

THE THEORY of public-expenditure criteria poses both theoretical and conceptual problems for the economist attempting to make it operational, *i.e.*, to prescribe for specific projects designed to serve the community. In exposing some of the limitations of current economic analysis for this purpose I hope to point the way to research and subsequent modification and extension of the theory in directions which will make it more useful in the determination of public expenditures for community needs such as the control of air pollution.

The question I pose as a jumping-off point is, What guidelines can economic analysis in its present state offer for the expenditure of public monies to increase the well-being of the community? Specifically, to what extent do the tools of economic analysis enable the economist to execute meaningful studies and dispense practical advice on the optimum direction and size (they can be negative[1]) of public expenditures for such programs as air-pollution control?

There are a good many economic analysts who believe that the nature of the assumptions underlying most of the body of existing economic theory renders it seriously inadequate for this complex assignment. There are grounds for asking, for example, whether it is realistic to isolate economic from political man as the basic decision-making unit in this area. This may be unrealistic and consequently a path to naïve policy prescription. Perhaps it can be shown, particularly when it comes to controlling air pollution, that man's "politically-revealed preferences are 'higher' than market-exhibited ones." [2] To mention another example, in much of the literature on public-expenditure policy, the so-called compensation principle assumes an important role, yet its relevance and usefulness have been the focal point of extended debate. The issues raised are fundamental: whether it involves an "undue sanctification of the status quo," an argument objecting on ethical grounds to the nature of the implicit value judgments embodied in the principle, or whether these value judgments are "inconsistent with the possibility of rational choice by the community as a whole." [3]

The attempt to make economic analysis operational in the public sector goes back a long way in the economic literature. In the opinion of some economists the results have been meager, if not downright disappointing. The difficulties stem not only from the crudeness of the tools, but from the special socio-economic problems encountered in the pursuit of an operational theory in this sector of the economy. We are faced with the divergence between the factors to be considered in reaching market decisions and in reaching social decisions in the allocation of resources; third-party or indirect effects of policies (externalities) have to be taken into account. As far as practicable, nonmarket social goods have to be considered in the economic calculus. As Allen V. Kneese suggests, "values must be introduced into the decision-making process." [4] He argues in a discussion of the economics of pollution control:

> The U.S. economy generally depends upon private enterprise and market processes for the generation of values and on private decisions to incorporate them into the economic decision-making process in an efficient fashion. For a variety of reasons, unregulated market processes cannot deal efficiently with pollution. Consequently, there are adequate grounds for public intervention and planning in this area, even though the general rationale for a market economy is

accepted. Indeed in large measure, such intervention can be justified by the desirability of moving actual results more closely into line with ideal market results. Further, there are grounds for considering values not arising from market-type valuation at all.[5]

The problems of the economist are often further complicated by the nature of his relationship with the public-policy maker whom he must advise. The policy maker often does not spell out his aim sufficiently in his request for an economic analysis and prescription. In a very perceptive discussion of the problems of the economist in advising and researching in the area of health-service policy, Dr. Jack Wiseman emphasizes "the need for a clear understanding of the relation between the apparent aims and the methods of cost-benefit studies." [6] He notes that in "actual studies of investment in health" the researches often proceed "on the basis of a set of assumptions about other aims of policy (other than the rate of return) that are never made satisfactorily explicit." [7] Dr. Wiseman maintains, "The essential matter is that the studies do not provide 'pure' information either about the implications of any one policy aim or about an explicitly stated group of aims. Rather, they measure the rate of return to 'investment in health' or some aspect thereof, in relation to an existing environment." Wiseman maintains that since the environment (the existing size, character, and cost of health services, the "investment" in such cooperating services as education, and the productivity of labor) is itself the product of a "complex set of policies and aims," the rate of return to health investment can only be "satisfactorily interpreted" in relation to the constraints imposed by these policies and aims.[8]

Arguing that economic policy is rarely concerned with the attainment of "the best of all possible worlds" Dr. Otto Eckstein asserts that it is of utmost importance to realize that economic policy by definition seeks to improve economic welfare *in the face of constraints*. According to Eckstein, the economist must, in devising a policy model, recognize and build the relevant constraints into his analysis. The question of how many and which ones to include presents the crucial difficulty and decision. There comes a certain point, however, where the constraints and assumptions can be so specific that they produce "bad economics." This is, I suppose, a way of saying that the narrowed-down solution often is inadequate, unrealistic, or impractical for policy purposes. But as Eckstein himself points out, "the line between realism and bad economics" is often hard to draw.[9]

Planning under Constraints

There are many types of constraints, originating in institutional or physical limitations, under which public policy must operate. Building these into an economic study not only makes the analysis more applicable, but gives shape to the problem under study and determines the general nature of the solution; therefore, it may be useful to look at the nature of the constraints encountered. In my brief survey, I lean heavily on Dr. Eckstein's excellent discussion.[10] Physical constraints, such as the production function, relate physical inputs to outputs. A closely related constraint is that limiting in cost curves the extent of discontinuities beyond which cost data will not be accepted.

Legal constraints require that a program or project fit within existing laws, such as water laws, property laws, treaties, and so on. Eckstein warns, however, that in admitting legal constraints, laws which could be affected by the analysis must not be assumed as fixed. He feels that this is one of the areas in which the economist "is in peril of accepting *so many* constraints that he will exclude the interesting solutions." Administrative constraints reflect the capability of a sponsoring agency. They include such things as the limits on the rate of a program's expansion due to personnel ceilings and shortages of administrative know-how. Excessive centralization of decision-making, over-complex planning needs, or too many variables imposed also can hamper and constrain programs. Distributional constraints may impose a fixed pattern of distribution of benefits and costs or "side conditions" of minimum benefits for different groups.

Financial or budget constraints set limits to the availability of funds for given projects. These constraints are of primary importance in the way in which we go about deriving expenditure criteria; in actuality, it goes without saying that if public monies were to be available in unlimited quantities, then we would not have to expend time and effort in determining the optimum allocation of resources.

Eckstein has explored this problem in detail;[11] the following gives some idea of the type of approach which has been devised to cope with the financial constraints:

> If there is only one constrained financial resource and one category of benefits, the criterion requires that the rate of net benefit per dollar of the constrained funds be maximized. This maximization is accomplished by computing ratios of benefit to constrained funds for each project (or smaller unit of choice where possible), ranking projects by these ratios and going down the ranked list to the point where the scarce funds are exhausted. Although the ranking is by ratios, it is not the maximization of the ratio which is the objective but rather the total net gain that is possible, given the constraint.[12]

There are, of course, many other types of constraints such as the introduction of uncertainty into the situation, political realities, and so on. The problem often is to identify all of the constraints involved.

Welfare Economics—The Economist's Toolbox

The nature of the constraints under which economic analysis must operate having been demonstrated, the question which logically follows is, What is the nature of the economic analysis? Can it operate effectively under the kind of constraints described, or do these constraints subtly shape the very structure of the theory? The next section sets out and evaluates the body of economic theory (not statistical techniques) which has been built up to guide public-expenditure policy. It seems advisable, also, to examine aspects of economic analysis which purport to indicate on what basis private firms may be induced to make expenditures on projects which would otherwise have to be taken care of by public bodies (control of air pollution, for example). This approach fits particularly the case where the constraints adopted in the public area have brought a solution of zero outlay by the public sector for projects which could, nevertheless, promote the community's general welfare. Of course, even in such instances it may not be absolutely correct to say that no public monies will be spent, for some resources may have to be allocated to stimulate outlays in the private sector by demonstrating the community's need for the expenditure and the possible net gains for the firms or individuals involved. Such an attempt would be particularly useful where firms allocate funds for community service.

The analytic principles designed to guide public policy can be evaluated with respect to both their internal consistency and their application and special extensions—for instance, the application of the theory of public-expenditure criteria to such problems as controlling water or air pollution. As we proceed, the limitations of the conventional body of theory which have challenged working economists to provide a practicable framework for determining levels and directions of expenditures of public funds on the control and alleviation of air pollution will become apparent. As a matter of fact, one of the crucial problems, namely, constraints, has already been discussed. In this instance, what rises to the surface as an essential prerequisite for an operational theory is the need to integrate economic criteria with those implicit in other factors shaping expenditure policies, particularly social, political, and psychological factors. Especially important are the concerns within the domain of the social psychologists (the factors shaping group psychology and attitudes), for these often translate into the political constraints shaping public-expenditure policy.

John V. Krutilla has written that engaging in refined theoretical discussion is uniquely the province of the academic; but he has also asserted that thinking "systematically about problems and basing decisions on such analysis are likely to produce consequences superior to those that would result from 'purely random' behavior." He further states:

> The academic theorist without responsibility for policy can afford to (and probably should) be puritanical without regard to whether or not this is immediately constructive. On the other hand, the producing economist in government, charged with responsibility to act under constraints of time and information, will often be grateful for perhaps even a perforated rationale to justify recommendations "in the public" interest.[13]

That body of economic theory most relevant to the subject matter of this paper falls under the general heading of "welfare economics." Closely related to this is the evolving theory of the "public household." Although I do not intend to go off on a purely methodological excursion, an examination of the topics and techniques of welfare economics is essential as the basis for ascertaining the nature and extent of its applicability to decision-making in specific programs (such as air-pollution control) undertaken by national, state, or local governmental bodies or authorities. We should be, then, in a better position to evaluate existing programs and to establish guidelines for policy-oriented research.

My position on welfare economics itself is that it has been extended as far as it can be for practical purposes. As I. M. D. Little aptly puts it, ". . . any further extension of welfare theory is unlikely to be at all valuable except as a mathematical exercise." [14] Now to the substance of the problem. Melvin Reder defines welfare economics as the branch of economic science that attempts to establish and apply "criteria of propriety" [15] to economic policies. Welfare economics makes "explicit" the criteria (for judging public policies) which were implicit in the works of such classical economists as Smith, Mill, Ricardo, and the like. The norm customarily adopted by welfare economists, according to Reder, is that the welfare of the community as a whole should be maximized. Although this is unambiguous once welfare has been adequately defined, welfare has been defined in diverse ways and these are reflected in the appropriateness of economic policies. Even when welfare is adequately defined, the difficulties in applying the strictures of welfare theory are not erased, for the problem of measurement arises. And this problem of measurement—of what and how to measure—has not only given rise to most of the disagreement and debate over the applicability and relevance of welfare theory, but has led to a fairly acceptable pragmatic solution—through systems analysis or operations research, referred to as "benefit-cost" analysis in the welfare area.

It must be recognized that the world of economic analysis is a starkly simplified one. Production and economic organization are assumed to exist solely for the purpose of maximizing human satisfactions, and these are the sum, for society, of individual satisfactions. Rationality has been traditionally identified with such maximization, *i.e.*, rational economic man, who *knows* what is *best* for him, is the decision-making unit. As Kenneth Arrow astutely observes, given these conditions "the problem of achieving a social maximum derived from individual desires is precisely the problem which has been central to the field of welfare economics." [16] This formulation of the problem also implies interpersonal comparisons of utility.

The original formulations of welfare economics reflected the simple-minded utilitarian economics of the classical economists, who were concerned principally with specifying the optimum conditions under which the total satisfaction for the society would be maximized. It was assumed of course that *laisser-faire* as the basic form of economic organization insured maximum satisfaction, and even A. C. Pigou, who has been called the father of modern welfare economics, set out the argument of his "economics of welfare" "in terms of exceptions to the rule that *laisser-faire* ensures maximum satisfaction." [17]

The fundamental theorem of the classical welfare economics holds that a long-run competitive equilibrium (perfect competition is assumed) automatically insures the best of all possible worlds—an optimum allocation of resources. As William Baumol points out, this elementary theorem is strictly speaking true only under seriously limiting assumptions:

> The standard welfare economics deals only with commodities which are actually bought in the market and not with those which are free goods or for which no customers can be found at a profitable price. For old-fashioned welfare theory leans heavily on the marginal conditions of equilibrium, e.g., the condition of equality of price ratios to the marginal rates of substitution. But these conditions need not hold for free or unsaleable goods. In old-fashioned terms, if each consumer chooses not to buy a commodity the marginal utility of that item may well be less than its price (note the inequality again). Moreover the cost of production of such an unsaleable good must be greater than its price. For free goods the ratio of prices is not even defined. It follows that the standard theorem of welfare economics must be restated to read that (where the theorem is valid) a competitive economy will allocate resources optimally among commodities which are saleable without loss and which are not free. But which commodities will these be? We cannot as-

sume we know the answer in advance, for the answer is an economic question of costs of production and demand patterns. Moreover, though our intuition may tell us that this is so, we must prove rigorously that there can be no preferable allocation of resources to free or unsaleable goods. (Pigou long ago pointed out that the production of some competitively unprofitable items can conceivably yield a considerable addition to consumer's surplus.)

Old-fashioned welfare theory, by taking marginal utility to equal price, may end up requiring negative consumption of an unwanted commodity since even with zero consumption its marginal utility may turn out to be less than its price. Similarly, it cannot preclude the economic absurdity of negative prices for "free goods." [18]

Modern welfare economics, as we now know it, has evolved in response to fundamental criticisms of the utilitarian assumptions underlying the classical welfare economics. Following I. M. D. Little, who abandons the idea of maximizing welfare and is satisfied only with improving it, the basic criticisms of utilitarian welfare economics can be briefly summarized as follows: First, satisfactions cannot be summed. Therefore it is meaningless to refer to the happiness of the community as the sum total of the happinesses of individuals and the happiness of individuals as "the sum total of their satisfactions." This criticism has led to a "general acceptance" of the position that only the ordinal numbers, denoting relative position, and not the cardinal numbers, indicating absolute quantities, are of use in the evaluation of satisfactions. Thus, one can say that one has more or less satisfaction, but not *how much*. Second, the satisfactions and happiness of different people cannot be compared objectively or scientifically. Any such comparison is a value, or an ethical, judgment, not an ordinary empirical judgment. The third criticism, rising out of the preceding, is that welfare economics is by definition a "normative" study, because "no change could be made without harming someone and since . . . interpersonal comparisons of satisfaction are value judgments and essential to judgments about the welfare of society, welfare economics is unavoidably ethical." [19] This argument is not just academic; for what is involved is the nature of the social decision process and, implicitly, the nature of the constraints under which public officials move. The basic issue raised is whether "it is formally possible to construct a procedure for passing from a set of known individual tastes to a pattern of social decision making. . . ." [20] Although this is not the place to go into this technically involved discussion, it may be pointed out that it raises a fundamental question about both the role and the content of welfare economics. An equally fundamental issue is the meaning of the economic rationality assumed in the conception of economic choice which underlies much of the discussion of welfare economics. Little argues that because a welfare judgment implies that an individual is making a judgment whereas social decisions can be reached through the governmental process for reasons of convenience or necessity, they are different.[21] Directing himself to this point Kenneth Arrow raises issues which are at the heart of the matter:

> This distinction is well taken. I would consider that it is indeed a social decision process with which I am concerned and not, strictly speaking, a welfare judgment by any individual. That said, however, I am bound to add that in my view a social decision process serves as a proper explication for the intuitive idea of social welfare. The classical problems of formulating the social good are indeed of the metaphysical variety which modern positivism finds meaningless; but the underlying issue is real. My own viewpoint towards this and other ethical problems coincides with that expressed by Popper: "Not a few doctrines which are metaphysical, and thus certainly philosophical can be interpreted as hypostatizations of methodological rules." All the writers from Bergson on agree on avoiding the notion of a social good not defined in terms of the values of individuals. But where Bergson seeks to locate social values in welfare judgments by individuals, I prefer to locate them in the actions taken by society through its rules for making social decisions. This position is a natural extension of the ordinalist view of values; just as it identifies values and choices for the indivdual, so I regard social values as meaning nothing more than social choices.[22]

The "new welfare economics," discussed extensively in I. M. D. Little's *Critique of Welfare Economics,* developed in response to the basic criticisms of utilitarian welfare economics and has attempted to get around the knotty problems of measurement and quantification through various expedients. One such approach, which has by and large taken the place of the Marshallian type of analysis, is an analysis of the behavior of the rational consumer by means of an Edgeworth indifference curve, Pareto's "index of *ophélimité.*" Although this analysis still assumes that the individual attempts to maximize his satisfaction, this "no longer means achieving the largest sum total of satisfaction but rather reaching the highest level of satisfaction." Using this apparatus, the analysis then focuses upon the needs of the community as a whole, with the "compensation" principle as an important tool for policy determination. If we assume that "welfare increases (decreases) whenever one or more individuals become more (less) satisfied without any other individuals becoming less (more) satisfied," then the welfare of a community is maximized if its productive resources are used so as to make it impossible to make any person more satisfied without making at least one other person less satisfied. Thus, if the satisfactions of some individuals can be increased and at the same time any others who might be adversely affected by the process can be compensated for any injury, the total welfare is increased. This is the famous compensation principle first introduced by J. R. Hicks and N. Kaldor. Under this rule, if a person is made worse off by a given public policy, all is righted if he is compensated.[23]

Otto Eckstein has summarized the development and criticisms of this approach excellently in the article cited earlier in this paper. As he points out, the Kaldor-Hicks compensation criteria have been subjected to considerable criticism. It has been argued, for example, that if economic change caused a price change, the criteria might become inconsistent: ". . . the gainers could compensate the losers after the change, yet the potential losers might be able to compensate the potential gainers prior to the change." Also, censure has been focused on the assumption that an individual's or family's welfare is independent of his neighbors—that there are no "neighborhood effects" (externalities), such as envy. I. M. D. Little after introducing the so-called Scitovsky effect, which would impose limitations on those opposing a welfare-increasing change (by taking measures to prevent it they would lose more than they would gain), advocates a given course of action only if (1) the gainers could conceivably overcompensate the losers and (2) the ensuing distribution of income would be "good"; but this view, too, was open to severe criticism.[24] Despite the theoretical difficulties which have caused many leading students of welfare economics to throw up their hands in despair at the prospects for making it useful for formulating public-expenditure policy, Otto Eckstein still manages to be optimistic about the usefulness of welfare economics. However, he severely limits the scope of the economist in policy formulation:

> Its critics underestimate the usefulness of welfare economics. It is true that it has failed in the tasks which had been set for it: it has not (1) proved the superiority of laissez faire; (2) provided simple criteria for judging economic changes or economic optima, or (3) provided a method of isolating the economic aspects of policy from ethical considerations. But the failure to accomplish these objectives is due to their grandiose nature. There are more modest objectives of analysis for which welfare economics must play a crucial role.

Eckstein's program of action is as follows:

> What I propose is this. First, the rather casually dispensed advice of the critics of welfare economics should be taken seriously. I follow Baumol and seek to establish what interdependence effects should be measured and to indicate the methods that may be appropriate. I follow Graaff by emphasizing measurement rather than absolutist advice. But this should be no senseless retreat into hypothesis-testing unrelated to potential action, nor the collection of random sets of facts; rather it should be the establishment of decision-models which will reveal explicitly what actions will maximize the achievement of specified objectives.
>
> I do not insist that the economist be given the objectives in polished, formal manner. Rather, the economist must interpret the desires of the policy people whom he is serving and express them in an analytical form as an objective function. He then seeks to maxi-

mize this function, given the empirical relations in the economy and the institutional constraints that may be appropriate to the analysis. In this manner, the economist can play the role of technician, of bringing his technical equipment to bear on policy problems, with maximum effectiveness. The specification of the objective function thus is not primarily meant to let the economist play omnipotent being; rather it is a device for bridging the gap between the positive quantitative research which is the main stock-in-trade of the economist, and the normative conclusions which policy requires.[25]

Dr. Eckstein modifies the rigor of his position in a footnote in which he says he does not mean that an objective function [26] must always be specified when economics is used for policy purposes. In fact, he goes on to state that in most cases, "particularly where the analysis involves few steps as the mere marshalling of figures" specifying an objective function would be "excess theoretical baggage." But he does feel that once the analysis takes on some complexity, an explicit objective function becomes more important if normative recommendations are to be derived. Eckstein feels that the exercise of specifying, rather than implying, a functional relationship forces the technician to state his normative assumptions. Specifying an objective function can, at its best, become "a powerful analytical aid, eliminating uninteresting areas of exploration and permitting the ranking of alternatives." For example, the advisability or feasibility of a consumer attitudinal survey might be evaluated on the basis of the complexity and nature of the objective function hypothesized for the project. Proposing the survey with only some vague objectives specified would yield a far less helpful and perhaps a risky basis for deciding whether or not to undertake it.

Welfare Economics and the Individual Firm or Consumer

No matter what form is taken by the so-called welfare function used in the sense discussed above, it becomes clear that one of the more valuable contributions of the welfare economics is that it attempts to come to grips with the problem of maximizing the welfare, however defined, of the community as a whole; and it requires the policy maker in applying the insights and tools of welfare economics to take into account an important set of considerations which the consumer or the individual firm often, perhaps not deliberately, ignores —namely, the effects on the community around him of his consumption and/or production. These are referred to in various ways as "neighborhood effects," "spill-over effects," and the like.

Now, as Allen Kneese points out, an essential condition for an optimum use of resources through the market mechanism is that "the full costs and benefits of performing a given act fall upon the unit performing it." [27] This implies, immediately, that the costs and benefits *can* be measured, including the neighborhood effects. Techniques for measuring these have been developed. They are lumped under the general heading of welfare "benefit-cost" analysis. These techniques will be discussed shortly, but let us consider first the costs or benefits which can not be so easily valued, or are in some instances not valued by those who might be benefited by them in *our* judgment.

Richard Musgrave in developing his theory of the "public household" has attempted to come to grips with these problems in a very perceptive approach integrating much that has been done in this area. He first explores the situations calling for adjustments in the allocation of resources because of dissatisfaction with the results obtained by the unfettered operation of the market mechanism—cases where "the forces of the market cannot secure optimal results."

Musgrave distinguishes two broad categories which call for public intervention. The first is the wide range of situations where the market mechanism brings about varying degrees of inefficiency in the allocation of resources, "inefficiencies that arise collateral to the satisfaction of private wants." The second covers situations "where the market mechanism fails altogether and where the divergence between the social and private product becomes all-inclusive." [28]

The kinds of market situations lumped under the first category include what we generally call imperfect competition and monopoly, where resource allocation "diverges from that obtained under purely or perfectly competitive market conditions." It also covers the case in which, because of decreasing unit costs, firms can't operate most profitably at the point leading to optimal resource allocation. Particularly interesting to us is the inclusion in the first category of the situation in which external economies or diseconomies are generated by either individuals or firms. Of course, a most relevant example of this is the pollution of air by industrial processes. The nuisance is a cost, often indirect as well as direct, to the community. Yet it is not a direct cost to the firm creating the pollution. In other words, the private operations "involve social costs that are not reflected in private cost calculations and, hence, are not accounted for by the market." [29] Musgrave's judgment is that wherever possible the satisfaction of this kind of want (in the above case it would be the desire for relatively pure air) should be left to the market. He would, I suppose, advocate a tax subsidy, for example, to pay for air-purifying devices or for more expensive and less polluting industrial processes. That this approach is an oversimplification of the problem is apparent from the following situation. Suppose that those firms polluting the air were required, by law, to install preventive devices. The assumption, then, would be that the social costs would be accounted for by the market, *i.e.*, the costs could be passed on.

The situation where the market mechanism fails altogether is more complex and involves the satisfaction or lack of satisfaction of two kinds of wants for goods or services, "social wants," which are in line with consumer preferences, and "merit wants," which are not. I lean heavily on the work of Musgrave in my discussion of the economics of these two classes of public wants, although in certain respects I differ with his analysis of their role in illuminating the alternatives for public policy. Social wants should in one sense cause public-policy planners a minimum of difficulty. They are identifiable wants and it is only because everybody consumes them and no one can be excluded by the market that they are not candidates for private production and sale. But how much does the public want them? They are not sold in the market; therefore, another means must be used to determine the consumer demand or preference. Professor Alan T. Peacock in discussing goods produced by government, such as defense and law and order, points out that because they are indivisible by their very nature, even those who are not prepared to pay for them cannot be denied their benefits. He concludes, "Escape for one means escape for all, and a pricing solution is simply not possible." [30]

The decision to spend public funds to supply a social want must be derived, as Musgrave puts it, from "the effective preferences" of the individual members of the society. These, in turn, reflect the individual's tastes and "proper" share in national income. His solution is that "a political process must be substituted for the market mechanism, and individuals must be made to adhere to the group decision." [31] This approach assumes that individuals can evaluate social wants, that they want them along with the goods and services which can be purchased in the private market. In a democratic society, according to Musgrave, it is assumed that public preferences are based upon some sort of summing of individual demands for social goods; I have already discussed the criticism of this position. An alternative view, reflected in other forms of political organization, is that social wants are collective, experienced by the group as a whole or by its leaders rather than by individuals. Here is Musgrave's judgment:

> I see no reason why individuals should not be able to evaluate the benefits they derive from the satisfaction of social wants, along with the benefits they derive from the satisfaction of private wants. To be sure, it may be simpler to assess the advantages of installing a lock in one's own house than to appraise the precise benefits one derives from military protection aganst foreign invasion; or one may find it simpler to measure the advantages of improving one's own yard than to evaluate one's gain from the installation of public parks. Such difference in degree may exist, but they are not inherently a matter of public versus private wants. Similar distinctions arise between various types of private wants, some of which are more immediate (such as medical consultation in the case of illness) and some of which are more remote (such as preventive medical care). Considerations of this sort, therefore, do not contradict our basic proposition that social wants are an integral part of the individual's preference pattern.[32]

The most difficult category of public wants for which to determine effective public policy covers those needs defined above as "merit wants." In fact, in my opinion it may be a misnomer to refer to them as "wants." Musgrave describes them as wants met by services subject to the exclusion principle and *satisfied* by the market— *i.e.*, only those willing, and able, to pay get them. "They become public wants if considered so meritorious that their satisfaction is provided for through the public budget, over and above what is provided for through the market and paid for by private buyers."

In providing for merit wants, public policy, it is implied, allocates resources in a manner which ignores consumer preferences; for the needs which are being provided for have *not* been elected in the market process. Consumers have chosen to spend their money on other things. The expenditures on merit goods take place not because the services are consumed in equal amounts and hence (like social needs) can not be sold on the market, but because individual choice is being corrected. This is a most important distinction, and in essence, brings out the nature of the decisions facing public planners. The spending of public funds on merit needs involves a conscious decision to interfere with the want pattern of others, even if they are the minority; [33] this is particularly important in the case of air pollution, where the market has not provided for clean air.

It should now be apparent that the economics of the process determining public expenditures must, somehow, take into account a host of social, political, and psychological factors which are implicit in the constraints discussed above. We might ask to what extent in ignoring this the empiricism of modern economics, like philosophic empiricism, has been "concealing phenomena instead of elucidating them." [34] It is in these areas that some of the most difficult and critical problems remain. Is the distinction between merit goods and social goods really relevant, even if valid? What is the nature of that rational choice which tolerates dangerous levels of air pollution—the rational choice upon which the economic principles expounded here rest? Are economic preferences immutable? How do they change over time? These are areas to which high priority must be given in future research.

Benefit-Cost Analysis and Public Expenditure

Whether a need be a merit or a social want, once public policy has decided to provide for it, the public body is faced with the problem of spending its monies most effectively. Doing so is not as simple as it sounds. Even the situation in which the political decision is to provide certain services which people want, and which they *prefer* to be compelled to pay for by tax or fee (rather than to purchase through the open market), poses a difficult problem of valuation to the public body. But what happens in the situation where the pricing mechanism could not carry out its function even if purchase of the service through the open market were desired? The always-lurking dilemma is that "if 'output' of government services cannot be valued, then neither can we determine with any precision how much should be produced nor what the relationship is between the change in the value of inputs and the change in the value of output." [35]

The expanding role of government in modern society and the corresponding necessity to develop a systematic basis for making decisions on public expenditures has stimulated considerable research, primarily in the United States. The tools developed, it is hoped, will cope with the knotty problems we have discussed, serving for the public sector of the economy the function fulfilled by the price mechanism in the private sector, *i.e.*, the allocation of resources efficiently and in accordance with society's preferences, however they are measured. This is, it can be seen, the economist's way of formulating the problem. However, it may well be that putting the decision-making tools within this market framework may have retarded the development of effective means to handle the economics of social policy.

The most widely used approach, described by Roland N. McKean as only a "partial substitute" for the pricing mechanism, is benefit-cost analysis, sometimes called cost-benefit analysis. Although many readers of this paper will be familiar with the approach, this tool warrants close inspection because of the increasing application to problems of economic welfare such as air-pollution control.

For a number of reasons benefit-cost analysis, looked at narrowly, can not be a perfect substitute for the price system. It permits only the "occasional comparison" of policies in contrast to the day-to-day operation of the price mechanism encouraging "frequent examination of numerous alternatives." Furthermore, although like the price mechanism it enables policy makers to identify alternative courses of action, the results of benefit-cost study do not by themselves generate strong incentives to undertake the optimum project. Yet, its practitioners feel it can be an indispensable tool for economic planning:

> . . . it is extremely important at least to be able to identify preferred policies and practices. Unless we can point to the better actions, we cannot possibly expect

officials to choose better rather than worse ones, nor can we devise institutional modifications that would provide incentives leading to the better policies. Indeed unless we can identify preferred actions we cannot even tell where political or administrative processes are distorting incentives or leading to poor decisions.[36]

The choice among alternatives is based upon a compilation or demonstration of the costs, or disadvantages, and the benefits, or advantages, of the various alternatives open. Many techniques for evaluating such alternative courses of action upon the basis of estimates of costs and gains are encompassed under the general heading of benefit-cost analysis. Although the analytic basis employed to evaluate costs and benefits is founded directly upon the methods used by private firms in arriving at their policies, there is one significant difference. Benefit-cost analysis explicitly attempts to measure externalities and other divergences between the private and the social product—the social *marginal* product, to be more precise. In contrast to the economic analysis of the firm, which on the assumption of profit maximization, is essentially *descriptive* with "causal" overtones, benefit-cost analysis is essentially designed to be *prescriptive*.[37]

In actual practice many types of systematic cost-gain computations throughout the economy are very similar to benefit-cost analysis; and this has rather profound implications for the application as well as the broadening of the approach. For example, operations research, now widely used in both the public and private sectors of the economy, was originally designed to analyze alternative operations or ways of carrying out tasks or missions during World War II. It is now generally employed in industry and government for comparisons of alternative methods of operation, often with given equipment and resources. Using various statistical techniques, in its general framework it is essentially the same as benefit-cost analysis; for it attempts to estimate the costs or sacrifices and the gains or achievements implicit in the available courses of action.[38] Systems analysis compares, for the purpose of development or procurement, costs and benefits of relatively complex systems. Concerned with choices among complex systems involving investments, operating supplies, personnel, and modes of operation, systems analysis is also "basically similar to benefit-cost analysis." In fact, as Roland Mc-

Kean observes, all policy-oriented economic analysis "has this same general character." [39]

In their application, benefit-cost techniques can become involved and sometimes prohibitively expensive. In fact, one specialist in the field has suggested, half seriously I presume, that we may well reach the point where benefit-cost studies of benefit-cost studies will be worth undertaking.

A few examples may best demonstrate the complex nature of the task faced in benefit-cost studies, and then we can look at various problems involved in such studies in the water-pollution area, as the closest parallel to the problems of designing air-pollution benefit-cost studies. In measuring the benefits of watershed treatment in reducing flood damage, for example, the analyst must take into account a considerable number of direct and indirect effects of the proposed project. Roland McKean has subjected these to close scrutiny. A few of the more significant estimates that would have to be made for such a project would measure the impact of the proposal on (1) water runoff from dozens of types of terrain in dry and wet years; (2) peak flood stages in several rivers; (3) the lengths of time that various areas would be inundated; (4) the diverse physical damages caused by inundation; and so on. The value of the damage reduction also would have to be measured. Other refinements could not be ignored; among these would be the effects of watershed treatment on both the sedimentation and the depth of river channels, on the life of reservoirs, and on the purity of public water supplies. Even the effect of the proposal on the location of people and their assets (the values risked in the watershed area) could not be neglected. McKean points out that "just one" of the watershed-treatment proposals might encompass forest planting, revegetation, channel improvement and stream-bank stability, measures for forest-fire control, the creation of ponds and reservoirs, pasture development, road and highway protection, gully stabilization and sediment control, the construction of terraces and other structures to divert flows, and the construction of special channels and waterways.[40]

The evaluation of defense proposals demonstrates dramatically one of the most difficult and stubborn tasks in any benefit-cost project, namely the estimating of external economies and diseconomies, which Roland McKean lumps together as the "spillover effects" of any project.

This turns out to be one of the more exacting tasks of cost-benefit analyses, for important spillovers are not always obvious or easy to measure. For example, tactical bombers and missiles, if equipped to carry A-bombs, may contribute to a different mission—that of strategic deterrence—but how much? On the other hand, if equipped only to deliver A-bombs this tactical force may well increase the likelihood of A-war, which is surely a negative contribution to strategic deterrence. As another example, the location of strategic bases near large cities may increase the difficulties of another jurisdiction, the one in charge of civil defense. (The location of installations would affect the enemy's targeting should deterrence fail, affecting the problems of civil defense and also the number of mortalities.) Or a nation's forces in N.A.T.O. may contribute to limited war capabilities elsewhere, but again, how much? Perhaps the most important spillover of all is the following. In choosing strategic defense postures a nation should be alert for spillover effects on the disarmament or weapons control mission. For two retaliatory forces may be equally effective in providing deterrent capability, but one may facilitate reaching mutually advantageous agreements on weapons control, while the other may make such agreements harder to achieve. By the same token, of course, in appraising disarmament proposals, a nation must keep a sharp lookout for, and attempt to weigh, any interim spillover on deterrent capabilities.[41]

This example makes clearly evident the fact that there are certain costs and benefits which either defy measurement or at best can only be measured in units which are not comparable. McKean suggests that even in such an apparently insoluble case the benefit-cost analyst still has several courses open to him. He can calculate "efficient solutions" demonstrating relevant combinations of attainable payoffs. He also can approach the problem by indirection by calculating, for example, the value that must be assigned an intangible item in order to make it preferable to some other item.

Benefit-Cost Analysis in Water Pollution as a Model for Air Pollution Study

We now turn to the use of benefit-cost analysis in the area of water pollution; for it is the area in which pioneering work has been done, which is, in a sense, the prototype research for air-pollution study. No matter what the exact methodology adopted, effective economic analysis of pollution policies requires knowledge of costs. Although we can only allude to the technical complexities involved in developing methods to handle the "increasingly complex and pressing character" of water-pollution problems, it is clear that the nub of the problem in this area has been the necessity to devise methods that can efficiently handle the many variables and constraints involved in selecting the most practicable system from a large number of possible alternatives.

A fundamental condition faced in designing public policies to abate water pollution is that the "unregulated market" not only does not cope with the problem, but is itself the source of much of the problem. Dr Kneese deals with this aspect of the problem at considerable length in his discussion of the considerations of economic efficiency and social policy involved in the pollution problem. He attempts to isolate the principal issues by analyzing the operations of a hypothetical profit-maximizing private firm, producing everything and controlling all of the plants and businesses in the area, to illustrate various aspects of the economics of the disposal of waste into bodies of water, as well as to face up to the question of how the pollution problem might be handled in such a simplified world. This firm, producing either in competitive markets or under regulations requiring marginal cost pricing, would be faced with the problem of minimizing the overall cost of disposing of the wastes generated in its wide range of activities; because certain of its interests would be harmed by water pollution, this problem, too, would be included. The significance of this example is that for the hypothetical firm the whole problem of basin-wide water-resources management "becomes a matter of internal economies." And at this point the competence of the economist in suggesting the most profitable courses of action for the firm depends upon his ability to utilize and devise proper tools for measuring alternative costs and benefits. Kneese suggests that the firm would select the combination of water-quality control measures (water-supply treatment, sewage treatment, flow augmentation, coordinated releases, and so on) and pollution damages that would minimize the firm's overall costs of waste disposal. The amount of waste would be determined by the level of output at the point of most profitable operation. In this situation the firm would be forced by the economics of profit maximization to undertake pollution control, for any economic activity harmed by pollution belongs to the firm. How would the multi-firm proceed in this simplified world?

> This would be accomplished by equating the incremental or marginal costs related to waste disposal for all alternatives. For example, if sewage treatment and pollution damages . . . were the only alternatives, the firm would operate so as to equate marginal treatment costs with the reduction in marginal residual damages. If it did not, there would be an opportunity to reduce over-all costs by shifting between the alternatives. . . . As part of its general profit-maximizing activities, the firm would integrate its pollution control activities with other aspects of its water-related operations. Thus, in computing the costs of alternative quality control devices, it would consider complementary and competitive relationships between different water uses. Accordingly, flow-augmentation costs would have to be determined in light of the fact that this alternative is complementary with navigation, for example, and to a degree with flood control, but at least partly competitive with irrigation. Moreover, the firm would consider the full marginal costs of producing particular products including the costs imposed on other activities by waste disposal.[42]

But does this imply that the firm is taking into account all of the costs of water pollution? The answer is a clear-cut *no*, and the conclusion suggested is that the market results, even under this hypothetically simplified situation, must be "amended" by *public* policy so as to maximize the public benefit provided by water resources. Kneese makes it clear, for example, that the hypothetical basin-wide firm would not be adequately concerned with "aspects of quality in water bodies to which the public is exposed in the course of its everyday activities," because participation in the recreational and aesthetic enjoyment of the waters cannot "be parcelled out and sold." In the context of our earlier discussion it is a social good. Hence, there can be no market for this product whose quality is threatened by the general environmental effects of pollution. Even the all-inclusive firm would not include the benefits of this public service in its expenditures for pollution control. Other examples are readily available.

In the real world, the problem of externalities cannot be defined away; single firms do not encompass the economies of water basins. The pollution problem can only be handled through the intervention of public bodies. By and large they undertake formal benefit-cost studies of water-quality improvement, although these have been confined generally to consideration of the economics of low-flow augmentation, "with water supply and sewage treatment usually the only alternatives considered." Industrial and navigation benefits as well as benefits to public water supplies have been treated "in terms of avoided costs." The latter differ from the former generally in that, like drinking-water standards, they are not measured in terms of market prices. Where market-based calculations can be made, the solution follows conventional lines.

> The results of all planned systems of waste disposal which can be thought of as reduced damages adequately valued by market-based calculations, may be treated as benefits with which the costs (construction and operation of structures) can be compared. If all pollution effects can be adequately valued, the benefit-cost relationship has its conventional meaning and minimization of the costs associated with waste disposal is formally identical with maximization of the (positive) difference between benefits and costs. If constraints are admitted, they must be viewed as objectives or requirements which must be attained but which are not necessarily associated with any benefit to be valued in terms of money. The objective of cost minimization may then be alternatively stated as being the maximization of the positive difference between benefits and costs or the minimization of the negative difference, whichever the appropriate case may be,

provided that the requirements of the constraints are met. It may be that a particular system cannot be carried beyond the constraints without decreasing net benefits or what is the same thing, increasing the total costs associated with waste disposal (costs of the project plus damages and foregone opportunities). If total costs continue to decline (equivalently if net benefits continue to increase or net costs continue to decline), this means that the marginal product of investment in abatement is positive.[43]

Setting minimum cost also involves specifying both an interest rate and an opportunity cost—tasks which may seem deceptively routine. In the usual benefit-cost analysis some interest rate must be employed in computing the present value of benefits. The rate which would have to be applied to costs to obtain the present value of benefits, the marginal benefit-cost ratio, can then be compared to the opportunity cost, "the rate at which present value in foregone elsewhere." [44] Now, what the latter is assumed to be translates into the assumptions made as to which interest rate is to be considered, a decision not so easily made, and, in fact, the subject of much controversy in the literature on public-expenditures criteria. This is not the place to resolve this issue; but what can be suggested is that in any benefit-cost analysis the interest-rate assumptions must be carefully scrutinized and evaluated. Otto Eckstein, in the article cited above, discusses this matter extensively. In a criticism of Eckstein's approach to the problem, Jack Hirshleifer takes issue with Eckstein's conclusion that the planners' decision as to what "social" rate of discount to use remains necessarily a value judgment. In general, Hirshleifer's dissent is based upon his contention that Eckstein overemphasizes time preference in his analysis. Rather, time preference *and* time productivity interacting equally determine the market rate of interest. ". . . the rate of discount adopted for investment decisions will affect the rate of growth of income, which cannot therefore be taken as a datum in determining a 'social' rate of discount." [45]

Pollution damage can take a number of forms, some to which constraints not always market based are applicable and some to which they are not. As a consequence, it may happen that the overall benefits are exceeded by the overall costs of an abatement system even though marginal benefits still exceed marginal costs. In this case, it will not be efficient policy to conclude on the basis of the negative overall benefit-cost ratio alone that a project is either inefficient or undesirable. Rather, the position of the decision maker may be that the best system ought to be that which meets the constraints set by social policy at minimum cost and expands "as long as total costs associated with waste disposal fall." [46] The public body setting social policy is, as we have already suggested, also responsible for pollution damage for which market evaluations do not exist: effects on the environment, on public health, and so on. And this raises the tricky problem of approximating market valuations.

Allen Kneese has succinctly illustrated the difficulties in the water-pollution area of devising proxies for the benefits of pollution control, in a discussion of the serious shortcomings of proposals to employ changes in property values as the benefit measure. Not only are there great difficulties involved in distinguishing the effects of pollution abatement from the many other factors determining property values, but a rise in values in the area affected might be at the expense of another area which might now be relatively less attractive to the market and/or affected adversely by the increased supply of desirable properties. Kneese's position is that, in the case of enhancement of values resulting from pollution control, a rise in the value of properties near the cleansed stream measures from the point of view of national benefits "too much and too little." The value rise may reflect, in part, the discounting of the net advantage of locating in the now more attractive area. Not only may costs of production be initially lower in this area, but residential property values may rise because of the enhanced recreational potentials of the cleansed stram. Unfortunately, the increase in welfare due to the latter is "inextricably intermingled with the portions that represent a mere transfer and that are counterbalanced by decrements elsewhere." Also, as long as there is public access to the new recreational area, property value increases will understate the total welfare gain. Kneese concludes as follows: "It appears that changes in property values are an inadequate and possibly highly deceptive representation of the real gains from pollution control." [47]

Conclusion

As Lord Robbins has stated: "There can be no doubt that throughout history economists of all schools have conceived their work as having the most intimate bearing on politics, both in the sense of the theory of political action and of the *actual practice of affairs.*" [48] (My italics.)

The purpose of this paper has been twofold. First, I have tried to facilitate clear thinking about the nature of choices involved in the expenditure of public funds for social objectives such as the control and alleviation of air pollution. Second, toward this end, I have critically evaluated relevant aspects of the tools which economics has evolved to analyze and prescribe in these areas. It is of course obvious that effective public policy should be based upon the fullest knowledge of the implications of various alternatives. Granted the limitations of our tools, it is in estimating the economic effects of the various alternatives that economic analysis becomes a vital part of public-policy formulation and implementation.

It was not the intent of this paper, however, to prescribe practices for the economic analysis of air pollution control projects; I attempted, rather, to demonstrate the limitations as well as the suggestive guides provided by the theory of public-expenditures criteria. Let me list, briefly, what some of these are.

First of all, the treatment of public wants—social and merit—as uniquely the province of public policy, as well as the distinction made between the two types, can serve as a realistic basis for facing up to the problem of air-pollution control, and specifically to the increased obligation of public authorities at all levels of government. In line with this view I have implied that in this area efforts to enlist and educate the private sector to shoulder the burden may yield incomplete returns, particularly because most of the costs of polluted air are external to the firms and individuals producing them.

Second, the constraints which must be part of any analysis and policy prescription must be clearly identified and kept to a minimum to avoid the danger of frustrating effective action.

Third, economic criteria must be integrated with the social, economic, and psychological factors which are part of the total problem of air-pollution control. Even identifying them is an ambitious blueprint for research. Quantifying them is obviously more difficult, but there is precedent, particularly in attempts to cope with water pollution. I have attempted to utilize relevant aspects of that experience for illustrative purposes.

The use of benefit-cost analysis for decision-making can of course be effective in determining air-pollution policy, but the difficulties and limitations brought out in the body of the paper point to the need for much systematic study of the use of this type of analysis before it is uncritically applied. Measuring spill-over effects is a good example of what I am talking about; coming to grips with this problem should be viewed as of the first order of importance, yet our tools and data sources present grave problems of application. I have shown, for example, that in some cases it does not necessarily follow that an adverse benefit-cost ratio means that a project is uneconomic or undesirable.

What further needs to be done in the study of the principles and practices which can serve as guides to public expenditures on the control and alleviation of air pollution? First, the experience here and abroad of other agencies in other fields ought to be most carefully appraised and culled for guidelines to air-pollution-control policy. Second, the special problems posed by the nature of air pollution—the fact that its principal sources are private firms and individuals in many diverse activities—points to the special need for interdisciplinary solutions, which of course can result only from a broad, interdisciplinary approach to research in the field. Finally, the issues of public economic and social policy raised by the need to control the pollution of our atmosphere require the setting of practical guidelines for relations between the various levels of government in cooperating and stimulating joint programs for the control of air pollution. Many issues are involved: the private versus the public interest; effects on resource use, income distribution, economic activity, and economic growth, to mention a few; and, finally, the difficult choices which must be made between alternative uses of public monies in this area. In any research on the problem of air-pollution control certain implications suggested by this paper warrant attention. How much weight ought to be given to the economic justification of expenditures on air-pollution control? The limitations of benefit-cost analysis, the unresolved debate on the goals and tools of welfare economics, the relative crudity of the tools of economic analysis in general—all of these stand in the way of obtaining objective criteria for expenditures of public funds on the control of air pollution.

NOTES

1. This would be a penalty tax. Expenditures might also be one place removed; that is, they might be expenditures to encourage outlays by individuals or firms.

2. Stephen A. Marglin, "The Social Rate of Discount and the Optimal Rate of Investment," *Quarterly Journal of Economics*, Vol. 77 (February, 1963), p. 99.

3. Kenneth J. Arrow, *Social Choice and Individual Values*, second edition, New York, John Wiley & Sons, 163, p. 45.

4. Allen V. Kneese, "Water Pollution—Economic Aspects and Research Needs," Washington, D. C., Resources for the Future, Inc., 1962, p. 17.

5. *Ibid.*

6. The methods of this approach will be evaluated below.

7. Jack Wiseman, "Cost-Benefit Analysis and Health Service Policy," in Alan T. Peacock and D. J. Robertson, *Public Expenditure: Appraisal and Control*, Edinburgh, Oliver and Boyd, 1963, p. 142–3.

8. *Ibid.*, p. 141.

9. Otto Eckstein, "A Survey of the Theory of Public Expenditure Criteria," in *Public Finances: Needs, Sources, and Utilization*, Conference of the Universities National Bureau Committee for Economic Research, Princeton, Princeton University Press, 1961, p. 450.

10. *Ibid., passim.*

11. Otto Eckstein, *Water Resource Development*, Cambridge, Mass., Harvard University Press, 1958, pp. 47–80.

12. "A survey of the Theory of Public Expenditure Criteria," *op. cit.*, p. 452.

13. John V. Krutilla, "Welfare Aspects of Benefit-Cost Analysis," *Journal of Political Economy*, Vol. 69 (June, 1961), p. 234.

14. I. M. D. Little, *A Critique of Welfare Economics*, New York and London, Oxford University Press, 1957, p. 1.

15. Melvin Warren Reder, *Studies in the Theory of Welfare Economics*, New York, Columbia University Press, 1947, p. 13.

16. Arrow, *op. cit.*, p. 3.

17. Joan Robinson, *Economic Philosophy*, Chicago, Aldine Press, 1962, p. 74.

18. William Baumol, "Activity Analysis," *American Economic Review*, Vol. 48 (June–December, 1958), pp. 865–6.

19. Little, *op. cit.*, pp. 13–4.

20. Arrow, *op cit.*, p. 2.

21. I. M. D. Little, "Social Choice and Individual Values," *Journal of Political Economy*, Vol. 60 (October, 1952), pp. 422–32.

22. Arrow, *op cit.*, p. 106.

23. Eckstein, *op. cit.*, p. 442.

24. Little, *A Critique of Welfare Economics*, op. cit., pp. 98 ff.

25. Eckstein, *op. cit.*, pp. 445–6.

26. One example of a form of the welfare function, an objective function stressing economic efficiency only, is that which the welfare theorists of the Kaldor-Hicks school attempted to give strong normative significance to via the compensation principle mentioned above: $N = (y_1 + y_2 + \ldots + y_n)$, where y expresses the gain (or loss) of real income of the individuals from 1 to n. It might be mentioned that economists have come increasingly to use the language and apparatus of mathematics. They now talk of functional relationships among variables in contrast to discussions of tendencies or causes which used to characterize the economic literature. How much this really adds to our insight is problematical, for the existence of a functional relationship between two or more variables simply indicates that the values or magnitudes of the variables are uniquely related."

27. Kneese, *op. cit.*, p. 20.

28. Richard A. Musgrave, *The Theory of Public Finance*, New York, Mc-Graw-Hill, 1959, pp. 6–8.

29. *Ibid.*, p. 7.

30. Alan T. Peacock, "Economic Analysis and Government Expenditure Control," in Peacock and Robertson, *op. cit.*, p. 4.

31. Musgrave, *op. cit.*, pp. 10–11.

32. *Ibid.*, p. 11.

33. Of course, initial expenditures may be for educating the public to the desirability of the service, thus changing their preference pattern—for example, by illustrating the deleterious effects of air pollution.

34. See M. Merleau-Ponty, *Phenomenology of Perception*, translated by C. Smith, New York, Humanities Press, 1962, p. 21.

35. Peacock, *op. cit.*, p. 4.

36. Roland N. McKean, "Cost Benefit Analysis and British Defense Expenditure," in Peacock and Robertson, *op. cit.*, p. 17.

37. Krutilla, *op. cit.*, p. 226.

38. For an excellent discussion see "Economics and Operations Research: A Symposium," *Review of Economics and Statistics*, Vol. 40 (August, 1958), pp. 195 ff.

39. McKean, *op. cit.*, p. 20.

40. McKean, *op. cit.*, pp. 20–1.

41. *Ibid.*, p. 25.

42. Kneese, *op. cit.*, p. 22.

43. *Ibid.*, pp. 42–3.

44. *Eckstein, op. cit.*, p. 462.

45. J. Hirshleifer, "Comment," in *Public Finances: Needs, Sources, and Utilization*, Conference of the Universities National Bureau Committee for Economic Research, Princeton, Princeton University Press, 1961, pp. 495–6.

46. Kneese, *op. cit.*, p. 43.

47. *Ibid.*, p. 45.

48. Lionel Charles Robbins, *Politics and Economics*, New York, St Martin's Press, 1963, p. 5.

A Study of Pollution—Air:

A Staff Report to the Committee on Public

Works, United States Senate, September, 1963

THE PROBLEM

Air Requirements

Air is essential for survival. This statement applies not only to the air we need for breathing but also to the air needed to sustain the kind of world in which man presently lives. Heating our homes, running our factories, driving our cars, burning our wastes—all depend upon air. The amounts required are enormous. The supply of air is fixed as are our supplies of other natural resources such as coal, petroleum, iron ore, uranium, water, and other substances we gather from our environment. We realize that these are not limitless and must be conserved, and we must take the same view of our air resources.

Approximately a ton of air is required for every tankful of gasoline used by a motor vehicle. A ton of air occupies a volume of about 25,000 cubic feet. The billion gallons of fuel consumed annually by motor vehicles in the United States use 94 trillion cubic feet—or 640 cubic miles of air.

Other fuels need comparable quantities of air. Burning a ton of coal consumes about 27,000 pounds of air, and a gallon of fuel oil about 90 pounds of air, while approximately 18 pounds of air are used in burning a pound of natural gas. About 3,000 cubic miles of air must be provided annually to satisfy the oxygen requirements of the fossil fuels presently used in the United States alone.

Other nations also share the atmosphere and make demands upon it as a source of oxygen and a receptacle for waste products. While atmospheric purification processes may remove many pollutants before they can travel from one continent to another, it is quite evident, as demonstrated by nuclear testing in the atmosphere, that pollution can circle the earth a number of times before reaching the ground. Also, as will be discussed later in this report, air pollution has the potential for worldwide influences on weather. The present world population of 3 billion is expected to reach 4.5 billion by 1980. The increasing worldwide demands upon, and pollution of, the common air resource can reduce the quality of air which reaches the United States, making adequate control that much more essential.

What Are Pollutants?

What is the nature of airborne wastes, and where do they come from?

Matter exists in three forms—solid, liquid, and gaseous. Air itself is a mixture of a number of gases, principally nitrogen (78.09 per cent), oxygen (20.95 per cent), and argon (0.93 per cent). Small amounts of a number of other gases are normal constituents of air. Among these are neon, krypton, helium, hydrogen, xenon, and ozone. Carbon dioxide, although normally constituting only 0.03 per cent of the atmosphere, is of special interest and importance because of its role in the life processes of animal and vegetable life and its influence on the temperature of the atmosphere. Green plants, utilizing the energy of sunlight, manufacture carbohydrates from carbon dioxide and water, and release oxygen. Animals, including man, use the oxygen and release carbon dioxide. Carbon dioxide is also produced whenever we burn carbonaceous fuels, such as wood, coal, gas, oil, or paper. With the steadily increasing rate of consumption of such fuels, there is evidence of a gradual increase in the carbon dioxide content of the air, which in turn is believed by many scientists to be causing a rise in the temperature of the earth's atmosphere.

Air is never completely "pure." Other gases, such as sulfur dioxide, hydrogen sulfide, carbon monoxide, and methane, are discharged into the air by such natural occurrences as volcanic eruptions, forest fires, and the decay of vegetation. Wind and other disturbances distribute and suspend particulate contaminants in the form of tiny fragments of solid matter and liquid droplets. Some pollution of the air, from natural processes, is occurring all of the time.

The contaminants we discharge into the air mirror virtually all of our activities which utilize materials for domestic, commercial, agricultural, industrial, or other purposes. The burning of fuels to heat our homes, and to propel our automobiles, trains, planes, and missiles; the conversion of raw materials into finished goods; the application of pesticides and fertilizers to increase our crops; the exploration into the capabilities of nuclear energy; the burning of trash and garbage; the clearing of land; the construction of roads and buildings—each of these puts foreign substances into the air.

These foreign substances are not the only aerial pollutants which result from our activities. For after these pollutants enter the atmosphere, a great deal of chemical and physical activity occurs—much more than was realized only a few years ago.

Though not yet fully explained, recent research has revealed that complex reactions take place in the air. It is known that the rate and extent of some of these changes are influenced by energy from the sun. In many instances, the presence of airborne particulate matter also has significant effects. Apparently, contaminant gases may be attracted to, and concentrate on, the surfaces of these particles, and this leads to a speedup of chemical reactions. Some of these particulates have catalytic properties; that is, the ability to promote or speed up reactions without themselves undergoing a change. Only the exposed surface of a catalyst can provide this stimulus. The surface area of a solid increases tremendously as the material is divided into smaller and smaller pieces. The relative surface area of particles small enough to remain floating in air is enormous, and a small weight of such finely divided catalysts can exert remarkable effects.

Some of these atmospheric reactions result in the conversion of harmful compounds into secondary compounds which do no injury. On the other hand, secondary compounds can be formed which are more dangerous or otherwise more objectionable than those originally discharged into the air. For example, one of the compounds thought to be responsible for eye irritation in the type of smog first noted in Los Angeles is peroxyacetyl nitrate—referred to, for short, as PAN. This substance is produced in the air by the action of sunlight on automotive exhaust gases.

The term "smog" originally referred to a combination of smoke and fog, such as is frequently encountered in London, where coal is widely used for domestic heating as well as industrially. The word later was applied to the pollution problem of the Los Angeles area, even though neither smoke nor fog is particularly involved. It is through studies of this problem that much of the existing knowledge of atmospheric reactions was developed. Our scientists now refer to this type of pollution as "photochemical smog," since it has been shown to arise largely from a series of chemical reactions brought on or accelerated by solar energy. The principal primary contaminants involved are hydrocarbons and nitrogen oxides. The motor vehicle is one of their chief sources.

Photochemical smog, in objectionable amounts, is being found with increasing frequency in a number of cities throughout the Nation. As the basic ingredients are present everywhere and our urban population continues to grow, such smog will occur, with increasing intensity, in an ever greater number of localities.

The effects of photochemical smog are not necessarily limited to those areas where the pollutants are emitted. Since several hours may be required for the transformation of the original pollutants into the more harmful secondary products, the air mass involved may drift a considerable distance from the primary pollution sources before its maximum potential for adverse effects is reached. Thus control measures are often required, not only for the benefit of the community where the pollution arises but also for the protection of its neighbors.

The Magnitude of Pollution

Pollution of natural origin, as from volcanic eruptions, forest fires, and dust storms, is generally uncontrollable, but fortunately, in most localities, is rarely of major significance in terms of the total air pollution problem. The problem owes its importance to man and his activities.

As the number of people on earth increases, there is more air pollution. The United States, in achieving the world's highest standard of living, however, is finding that air pollution is increasing at an even faster rate than its population growth would suggest. This is related to our increasing per capita production and consumption of goods and services, which entail a vastly greater utilization of combustible materials, as well as other activities which pollute the air. This trend has accelerated as our Nation has grown from a primarily agricultural economy to a highly industrialized one.

The steady rise in per capita income has enabled the average citizen to own more goods, to replace them more often, to travel more, and in various other ways to avail himself of increased material benefits. To supply these wants has required greater production and energy generation at rates considerably in excess of the rate of population growth.

From the Report of the National Fuels and Energy Study Group to the Committee on Interior and Insular Affairs, U.S. Senate, September 21, 1962, are the following projections of annual energy and fuels requirements:

	Present	1980
Power consumption (trillions of British thermal units)	41,000	82,000
Generation of electric energy (billions of killowatt-hours)	770	2,700
Oil consumption (billions of barrels)	3.4	5.7
Coal consumption (millions of tons)	400	800
Gas consumption (trillions of cubic feet)	10	20

NOTE.—These figures, which show a twofold overall increase of annual energy and fuel requirements, indicate that the demands on our fixed air supply will also increase greatly by 1980.

The quantities of pollutants discharged into the air are so great as to be difficult to visualize. For example, it has been estimated [1] that for every 1,000 gallons of gasoline used by cars, there are discharged 3,000 pounds of carbon monoxide, 200 to 400 pounds of hydrocarbons, and 50 to 150 pounds of nitrogen oxides, as well as significant amounts of such other contaminants as aldehydes, sulfur compounds, organic acids, ammonia, lead, and other metallic oxides. Applying these figures to the Nation as a whole gives the following figures for the daily discharge from motor vehicles:

	Tons
Carbon monoxide	250,000
Hydrocarbons	16,500–33,000
Nitrogen oxides	4,000–12,000

Translating the carbon monoxide figures into volume shows that vehicles discharge enough of this gas each day to pollute the air to a concentration of 30 parts per million, up to a height of nearly 400 feet over an area of 20,000 square miles, equal to the combined areas of Massachusetts, Connecticut, and New Jersey. Thirty parts per million is the concentration which for an 8-hour exposure is classified as "adverse" according to the State of California standards of ambient air.

Another example of the magnitude of pollution is obtained by estimating the sulfur dioxide produced by coal, which, while one of the most important, is certainly not the only source of sulfur dioxide pollution. Assuming coal with an average sulfur content of 2 per cent, the daily discharge would be 48,000 tons of sulfur dioxide. In terms of volume, this would be enough to pollute the air up to a height of 400 feet over an area of more than 46,000 square miles, an area larger than the State of Pennsylvania, to a concentration of 1 part per million, a concentration sufficient to damage vegetation.

Particulates, or minute separate particles of matter, discharged into our air may arise from many sources: incomplete combustion of fuels, wastes from metallurgical, chemical, and refining processes, and incineration—to name a few. Consequently, comparable, meaningful estimates of *total discharges* of solid particulate contaminants may not be practicable. However, we do have much useful information on the *concentrations* of particulates which are suspended in the air. Since 1956 the National Air Sampling Network of the Public Health Service has obtained data throughout the country on such contaminants, from communities of all sizes as well as from rural areas. One important finding from this network is the consistent relationship of particulate pollution to population, as shown in figure 1.

The Effects of Urbanization

The continuing movement of an ever larger percentage of the population into urban areas has concentrated the discharge of waste products from combustion into a very small proportion of the atmosphere, hereby intensifying the problem of air pollution. This results in the exposure of more and more people to more and more pollution without any corresponding increase in the available air supply.

Two-thirds of the population of the United States reside in the 212 standard metropolitan statistical areas, which have a combined area of 310,233 square miles, representing approximately 9 percent of the total land area of the United States. The concentration of population is perhaps even more emphatically shown by the fact that, in 1960, 95,848,487 persons resided in 213 urbanized localities

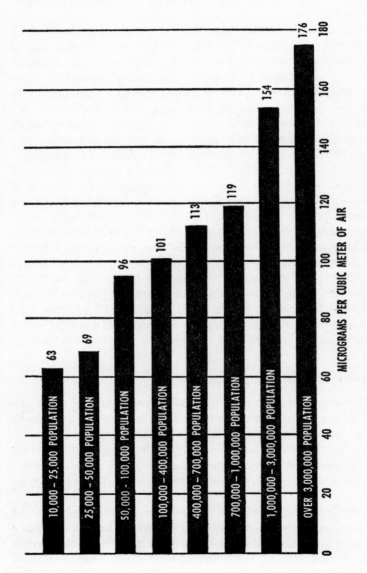

FIGURE 1. *Suspended Particles-Urban Stations by Population Class. 1957–1961 Geometric Mean Values.*

TABLE 1. *Estimated[1] number of places with air pollution problems and population exposed to air pollution[2]*

[1960 population in thousands]

Population class	All urban places		Major problem			Moderate problem			Minor problem			All problems		
	Number in class	Approximate population	Places Per-cent	Number	Approximate population	Places Per-cent	Number	Approximate population	Places Per-cent	Number	Approximate population	Places Per-cent	Number	Approximate population
Urban places:														
1,000,000 or more	5	17,500	100	5	17,500	0	0	0	0	0	0	100	5	17,500
500,000 to 1,000,000	16	11,100	70	11	7,800	30	5	3,300	0	0	0	100	16	11,100
250,000 to 500,000	30	10,700	45	13	4,800	45	14	4,800	10	3	1,100	100	30	10,700
100,000 to 250,000	81	11,600	25	20	2,900	50	40	5,800	25	21	2,900	100	81	11,600
50,000 to 100,000	201	13,800	20	40	2,800	35	70	4,800	45	91	6,200	100	201	13,800
25,000 to 50,000	432	14,900	10	43	1,500	25	108	3,700	45	194	6,700	80	345	11,900
10,000 to 25,000	1,134	17,600	8	91	1,400	20	227	3,500	37	420	6,500	65	738	11,400
5,000 to 10,000	1,394	9,800	3	42	290	12	168	1,200	35	487	3,400	50	697	4,890
2,500 to 5,000	2,152	7,600	2	43	150	10	215	760	28	602	2,100	40	860	3,010
Unincorporated parts of urbanized areas		9,900			3,800			2,300			2,300			8,400
SUBTOTAL	5,445	124,500	5	308	42,940	15	847	30,160	33	1,818	31,200	53	2,973	104,300
Urban & rural places under 2,500	14,345	11,100										[3]30	4,300	3,300
GRAND TOTAL	19,790	135,600	5	308	42,940	15	847	30,160	33	1,818	31,200	37	7,273	107,600
Percent of total U.S. population[4]		76			24			17			17			60

1. Accuracy of estimates not to be inferred from number of significant digits reported.
2. Urban places as defined by U.S. Department of Commerce, Bureau of the Census.
3. Problems are mostly minor.
4. Total U.S. population in 1960 was 179,323,000.

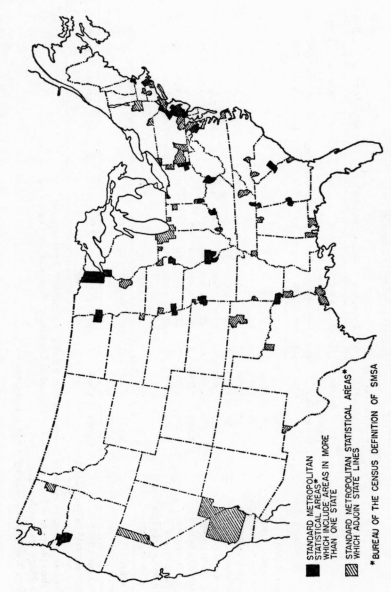

STANDARD METROPOLITAN
STATISTICAL AREAS*
WHICH INCLUDE AREAS IN MORE
THAN ONE STATE

STANDARD METROPOLITAN STATISTICAL AREAS*
WHICH ADJOIN STATE LINES

*BUREAU OF THE CENSUS DEFINITION OF SMSA

FIGURE 2. Potential Major Interstate Air Pollution Problems.

which have a combined area of only 25,544 square miles. In other words, 53 per cent of the people live on considerably less than 1 per cent of the land area. Over half of the people are so concentrated that they average more than 3,750 per square mile.

Further, in a number of areas, many urbanized localities are located closely enough together so that pollution from one can adversely affect another. Such problems are frequently of an interstate nature, as shown by figure 2.

In small communities, air pollution problems often affect only certain neighborhoods and are caused by a single source, or a few major sources, of pollution. As the size of a community increases, the proportion of the total area affected tends to increase, due to an increase in the number of pollution sources. While individual opinions will vary on the severity of a given situation, the estimates presented in table 1 reflect to a degree the views, in 1961, of a number of State and local control officials. These indicate "major" air pollution problems in 308 urban places. This is an increase of 84 over the number 10 years earlier. About one-quarter of the Nation's population resides in these 308 communities. About 7,300 places, housing 60 per cent of the population, are confronted with an air pollution problem of one kind or another.

The Influence of Weather on Pollution

Weather has an important influence on air pollution. Pollutants may be dispersed by one or another degree in two principal ways: Horizontally by wind and vertically by rising air currents.

Daily variations in wind speed depend on large-scale high- and low-pressure systems. As a rule, however, the wind blows hardest in the early afternoon, with the minimum speed generally occurring during the early morning hours.

The weather patterns are also influenced by hills, mountains, lakes, and oceans. During warm weather, the air over land heats more during the day than does air over water. The lowest air layer on land warms quickly, making the air unstable, so that it rises. This induces an inland flow of cooler air from the sea, and sets up the well-known sea breezes. These breezes generally extend upward less than 2,000 feet, and gradually decrease both in speed and height as they move inland, diminishing by about half in 10 to 15 miles.

Above these breezes there is a return circulation from land to water. At night, particularly on clear nights, the land cools faster than the water and so cools the low air layer on the land quickly. The heavier land air spills seaward, where the lower air stays warm longer and sets up a land breeze, thus reversing the airflow pattern. These breezes, prevailing from about 2 hours after sunset until 2 hours after sunrise, are not as strong, and extend up only a few hundred feet.

Similar patterns develop in mountainous locations, due to different rates of heating and cooling along the slopes of the valleys. On clear days the earth's surface heats rapidly, and promptly warms the adjacent layer of air. Strong convection currents then flow up sloping surfaces. They induce colder upper air to subside into the valley, giving strong air circulation over the terrain. On clear nights the earth's surface cools faster than the upper air and cools the lower air first. Cooled air flows downward and accumulates in valleys, causing stagnant inversions by trapping warm air above.

While such local flows can sometimes prevent periods of sustained exposure, they can also result in polluted air flowing back across the source area, thereby permitting higher concentrations to build up through additional discharges into the already polluted air.

Wind speed also changes with the seasons. As an example, in both the Appalachian Mountains in the east and over the Great Basin area in the west, there will be, in fall and early winter, long periods of atmospheric stagnation, with only light winds, or none.

The rate at which pollution can rise depends upon changes in the air temperature with height. Ordinarily, air becomes cooler with increases in height. If the temperature drops more than 5.4° F., per 1,000 feet, warm polluted air, being lighter, will continue to rise. But if the temperature decrease with height is less than 5.4° F., a stable condition occurs and pollutants tend to remain in the air layer into which they are discharged.

If a layer of warm air is above air which is cooler, the normal temperature gradient is reversed. The layer of warm air then acts as a "lid," and pollution does not rise above it. This is a thermal inversion.

Such inversions are common in all areas of the United States, occurring between 10 per cent and 50 per cent of the time at elevations of 500 feet or less, as shown by the following table:

Annual percent of hours of inversion based at or below 500 feet

Region:	Per cent
Atlantic coast	10–35
Appalachian Mountains	30–45
Great Lakes	20–30
Gulf coast	10–35
Central Plains	25–40
Rocky Mountains	35–50
Northwest Pacific coast	25–30
West coast	35–40

The intensity and duration of inversion depends upon how rapidly the earth cools at night and warms in the morning. These rates are affected by clouds, topography, and the season. Fall months generally have more total hours of inversion conditions, but a single inversion condition is likely to last longer during the winter.

The importance of inversions to the air pollution problem is shown by the following example.

Inversion conditions developing over a city during the night frequently persist until 3 or 4 hours after sunrise. This means that the pollution from the morning traffic peak is held down until late morning or early afternoon. Again, conditions which restrict the dilution of pollution often arise at the time of the peak of evening traffic. Ironically, the two daily periods of maximum automobile traffic frequently coincide with the two daily periods least satisfactory for the escape of pollution.

Figure 3 illustrates how various combinations of temperature and wind conditions can affect the dispersal of pollution.

EFFECTS OF POLLUTION

The insidious effects of air pollution are many—all of them undesirable. Pollution harms our health, reduces our crop yields, damages our property, affronts our senses, and lessens our enjoyment of life.

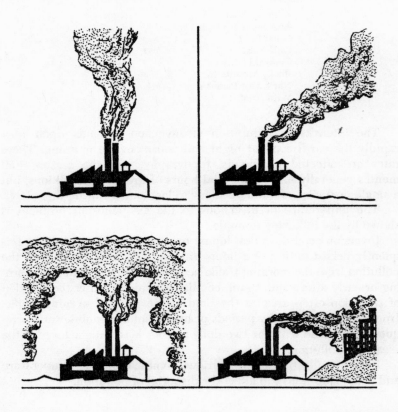

FIGURE 3. *Effects of Wind and Temperature on Spread of Pollution.*

What Does Air Pollution Do to Health?

The cost of illness, of decreased strength, and of shortened lifespan cannot be measured in dollars. There can be no price tag for the health effects of air pollution. If there could be, its amount would far exceed all other costs combined.

In London, England, in December, 1962, at least 340 people died because of a smog which persisted for only a few days.

Other catastrophes of this type, brought on by periods of inversion and weather stagnation, have occurred in the past. Some of them probably were not even recognized. London itself had similar weather conditions in December, 1952, which brought on a "pea soup" fog lasting 5 days. A review of the records, some months later, showed that there were 4,000 more deaths than usual during the week beginning with the first day of the fog. Following this disaster, the British passed a Clean Air Act designed to reduce pollution. Improved coal burning practices required by that act have reduced the amount of particulate matter in the air. This is credited, in part, with the lower death toll from the 1962 smog, in which sulfur dioxide levels were similar to those in 1952. Other measures undoubtedly also helped. For one, there was available an emergency plan for prompt hospitalization and treatment of acutely affected persons. Also, as a result of an educational program, many people minimized their exposures by remaining indoors as much as possible and by otherwise protecting themselves. Consequently, only 340 deaths were officially ascribed to the 1962 episode.

While the air pollution problems of the United States differ from those in Great Britain, similar calamities have occurred in this country. Until recently, the one usually mentioned was that which struck Donora, Pa. in October, 1948, where one-third of the population of 14,000 became ill and 17 died. This episode was recognized immediately as a disaster. In contrast, an episode that occurred in New York City in November, 1953 was not recognized until statistical evidence presented almost 9 years later disclosed that during a brief period of weather stagnation at that time, in which unusually high levels of sulfur dioxide and smoke shade had been recorded, the number of deaths in New York had been approximately 200 in excess of normal.

This disaster attracted far less attention than the loss of a comparable number of lives in the collision of airliners over the same city. With respect to this accident, it might be added that the conditions of poor visibility which may have been in part responsible for the collision were undoubtedly aggravated by air pollution.

Of much greater overall significance than acute episodes is a growing body of evidence that long-term, low-level air pollution can contribute to and aggravate certain diseases. As the "Report of the Panel on Health Considerations" at the 1962 National Conference on Air Pollution states:

> It would be a mistake to leave this conference with the impression that there is insufficient evidence for action—now. The evidence that air pollution contributes to the pathogenesis of chronic respiratory disease is overwhelming. The classical concept of one agent being responsible for one disease is * * * an investigational convenience * * * the demonstration of a cause and effect, or one-to-one relationship is an unrealistic approach to this problem * * * the interactions of various chemical irritants, of infectious agents, and of carcinogenic substances together with meteorological factors as affecting human respiratory health, are entirely what should be expected of complex man in his complex environment. Neither these complicated interactions nor the variabilities of the types of pollution in different communities should be used to camouflage the need for action.

Prolonged exposure to low levels of airborne toxic substances may have many health effects. Primary interest centers, logically, on the respiratory system through which these poisons most easily enter the body.

There is strong evidence that air pollution is associated with a number of respiratory ailments. These include: (1) nonspecific infectious upper respiratory disease, (2) chronic bronchitis, (3) chronic constrictive ventilatory disease, (4) pulmonary emphysema, (5) bronchial asthma, and (6) lung cancer.

(1) The "common cold" and other *upper respiratory tract infections* have been shown to occur more frequently in areas which have

higher pollution levels. This has been demonstrated by investigators in Great Britain, Japan, and the U.S.S.R., as well as in the United States. Epidemiologic studies make it clear that acute nonspecific upper respiratory disease accompanies moderate levels of air pollution common in our communities.

The laboratory provides further evidence that pollution makes us more susceptible to such infections. Experiments have shown that animals inhaling the organisms which produce pneumonia are more likely to develop the disease if they are first exposed to low concentrations of ozone or nitrogen oxides.

Ciliary activity, the wavelike motion of the microscopic hairlike formations which line the air passages, is an important protective mechanism for removing infectious agents and injurious chemicals from those passages. It is decreased or stopped as a result of breathing irritant air pollutants. This too has been proved by laboratory experiments.

(2) Nearly 10 per cent of all deaths in Great Britain result from *chronic bronchitis*. Many studies there have shown positive connections between air pollution and the occurrence, severity, and aggravation of this disease.

Partly because of differences in definitions and terminology, chronic bronchitis has generally not been a well-recognized clinical entity in the United States. However, the condition, or a very similar one, is beginning to be found more often than had been suspected. One investigation, using the British criteria, found chronic bronchitis in 21 per cent of men 40 to 59 years of age.

(3) The effort required for breathing is increased as a result of breathing irritant air pollution. Studies have shown that pollution, at levels sometimes occurring in urban environments, can cause a constriction in breathing passages. This can lead to a long-continued nonspecific respiratory condition referred to as *chronic constrictive ventilatory disease*. While healthy individuals may not notice the extra breathing effort imposed by airway constriction, this added burden may be serious, even unbearable, for persons whose hearts or lungs are already functioning marginally.

(4) *Pulmonary emphysema* is a disease in which the very fine air sacs of the lung become abnormally stretched, resulting in a loss of functioning vital lung tissue. The growing importance of this disease is shown by figure 4, which indicates the rapid increase during

recent years in deaths attributed to emphysema. The extent and cost of this disease are further emphasized by social security figures. Among 179,419 persons receiving monthly payment in 1960 for disability from serious illness, pulmonary emphysema was the proven primary medical diagnosis in 6.9 per cent (or 12,380) of the cases. Only arteriosclerotic heart disease, including coronary disease, exceeded this number, accounting for 19.9 per cent. It is estimated that the payments to individuals for whom emphysema is the primary medical diagnosis is about $60 million per year.

Pulmonary emphysema seems to be increasing especially in urban areas. Air pollution is suspected of being responsible for much of this. In addition there is the demonstrated fact that individual patients with emphysema become worse when exposed to irritant air pollution.

(5) *Bronchial asthma* is another condition which, in many instances, is definitely made worse by air pollution. There is, of course, a long list of stimuli capable of triggering asthmatic attacks and it is not surprising that irritant air pollutants are included in the list. It is interesting to note that one of these, sulfur dioxide, has been reported to be an allergenic agent with respect to asthma.

As early as 1946, a condition considered to be an epidemic of asthmatic bronchitis appeared among American troops stationed in the highly industrialized Yokohama area of Japan. The condition soon appeared also among dependent family members living in the area. In time, the condition was also recognized as occurring in our military personnel in the Tokyo area. The cases did not respond to usual medication for asthma, but the symptoms generally disappeared when the individuals were evacuated from the area. If allowed to remain in the area a few months to a year, many individuals develop permanent lung disability, probably in the form of pulmonary emphysema.

The condition is still under detailed study. Among the findings thus far are the following: it is estimated that 3 to 5 per cent of the exposed American personnel develop the disease; it occurs in epidemic form in late fall and early winter, when the usual allergens of plant origin are not present in the air; it is unclear whether the native population have the disease, although it is known that they do have true allergic bronchial asthma; few of the patients report a history of allergy in themselves or their families; removal from the

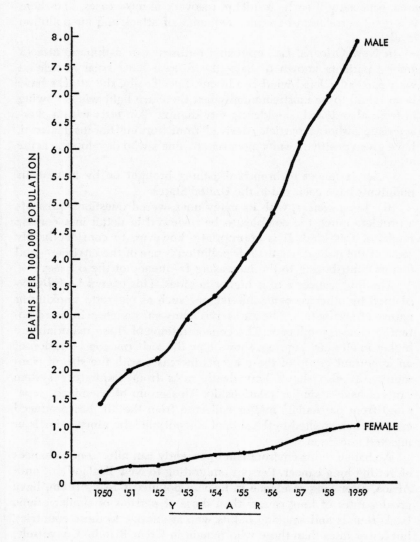

FIGURE 4. *Death Rates from Pulmonary Emphysema by Year and Sex. United States 1950–1959.*

area, especially if early, results in recovery in most cases; and there is a good correlation between frequency of attack and air pollution levels.

In New Orleans, La., epidemic outbreaks of asthmatic attacks among patients known to have the disease have been associated with particular local wind conditions. Specifically, the attacks have been found to be most common when there are light winds flowing in from abandoned, smoldering city dumps. Skin tests with a characteristic airborne particle, derived from burning fibrous material, have given positive results among individuals who develop the acute attacks.

Other instances of bronchial asthma brought on by irritant air pollutants have occurred in the United States.

(6) *Lung cancer*, with its many unanswered questions, presents a problem much too complex to be reviewed in detail in a concise report of this kind. It is appropriate, however, to consider briefly some of the indications that air pollution is one of the environmental factors contributing to the increasing frequency of the disease.

The lung cancer rate is higher in cities. This cannot be fully explained by other recognizable factors, such as cigarette smoking or nature of occupation. The air carries many substances which are potential cancer producers. The concentrations of these materials are higher in city air. Figure 5 shows how the airborne concentration of an important group of these agents increases with the size of community. It also shows how death rates from respiratory system cancers have a similar relationship. This group of chemicals, separated from particulate matter collected from the air, has produced cancer when applied to the skin of susceptible laboratory animals or injected into them.

A change in air environment apparently can affect one's chances of getting lung cancer. Persons emigrating to New Zealand or South Africa, after long residence in heavily polluted Great Britain, have greater rates of lung cancer than those of persons of similar ethnic backgrounds and smoking habits who are native to those countries, but lower rates than those who remain in Great Britain. Conversely, persons coming to the United States from Norway have lower cancer rates than native Americans of similar backgrounds but higher rates than among those who remained in the cleaner air of their own country. These relationships have been demonstrated in four independent studies.

Mice which had recovered from induced influenza developed lung cancer after inhaling ozonized gasoline, a substance quite similar to the photochemical smog found in many areas. Similar mice which did not inhale the ozonized gasoline did not develop cancer. Likewise, mice which had not had influenza did not develop cancer, even though they were exposed to the ozonized gasoline.

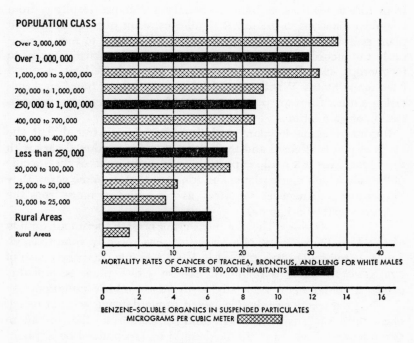

FIGURE 5.

These and other findings give strong indications that air pollutants, either alone or acting in conjunction with other factors, contribute to the development of respiratory cancer.

Air Pollution Is Costly to Agriculture

The nature and extent of air pollution damage to vegetation has been changing, just as air pollution has been changing. Until recent years, the destruction of foliage on a serious scale was primarily due to sulfur dioxide, of which classical examples occurred at Copper Hill, Tenn., and in the State of Washington from the smelter at Trail, British Columbia.

With the expansion and development of new industrial processes and products, a variety of contaminants is now sometimes present in harmful concentrations. Augmenting the problem are the emissions from motor vehicles and the secondary pollutants resulting from chemical reactions in the air. A significant result of these additional plant poisons has been the rapid spread of damage to many previously untouched areas of the Nation. Reports of extensive injury to farm crops, as well as to ornamental shrubbery, have been received from many States. Whether reported or not, without question, vegetation suffers from air pollution in and around every large concentration of population.

Recent research in plant pathology has demonstrated that the kinds of plants affected and the nature of injury produced vary with the agent. This has made it possible to identify some of the specific pollutants which injure plants and to prove that, in some cases, they have caused damage as far away as 100 miles or more from the point where they originate.

Ozone · The Southeastern Forest Experiment Station of the U.S. Department of Agriculture has recently reported evidence, based on studies of trees in West Virginia, that the cause of *emergence tipburn,* a blight of eastern white pine, is probably ozone, a contaminant associated with motor vehicle pollution.

The great economic significance of ozone damage was not recognized until 1958, when it was found, in California, that lesions in grape leaves observed in the field could be reproduced by a 3-hour fumigation with only one-half part per million of ozone. Ozone has also been shown to be responsible for flecking of tobacco leaves in the eastern part of the United States.

As a result of observed damage to spinach crops in New Jersey in 1958, studies were begun in that State the following year. A recent report from the New Jersey Department of Plant Pathology stated that, so far, they have observed ozone injury not only to spinach, but also to alfalfa, rye, barley, orchard grass, tobacco, petunia, radish, red clover, bean, parsley, grape, and perhaps chicory, endive, broccoli, carnation, and pine. Results of a similar nature were obtained from fumigations conducted in Utah.

That this kind of damage is not limited to the immediate vicinity of great cities is indicated in the New Jersey report, which concludes with this statement:

> With the sources of contamination, cars, home, and industrial fires, refineries, etc., being so numerous both in and bordering New Jersey, it is not surprising that test tobacco plants placed in 14 different locations in New Jersey during the growing season just past, showed injury from ozone in every location. It appears therefore that this is a problem which, while being most serious near such cities as Philadelphia and New York, can be expected to affect sensitive plants in all areas of the State.

By 1961, damage from oxidants had already been observed in 19 States (Arizona, California, Colorado, Connecticut, Delaware, Hawaii, Illinois, Indiana, Maryland, Massachusetts, Missouri, North Carolina, New Jersey, New York, Ohio, Pennsylvania, Utah, Washington, and West Virginia), the District of Columbia, and the Province of Ontario, Canada, as well as in Baja California, Mexico. In 1955 it was reported that such damage had been seen in Bogotá, Colombia; Cologne, Germany; Copenhagen, Denmark; London and Manchester, England; Paris, France; and São Paulo, Brazil.

Fluorides · Fluorides are another class of contaminants that have caused extensive vegetation damage. Being primarily of industrial origin, fluoride damage is generally associated with specific, fixed sources. In many such situations livestock, foraging on vegetation on which airborne fluorides have been deposited, have suffered serious adverse effects.

Although hydrogen fluoride and sulfur dioxide are both acid gases, their effects on vegetation vary. Corn and peach, for example, are quite susceptible to hydrogen fluoride, but both are resistant to sulfur dioxide. The reverse is the case for certain other species of plants.

Hydrogen fluoride is a gas which is extremely poisonous to vegetation. Some gladiolus plants have been injured by concentrations as low as 1 part per 10 billion parts of air.

Others · Examples of some vegetation-damaging pollutants have been given. Others of importance, such as ethylene and peroxyacetyl nitrate, have also been identified. Much additional research is needed to ascertain the full cost to agriculture of air pollution. In addition to visible damage, retardation of plant growth and reduction in yield require careful study. Effects on livestock also should be investigated more thoroughly.

The economic losses are presently difficult to measure. As interest in air pollution effects on vegetation grows, the vast cost is beginning to be appreciated. This is exemplified by the report from the Panel on Agricultural, Natural Resource, and Economic Considerations at the 1962 National Conference on Air Pollution, which states:

> The agricultural losses resulting from the adverse effects of all of the presently recognized pollutants have been estimated to amount to hundreds of millions of dollars a year.

Property Losses Are Enormous

Accurate data are not available on the extent and cost of air pollution damage to property. Various cost estimates have been made. One frequently employed is $65 per capita per year. This would represent an annual cost to the Nation of over $11 billion. Whatever yardsticks are employed, it is clearly evident that the cost of property damage alone from air pollution is great—far greater than the amounts devoted to its abatement by industry and all levels of government.

Air pollution causes the accelerated deterioration of materials, structures, and machines of all kinds. This in turn greatly increases maintenance and replacement expenditures. In addition, air pollution is responsible for a general depreciation in property values which affects neighborhoods and even entire communities.

Most common materials are adversely affected by pollution. Metals corrode, fabrics weaken and fade, leather weakens and becomes brittle, rubber cracks and loses its elasticity, paint discolors, concrete and building stone discolor and erode, glass is etched, and paper becomes brittle.

Sulfur dioxide, a common contaminant in the air of virtually all towns and cities, causes deterioration of many materials. It attacks metals, particularly iron and steel. Limestone, marble, roofing slate, mortar, and other carbonate-containing stone, are partially converted to water-soluble sulfates, which are leached away by rain. Sulfur dioxide has an affinity for leather, causing it to weaken and rot. Costly damage to upholstery and book bindings has been produced by its action. Cotton, wool, and nylon are all weakened by sulfur dioxide.

Another sulfur compound, hydrogen sulfide, reacts with lead compounds to form black lead sulfide. Houses covered with lead-based paints often suffer severe discoloration from even single exposures to this gas.

Hydrogen sulfide also tarnishes copper and silver. The coating formed on open electrical contacts of these metals can increase electrical resistance and may result in welding the contacts together in the closed position.

Important among the many property-damaging effects of photo-chemical smog is the excessive cracking of rubber. This is due to oxidants in the atmosphere, particularly ozone. So rapid is the action that measurement of crack depth in rubber is used as a method for determining ozone concentrations in the air. Ozone also causes deterioration in a number of dyes and fabrics, of both natural and synthetic materials. Fading is also produced by nitrogen oxides.

The primary effect of airborne solid particulate matter is soiling. While this does not directly result in deterioration of materials, such as fabrics or structures, the removal of the deposited grime is often costly and may shorten the life of such materials; for example, clothes wear out more from laundering than from wearing.

The presence of particulates apparently greatly accelerates the destructive action of those gases which corrode metals, just as particulates mixed with inhaled gases apparently increase the harmful effects of the gases on the respiratory system.

The cost, because of air pollution, of replacing or protecting precision instruments and other equipment affected by pollutants is undoubtedly high. The complex and expensive control systems which are becoming so commonplace in modern technology can be ruined, or seriously damaged, by the corrosive action of gaseous pollutants or by deposited dust. To prevent such damage, many industries—for example, those engaged in the manufacture of high-precision components for telecommunication or space vehicles—must clean, at considerable expense, air admitted to the plants in which such items are produced.

In the average home, air pollution is responsible for additional expenses—for example, more frequent painting of exterior and interior walls and more frequent cleaning of clothing and home furnishings, such as rugs and draperies—which can easily add up to substantial amounts per year. In neighborhoods where residents are unable or unwilling to incur such expenses, the resultant depreciation of property values may cost even more, to both individuals and the community.

Air Pollution Is a Safety Hazard

Air pollution represents a definite hazard to land, water, and air transportation, because it reduces visibility. Any source of dense smoke close to a modern high-speed highway can pose a serious threat to travelers. In at least two recent instances—one in Pennsylvania close to a smoldering culm pile, another in Louisiana near a burning dump—the sudden application of brakes by a single motorist led to a chain reaction which involved the wrecking of a number of vehicles and injuries to many of their occupants. The same thing has occurred on the New Jersey Turnpike. Similar accidents as well as unexpected delays on this account are probably frequent throughout the Nation.

Air pollution is not only hazardous, but also costly, where aircraft operations are involved. Normal fog, of course, sometimes slows up air travel. The addition of pollutants to the fog often reduces visibility enough to ground aircraft which are not fully equipped with appropriate blind-flying instruments. Even when planes have the best available instruments, the aggravation of poor weather conditions by pollution results in delays in landings and departures at busy airports. This is costly to people traveling on business and very expensive to the carriers. As long ago as 1946, a survey showed that the number of hours during which visibility was cut to 6 miles or less at Newark Airport as a result of smoke alone, or smoke in combination with other obstructions, totaled 4,359 hours, or almost 50 per cent of the total hours during the year.

A review by the Civil Aeronautics Board of 1,660 record cards, representing one-third of the aircraft accidents in the United States in 1962, showed 6 in which "obstructions to vision" (by smoke, haze, sand, and dust) were listed as a cause. Two of the six aircraft were classified as large, one of them being a commercial carrier. If the sample studied is representative, a total of 15 to 20 plane crashes in 1962 may be attributed to this cause.

Pollution contributes to fog formation and undoubtedly aggravates visibility problems in which natural conditions play a major role. Where accidents are attributed to impaired visibility due to weather, it is likely that, in many instances, the risk had been increased by air pollution.

Air Pollution Affects Our Weather

Air pollution causes many local changes in the atmosphere. It decreases the amount of sunshine reaching the earth, cutting down particularly on ultraviolet radiation. It reduces the natural illumination, which requires us to provide more artificial light, particularly in winter. It increases the frequency and density of fog, with the resultant loss of visibility and its attendant hazards. It increases cloudiness. Under some circumstances, it increases local precipitation in urban areas.

As stated earlier, there is evidence that the amount of carbon dioxide in the atmosphere is increasing as a consequence of human activities. This increase is raising the temperature of the earth's atmosphere by intercepting infrared heat waves going out from the earth into space. An increase in heat will lead to more violent air circulation and thus to more destructive storms.

Air pollution's effects on the weather, therefore, can be significant on a large scale as well as locally.

Recreational, Aesthetic, and Psychological Effects

The recreational, aesthetic, and psychological effects of air pollution overlap not only each other but also the economic effects. The contraction of the horizon by curtains of smog that can slow up or cancel air flights can also spoil the tourist's view of a natural wonder. The growing of green things that is one man's income is another man's recreation and a source of aesthetic satisfactions. When ozone blights a pine forest, it may not only destroy industrial resources, but also ruin the forest for vacationers or sportsmen.

This is also true of simpler and commoner occurrences. A man may touch a soot-coated window ledge or car fender and then the cuff of his freshly laundered shirt. The economic effect of the resulting black smudge may be no more than a few pennies in laundry bills, but the effects on his disposition and peace of mind may be substantial. The golfer—or anyone who is out of doors for pleasure —enjoys seeing the open sky, unclouded by manmade haze.

There is also a certain overlap between this kind of effect and health considerations. No permanent health effects have been demonstrated as a result of smog-induced stinging and tearing of the eyes, but this is highly uncomfortable and irritating in more than the literal sense. Diesel exhaust is possibly a lesser health hazard than the exhaust from gasoline motors, but the motorist who is held up behind an idling bus is not thinking of long-range health effects; he simply resents the sight and the smell of those diesel fumes.

Wholly apart from health or economic considerations, the recreational, aesthetic, and psychological effects sometimes seem, to some groups and individuals, serious enough on their own account to call for remedial action. It will never be possible to measure these effects accurately in quantitative terms, if only because they affect different people differently. To the flower lover whose ornamentals refuse to grow, to the art lover who sees his city's memorial buildings and statues defaced by grime or slowly crumbling because of sulfur compounds, to the sportsman who notes the recent slaughter of ducks and fish by airborne crop sprays—these effects of air pollution may seem the most obnoxious of all.

HISTORY OF FEDERAL PROGRAM

Public Law 84-159

An identifiable Federal program in air pollution was not established until 1955, when Public Law 159 was passed by the 84th Congress. This was entitled "An act to provide research and technical assistance relating to air pollution control."

Prior to the passage of this act, only limited work had been done in the field of air pollution. The Bureau of Mines, for example, did some studies on the nature and control of pollution from fuel combustion, and the Public Health Service, under Public Law 78–410, conducted certain studies and investigations—in particular the one involving the Donora, Pa., episode of 1948.

Public Law 84–159 supplemented the authority provided by the Public Health Service Act (Public Law 78–410) to the Secretary of Health, Education, and Welfare: (1) To prepare or recommend research programs for devising methods of controlling air pollution; (2) to encourage cooperative activities by State and local governments; (3) to collect and disseminate information relating to air pollution; (4) to conduct research to devise and develop methods of prevention and abatement and to support such work conducted by other governmental and private agencies; (5) to conduct research, surveys, and investigations concerning any specific problem of air pollution, upon request of any State or local governmental air pollution control agency, and (6) to make grants to, and enter into contracts with, other governmental and private agencies and individuals for surveys, studies, research, training, and demonstration projects.

In 1960, Public Law 86–493 directed the Surgeon General to study the problem of motor vehicle exhausts and their effects upon human health, and to submit a report to the Congress within 2 years. This report, entitled "Motor Vehicles, Air Pollution, and Health," was published in 1962 as House Document 489.

Public Law 84–159 authorized a maxium appropriation of $5 million for each of 5 fiscal years. Subsequently, the time period of the authorization was extended by amendment of the act. Public Law 86–365 extended the authority for an additional 4 years to June 30, 1964 and Public Law 87–761 further extended the period to June 30, 1966.

No substantive change in the authority of the Public Health Service with regard to air pollution has been made since passage of Public Law 84–159 in 1955. An amendment, contained in Public Law 87–761, included a directive to continue work on motor vehicle exhausts as called for in Public Law 86–493. Public Law 86–365 added another amendment declaring the intent of Congress that Federal agencies shall cooperate with the Department of Health, Education, and Welfare and with State and local air pollution agencies in preventing or controlling air pollution from sources under the control of such Federal agencies.

Monetary appropriations for air pollution since inception of the Federal program are summarized as follows:

[in thousands]

	1955	1956	1957	1958	1959	1960	1961	1962	1963
Research:									
Intramural		535	823	1,263	1,279	2,061	2,908	3,831	4,462
Contract		519	803	1,157	1,157	1,059	1,824	1,786	2,278
Grants		462	530	700	700	444	450	1,944	2,892
TOTAL	186	1,516	2,156	3,120	3,136	3,564	5,182	7,561	9,632
Technical assistance		166	400	570	488	397	426	582	681
Training:									
Direct		40	79	135	136	151	233	258	299
Grants			105	170	100	100	113	113	450
TOTAL		40	184	305	236	251	346	371	749
GRAND TOTAL	186	1,722	2,740	3,995	3,860	[1]5,201	[1]7,057	8,800	11,069

1. Including transfer for research grants operations from NIH.

With the enactment of Public Law 84–159 in 1955, the Public Health Service began its work in air pollution through two mechanisms. One was the establishment of an engineering air pollution program which began limited technical assistance activities and research into the sources, nature, concentration, and control of air pollutants. Laboratory facilities for parts of this work were developed at the Robert A. Taft Sanitary Engineering Center in Cincinnati. The remainder of the work was undertaken through contracts and grants. The other mechanism was the creation, at the same time, of a medical air pollution program, for the primary purpose of evaluating health effects of air pollution. Since facilities were lacking at the beginning for conducting research, it was inaugurated almost entirely through grants and contracts. By 1960, sufficient progress had been made, and enough problem areas defined, to justify combining the two programs into the present Division of Air Pollution, which was established on September 1, 1960, and under which there is a coordinated approach to the overall problem.

While continuing to make use of the research resources of educational institutions and other private or public agencies through contracts or grants, the Division has also strengthened its own research capabilities. The passage of Public Law 86–493 in 1960, provided a particular stimulus to research, accelerating the development of facilities and personnel for the study of motor vehicle pollution problems.

Program Objectives

The Public Health Service air pollution program to date has been based on the philosophy that the primary responsibility for the regulatory control of air pollution rests with the States and local governments, and that the Federal role should be a supporting one of research, technical assistance to public and private organizations, and training of technical personnel.

The basic objectives of the program are threefold: (1) To improve the status of knowledge about the causes and effects of air pollution and about the means of controlling it within acceptable limits; (2) to apply present and future knowledge to the actual control of air pollutants through technical assistance to States, communities, and industry; and (3) to stimulate all levels of government, industry, and the general public to devote increased attention and greater resources to the prevention and control of air pollution. A National Advisory Committee on Air Pollution helps to guide the policies and program. The Committee has representation from industry, control agencies, and other interested segments of the public.

Research

Air pollution research conducted or sponsored by the Public Health Service has explored many facets of the problem.

In the field of engineering, the research has dealt with such matters as the amounts, character, and control of automotive exhaust and crankcase emissions; incineration of refuse and other combustion problems; and control procedures, including studies of contaminant behavior, collection mechanisms, and performance characteristics of control equipment. Field surveys of industrial sources have also been undertaken to determine the amounts and nature of materials actually being discharged by certain processes.

Chemical research has developed new and appropriate analytical methods of the necessary sensitivity, and with these has explored the chemistry and movements of the atmosphere, and examined and developed basic data on "clean" atmospheres.

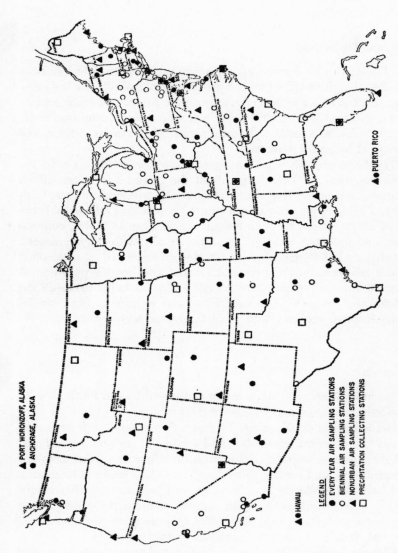

FIGURE 6. *National Air Sampling Network—1960*

LEGEND
● EVERY YEAR AIR SAMPLING STATIONS
○ BIENNIAL AIR SAMPLING STATIONS
▲ NONURBAN AIR SAMPLING STATIONS
□ PRECIPITATION COLLECTING STATIONS

▲ PORT WORONZOFF, ALASKA
● ANCHORAGE, ALASKA

▲● PUERTO RICO

▲● HAWAII

Air monitoring has been accomplished through the establishment of a national air-sampling network of approximately 250 stations (fig. 6) which provide data on suspended particulate matter in both urban and nonurban locations in every State on a year-round basis. A gas-sampling program is now also included at 50 of these stations. Since 1962 more complete data are being obtained by continuous automatic sampling and recording equipment located in eight cities.

Extensive investigation into the meteorological aspects of air pollution has accompanied other research activities of the Public Health Service. This has been accomplished through the closest possible cooperation of the Weather Bureau, with a number of its personnel being stationed in the Public Health Service laboratories. Research has been conducted on the relationships of meteorological variables to air quality, the diffusion of pollutants, and the effects of topography, vegetation, and structures on temperature and wind. Meteorological research has made it feasible to establish a nationwide program by which air pollution potential is forecast, with telegraphic warnings being sent to appropriate State and local officials when indicated.

Biomedical research has likewise been extensive and productive. Population surveys have provided meaningful data on many relationships of air pollutants to sickness or death.

In laboratories and hospitals, the mechanisms of response to pollutants have been studied and biochemical, physiological, and pathological measurements of reactions have been made. Studies have been made with a variety of toxic materials, with cancer-producing agents, and with allergens.

In addition to the effects on animal life, related research on vegetation has likewise been carried on, in close cooperation with the Department of Agriculture.

Technical Assistance

An extension of knowledge of air pollution has also been gained through such technical assistance activities of the Public Health Service as field surveys, demonstration grants, and short-term assistance to State and local agencies on special projects.

The primary objective of the technical assistance program, however, is to help in the establishment or strengthening of State and local air pollution control agencies. Such aid is rendered in a variety

of ways, dependent upon the specific situation. Since the inaugura-
tion of the Federal program, major technical assistance projects of
the Public Health Service have included 8 major field investigations,
16 statewide surveys and some assistance in 4 other State surveys, 12
local surveys to provide a basis for program initiation, and 32 short-
term technical studies of limited scope. In a number of instances,
personnel have been loaned to States or communities for periods of
up to 2 years. The locations and nature of such services are tabulated as follows:

MAJOR FIELD INVESTIGATIONS (APRIL 1955 TO MAY 1963)
1. Louisville-Jefferson County, Ky.
2. Nashville-Davidson County, Tenn.
3. Lewiston, Idaho-Clarkston, Wash.
4. New York-New Jersey area (in cooperation with the Interstate
   Sanitation Commission)
5. Jacksonville-Duval County, Fla.
6. Berlin, N.H.
7. Detroit-Wayne County, Mich.-Windsor area, Ontario (International
   Joint Commission) (continuing at limited level)
8. Interstate St. Louis Metropolitan area (in progress)

STATEWIDE AIR POLLUTION SURVEYS (APRIL 1955 TO MAY 1963)

1. Washington	9. Florida
2. Connecticut	10. Georgia
3. Tennessee	11. South Dakota
4. Texas	12. Colorado
5. New York	13. Kansas
6. North Carolina	14. Oklahoma (in progress)
7. Minnesota	15. Mississippi (scheduled)
8. Pennsylvania	16. South Carolina (scheduled)

Assistance was also given to conduct of statewide surveys in
California, Illinois, Montana, and Utah but main responsibility
rested with the respective States.

LOCAL SURVEYS (APRIL 1955 TO MAY 1963)
Surveys conducted primarily to provide a basis for program
initiation:

1. Portland, Ore.
2. Steubenville, Ohio
3. Denver area, Colo.
4. Birmingham, Ala.
5. Salt Lake Valley, Utah
6. Elmira, N.Y.

7. Charleston, S.C.
8. Hamilton, Ohio
9. Lynchburg, Va.
10. Washington, D.C. area
11. Spartanburg, S.C.
12. Dade County, Fla.

LOCAL TECHNICAL STUDIES OF LIMITED SCOPE (APRIL 1955 TO MAY 1963)

1. Short-term air quality measurement demonstrations done largely by PHS but with local participation:

(a) Phoenix, Ariz.
(b) Tucson, Ariz.
(c) Fresno, Calif.
(d) Washington, D.C.
(e) Birmingham, Ala.
(f) Richmond, Va.

(g) Providence, R.I.
(h) Spartanburg, S.C.
(i) Lynchburg, Va.
(j) Winston-Salem, N.C.
(k) Pittsburgh, Pa. (mobile laboratory)

2. Short-term technical studies done in conjunction with state-wide surveys:

(a) Atlanta, Ga.
(b) Minneapolis, Minn.
(c) St. Paul, Minn.
(d) Duluth, Minn.
(e) Fergus Falls, Minn.
(f) Asheville, N.C.
(g) Charlotte, N.C.

(h) Greensboro, N.C.
(i) Raleigh, N.C.
(j) Umstead Park, N.C.
(k) Kansas City, Kans.
(l) Topeka, Kans.
(m) Wichita, Kans.

3. Short-term technical studies done primarily to evaluate influence of specific sources of pollution (April 1955–April 1963).

(a) St. Bernard, Ohio
(b) Baccus, Utah

(c) Lexington, Ky.
(d) Galveston, Tex.

4. Short-term technical studies done primarily by other agencies but with substantial assistance from Division of Air Pollution:

(a) Denver, Colo.
(b) Hamilton, Ohio

(c) Wheeling-Weirton, W. Va.-Steubenville, Ohio area.
(d) El Paso, Tex.

LOAN OF PERSONNEL

Agencies to which Division of Air Pollution personnel were on loan 3 months or longer during calender year 1962:

Location	Purpose
California State Department of Public Health	Conduct studies of effects of carbon monoxide and lead on humans
Delaware State Board of Health	To establish air quality measurement program and to provide other support
Florida State Board of Health	To carry on program, to replace men who quit or had gone to school for further training
New York City	For training and orientation and to provide program support
San Francisco Bay Area, Air Pollution Control District	For training and orientation and to provide program support
New York State Air Pollution Control Board	For training and orientation and to provide program support
Oregon State Sanitary Authority	For training and orientation and to provide program support
Pennsylvania Division of Air Pollution Control	For training and orientation and to provide program support
Indiana State Board of Health	To help initiate new programs
Chicago Department of Air Pollution Control	Revise, rebuild, and prepare long-range plans for program; assist with technical studies
Metropolitan Washington, D.C.	Design, organize, and help operate oxidant sampling network

TRAINING COURSES

A major technical assistance function of the program is the training of personnel from State and local agencies, and also from industry. This is accomplished through a variety of short courses, usually of one or two weeks' duration, presented at the Robert A. Taft Sanitary Engineering Center in Cincinnati. These are supplemented by field courses presented in various convenient locations. Since inception of the training program in 1955, instruction has been given to 5,837 individuals through 116 presentations of 41 different courses. The nature of these courses is illustrated by the titles of those being presented during fiscal year 1964:

Sampling and Identification of Aero-Allergens
Elements of Air Quality Management
Control of Gaseous Emissions
Control of Particulate Emissions

Diffusion of Air Pollution, Theory and Application
Measurement of Airborne Radioactivity
Medical and Biological Aspects of Air Pollution
Microscopic Analysis of Atmospheric Particulates
Analysis of Atmospheric Inorganics
Analysis of Atmospheric Organics
Meteorological Aspects of Air Pollution
Atmospheric Survey
Design of Air Pollutant Sampling Trains
Source Sampling for Atmospheric Pollutants
Orientation in Air Pollution

TRAINING GRANTS

More extensive training at graduate level at a number of universities is also now being provided through training grants to these institutions and to some of their students. As of August 1, 1963, a total of $576,408 in training grants had been allocated during fiscal year 1964 to the following institutions:

University of Cincinnati	University of Michigan
University of Minnesota	University of Pittsburg
Harvard University	West Virginia University
University of Florida	University of Illinois
New York University	University of Southern California
University of North Carolina	Vanderbilt University

As of August 1, 1963, a total of $110,656 had been allocated during fiscal year 1964 for fellowships at the following schools:

Auburn University	Washington University, St. Louis, Mo.
California Institute of Technology	Columbia University
University of California at Riverside	Clarkson College of Technology, Potsdam, N.Y.
Massachusetts Institute of Technology	University of Cincinnati
University of Michigan	Ohio State University
University of Minnesota	University of Texas

Applications from other institutions for training grants and fellowships are under review on the expectation that a total of $1 million may be appropriated for those purposes.

Interagency Cooperation

Approximately 10 percent of the funds authorized for the Public Health Service, exclusive of moneys for research and training grants, goes into contracts with other Federal agencies for the conduct of air pollution research.

During 1963, (1) the Weather Bureau received $266,000 for meteorological studies of dispersal of community air pollution; (2) the Bureau of Mines $450,000 for a number of projects on sulfur dioxide removal from flue gas, desulfurization of fuel oil, pollutants from power station boilers, and removal of pollutants from motor vehicle exhaust; (3) the National Bureau of Standards' $125,000 for research on various aspects of chemical reactions and analytical procedures, (4) the Department of Agriculture $25,000 for research on agricultural effects of air pollution; and (5) the Library of Congress $12,550 for technical abstracts on air pollution.

A number of Federal agencies have interests in fundamental properties of either the upper or lower atmosphere. The research which they conduct often has some relationship to the subject of air pollution but, since air pollution is only incidental to the primary purpose of such research, it is not included in the foregoing discussion. Agencies engaged in such work include AEC, NASA, FAA, NSF, and the Departments of Defense, Commerce, Interior, and Agriculture. The Public Health Service maintains appropriate liaison with these agencies through the Interdepartmental Committee on Atmospheric Sciences of the Federal Council on Science and Technology.

STATE, LOCAL, AND NONGOVERNMENTAL PROGRAMS

In 1947 California adopted a statute authorizing the formation of county air pollution control districts. Oregon, in 1951, passed a law creating an air pollution study and control program. Since that time, many States have adopted air pollution legislation of some kind.

Inquiries by Senate Public Works Committee

On April 30, 1963, Senator Pat McNamara, chairman of the Senate Public Works Committee, sent letters to the Governors of all the States and territories requesting them to answer a set of questions on the status of air pollution control legislation in their respective jurisdictions and soliciting their opinions on certain proposed Federal activities in the field. By August 15 replies had been received from all but three of the States.

The questions asked by Senator McNamara were as follows:

1. "Does your State have air pollution control laws? If so, would you give a brief digest of their principal provisions?"

2. "If your State does not have air pollution control laws, is it contemplated that such laws may be enacted?"

3. "Do you have air quality standards and emission standards? If so, what measures are taken to obtain enforcement or compliance?"

4. "Do you have air pollution problems in your State which arise from sources outside your State? If so, do you have agreements with neighboring State or States to deal with the problem, and what provisions are made to handle the matter?"

5. "Does your State have a State-financed program of air pollution control research?"

6. "Would it be helpful to your State if the Department of Health, Education, and Welfare would recommend air quality standards and emission standards and assist in obtaining compliance with such standards?"

7. "General suggestions on how to cope with air pollution."

Supplemental information regarding State air pollution laws was also obtained from the Public Health Service, including information about the three States which had not replied to the questions. A detailed summary of the replies received, together with a digest of State air pollution laws, is presented in supplement I.

Briefly, 33 of the States and territories have some type of air pollution control laws and 18 do not. Fifteen have some control authority. Twelve have no control authority, but have local option legislation. Six provide only research and technical assistance. Of the 18 having no air pollution control laws, 10 indicated some interest in promoting such legislation. Three have studies of the problem underway, and 5 have made unsuccessful efforts to pass air pollution control legislation.

The States of California and Oregon have established air quality and emission standards which are enforced on a local or statewide basis. California also has motor vehicle emission standards. New York is in the process of establishing air quality standards and the establishment of such standards is authorized in seven States. Four States have emission standards for one or a few pollutants.

Nineteen units report having air pollution problems originating outside their jurisdiction, while twenty-nine report none so originating. Six States have formal or semiformal mechanisms dealing with interstate air pollution problems. Five States have made some attempt to cope with this problem by working along informal, cooperative lines.

Ten States have legislation authorizing air pollution control research, but only three conduct fairly extensive programs.

With respect to the Department of Health, Education, and Welfare recommending air quality standards, 37 States approve, 1 approves with qualifications, and 12 disapprove. Concerning emission standards recommendations from the Department, 33 approve, 1 approves with qualifications, and 14 disapprove.

With respect to the suggestion of Federal participation in the enforcement of air pollution control standards, 19 approve but 9 of these had qualifications, and 23 disapprove.

Budgetary Support for State and Local Programs

In 1961, the most recent year for which reasonably complete figures are available, only 17 States were spending as much as $5,000 per year on air pollution programs (table 2). Of the total expenditure of $2 million, 57 percent was spent by the State of California.

In 1961, there were 85 local agencies budgeting at least $5,000 per year each for air pollution control (table 3). Of their total expenditure of 8 million, 55 per cent was spent in California in seven local units, with the Los Angeles County Air Pollution Control District accounting for over 41 per cent of the money spent by local agencies throughout the United States. On a per capita basis Los Angeles spent 57 cents. The median expenditure for the 85 local programs was 10.8 cents per capita. The Division of Air Pollution of the Public Health Service reports that a satisfactory air pollution control program for a community with average present-day problems requires an annual expenditure of at least 40 cents per capita.

TABLE 2. *State air pollution programs, 1961 (those spending $5,000 per year or more)*

State	Land area (1,000 square miles)	(millions) Population 1960	Type of program [1]	Budget, fiscal year 1961	Personnel 1961
California	157	15.7	Technical assistance and research	$661,000	45
			Motor vehicle pollution control	500,000	17
Colorado	104	1.8	Technical assistance	10,000	[2] 4
Connecticut	5	2.5	do	7,200	1
Delaware	2	.4	Comprehensive	[3] 18,000	1
Florida Special district	54	5.0	Technical assistance throughout state	12,000	1
			Comprehensive in Polk-Hillsborough Counties.	50,600	7
Hawaii	6	.6	Comprehensive	10,000	2
Maryland	10	3.1	Conduct studies	37,700	3
Massachusetts Metropolitan Boston	8	5.1	Comprehensive	20,000	1½
			Regulatory program operated by the State	52,000	8
Michigan	58	7.8	Technical assistance and studies	20,000	[2] 19
Minnesota	80	3.4	Technical assistance	5,000	[2] 2
New Jersey	8	6.1	Comprehensive	104,000	14
New York	48	16.8	do	228,220	20
Ohio	41	9.7	Technical assistance and studies	95,000	7
Oregon	96	1.8	Comprehensive	63,000	8
Pennsylvania	45	11.3	do	60,000	9
Texas	264	9.6	Technical assistance and studies	[3] 22,800	{ 1 [2] 4
Washington	67	2.9	do	24,000	3
TOTAL		103.6		2,039,920	{ 148 [2] 29

1. Comprehensive includes regulation (control), technical assistance, studies, etc.
2. Part-time.
3. 1959 estimate.

TABLE 3. *Local air pollution control programs (with annual budget of $5,000 or more, Feb. 1, 1961)*

	Population 1960 (thousands)	Staff [1]	Budget (thousands)	Per capita budget (cents)	Staff per 100,000 population
Agencies with budgets of $25,000 or more per year:					
1. San Francisco Bay area, California	3,364	31.0	$560	16.7	0.9
2. Los Angeles County, Calif	5,970	373.0	3,402	57.0	6.3
3. Orange County, Calif	698	11.0	117	16.8	1.6

	Population 1960 (thousands)	Staff	Budget (thousands)	Per capita budget (cents)	Staff per 100,000 population
4. Sacramento County, Calif.[2]	500	4.0	50	10.0	.8
5. San Bernardino County, Calif	498	8.0	[2] 259	52.0	1.6
6. Riverside County, Calif	302	4.0	67	22.2	1.3
7. San Diego County, Calif	1,000	4.5	79	7.9	.5
8. District of Columbia [3]	746	6.0	42	5.6	.8
9. Polk-Hillsborough Counties, Fla.[4]	592	4.0	50	8.5	.7
10. Chicago, Ill	3,512	42.0	364	10.4	1.5
11. Indianapolis, Ind	469	6.0	38	8.1	1.3
12. Jefferson County (Louisville), Ky	606	11.0	63	10.4	1.8
13. Baltimore, Md.[3]	922	10.0	70	7.6	1.1
14. Boston metropolitan district, Massachusetts [4]	1,998	8.0	52	2.6	.4
15. Detroit, Mich	1,654	20.0	180	10.9	1.2
16. St. Louis, Mo	747	13.0	118	15.8	1.7
17. Newark, N.J.[3]	403	10.0	63	15.6	2.5
18. Buffalo, N.Y.[3]	530	6.0	59	11.1	1.1
19. New York, N.Y	7,710	74.0	734	9.5	1.0
20. Niagara Falls, N.Y	102	3.0	28	27.4	2.9
21. Syracuse, N.Y	215	5.0	36	16.7	2.3
22. Cincinnati, Ohio (area) [3]	542	18.0	165	30.4	3.3
23. Cleveland, Ohio	870	23.0	236	27.1	2.6
24. Cleveland Heights, Ohio	62	4.0	28	45.3	6.5
25. Columbus, Ohio	469	7.0	50	10.7	1.5
26. Dayton, Ohio [3]	258	7.0	55	21.3	2.7
27. Allegheny County, Pa	1,629	18.0	217	13.3	1.1
28. Philadelphia, Pa	1,971	23.0	166	8.4	1.2
29. Providence, R.I.[3]	206	8.0	31	15.0	3.9
30. Knoxville, Tenn.[3]	110	2.0	25	22.7	1.8
31. Harris County, Tex.[3]	1,243	6.0	42	3.4	.5
32. Salt Lake City, Utah	189	4.0	30	15.8	2.0
33. Richmond, Va	218	4.0	25	11.4	1.8
34. Milwaukee County, Wis	733	15.0	128	17.5	2.1
TOTAL OR MEDIAN FOR GROUP	40,929	802.5	7,629	14.1	1.6

Agencies with budgets of less than
$25,000 per year:

1. Birmingham, Ala	341	2.0	12	3.5	.6
2. Denver, Colo	494	2.0	15	3.1	.4
3. Dade County, Fla	935	[5] 1.0	5	.5	

	Popula-tion 1960 (thou-sands)	Staff	Budget (thou-sands)	Per capita budget (cents)	Staff per 100,000 popula-tion
4. Atlanta, Ga	485	1	13	2.7	.2
5. Cicero, Ill	69	[5] 1.0	5	7.2	
6. Peoria, Ill	103	1.0	8	7.8	1.0
7. East Chicago, Ind	58	1.0	11	19.3	1.7
8. Evansville, Ind	140	1.0	10	7.2	.7
9. Des Moines, Ia.[3]	208	[5] 2.0	11	5.3	
10. McCracken County (Paducah), Ky	57	1.0	12	20.9	1.8
11. Dearborn, Mich	112	[5] 2.0	5	4.5	
12. Grand Rapids, Mich	175	[5] 2.0	6	3.4	
13. Monroe, Mich	23	1.0	6	26.1	4.3
14. Wayne County, Mich	2,666	1.5	20	.8	.06
15. Minneapolis, Minn	478	1.0	11	2.3	.2
16. Omaha, Nebr	300	2.0	20	6.7	.7
17. Camden, N.J	125	1.0	7	5.6	.8
18. Hillside Township, N.J	21	[5] 3.0	5	23.8	
19. Perth Amboy, N.J	38	1.0	13	34.2	2.6
20. Trenton, N.J	114	1.0	5	4.4	.9
21. Illion, N.Y	10	1.0	5	49.0	1.0
22. Rochester, N.Y	316	1.0	10	3.2	.03
23. Tonawanda, N.Y	84	2.0	15	17.9	2.4
24. Watertown, N.Y	33	1.0	7	21.2	3.0
25. Asheville, N.C	59	3.0	16	27.2	5.1
26. Charlotte, N.C	201	2.0	19	9.5	1.0
27. Winston-Salem, N.C	111	2.0	12	10.8	1.8
28. Akron, Ohio	288	2.0	16	5.6	.7
29. East Cleveland, Ohio	38	1.0	7	18.4	2.6
30. Sandusky, Ohio	32	1.0	7	21.9	3.1
31. Toledo, Ohio	316	2.0	12	3.8	.6
32. Youngstown, Ohio	166	2.0	17	10.3	1.2
33. Zanesville, Ohio	39	1.0	5	12.8	2.6
34. Eugene, Oreg	50	1.0	10	20.0	2.0
35. Portland, Oreg	371	1.0	17	4.6	.3
36. Erie, Pa	138	2.0	15	10.8	1.5
37. Lehigh Valley, Pa. (area)	278	1.0	14	5.0	.4
38. East Providence, R.I	42	1.0	8	19.1	2.4
39. Pawtucket, R.I	81	1.0	5	6.3	1.2
40. Columbia, S.C	96	1.0	6	6.3	1.0
41. Chattanooga, Tenn.[3]	128	2.0	16	12.5	1.6
42. Kingsport, Tenn	26	1.0	7	26.6	3.9
43. Memphis, Tenn.[3]	492	2.0	13	2.6	.4
44. Nashville, Tenn	167	2.0	13	7.9	1.2
45. Roanoke, Va	97	1.0	11	11.4	1.0
46. Seattle, Wash	552	1.0	12	2.2	.2
47. Tacoma, Wash	147	1.0	8	5.4	.7
48. Wheeling, W. Va	53	2.0	17	32.1	3.8
49. Fond du Lac, Wis.[3]	33	1.0	7	21.4	3.0

		Popula-tion 1960 (thou-sands)	Staff	Budget (thou-sands)	Per capita budget (cents)	Staff per 100,000 popula-tion
50.	Green Bay, Wis.[3]	63	1.0	7	11.2	1.6
51.	Madison, Wis	126	2.0	14	11.1	1.6
	TOTAL OR MEDIAN FOR GROUP	10,475	73.5	548	7.8	1.0
	TOTAL OR MEDIAN FOR ALL AGENCIES	51,404	876.0	8,177	10.8	1.3

1. Not including clerical personnel.
2. 1960 fiscal year.
3. Staff believed to spend considerable time on work other than air pollution.
4. Operated by the State in which located.
5. Part time.

State Efforts

The scope and nature of State programs vary considerably. Depending on the exact meaning given the word "enforcement," four to six States "enforce" air pollution regulations. More common activities are technical assistance and development of local programs. Six or more States do air quality monitoring on a statewide basis, and about the same number review and approve plans for certain installations which may cause air pollution. In New York, plans for some installations, prior to construction, must be approved by the State air pollution control board or by qualified local agencies. California has established a program for the purpose of limiting emissions from motor vehicles, and New York has followed suit to the extent of legislating for the purpose of preventing emissions from crankcases.

Among other activities of State programs are training, dissemination of information, nuisance abatement, laboratory services for local agencies, studies of pollutant emissions, and research of various types. Due to limited budgets, only a few States can engage in many of these various activities to a meaningful extent. In the 17 States having programs in 1961, the average annual expenditure for air pollution control was only 2 cents per capita, and the median was 1.2 cents. The total full-time personnel employed for such work was 148, with 29 others being engaged on a part-time basis.

Local Programs

Nine States have adopted laws which authorize cities or counties to operate air pollution control agencies with authority transcending municipal boundaries or to otherwise undertake interlocal cooperation. Thus the 85 local air pollution control agencies serve more than 85 communities. For example, the San Francisco Bay Area Air Pollution Control District serves 89 urban places of various sizes. However, of 218 urban places with more than 50,000 population which have a major or moderate air pollution problem, only 119, or 55 per cent, are served by a control agency. Table 4 shows the numbers of communities of various population classes receiving services from agencies appropriating $5,000 or more per year for air pollution control. As indicated in footnote (^{1}), no consideration of program adequacy is given.

In local agencies, in contradistinction to most State programs, there is greater emphasis on control and abatement activities. An important aspect of this is prevention of new sources of excessive pollution. This is attempted by registration or permit systems for new installations. Under such systems the air pollution agency must be given notice of new installations of equipment which may discharge pollution. This eliminates the necessity of searching them out. In some instances plans for the installation may be required before the permit is issued. However, only about three-fourths of the agencies serving communities of 200,000 or more population provide for plan review, and many of these only review plans for combustion equipment and do not review plans for other process equipment which may cause air pollution. In smaller communities only about one-third of the control agencies do plan reviews. Thus many new sources of pollution are constantly developing even in localities where control programs exist. It can be added, also, that abatement or elimination of existing sources is generally more difficult than the prevention of new ones.

Enforcement is not the only approach used by local control

agencies. Many, some to a large degree, attempt to obtain corrections by education and persuasion.

Some local agencies do monitoring of the air to determine concentrations of pollutants, but the majority lack the funds, equipment, or qualified personnel to obtain such basic essential informa-

TABLE 4. *Urban places served by a local air pollution control agency*

[Places with 2,500 or more people; agencies spending $5,000 per year or more]

Population class	Number of places in class (1960)	Number of places with major or moderate air pollution problem (from table 1)	Places served by local air pollution control agency [1]		Per cent of places with major or moderate problem [3]
			Number [2]	Per cent of total	
1,000,000 or more	5	5	5	100	100
500,000 to 1,000,000	16	16	13	81	81
250,000 to 500,000	30	27	20	67	74
100,000 to 250,000	81	60	32	40	53
50,000 to 100,000	201	110	49	24	45
25,000 to 50,000	432	151	80	19	52
10,000 to 25,000	1,134	318	[4] 125	11	39
5,000 to 10,000	1,394	210	[4] 93	7	44
2,500 to 5,000	2,152	258	[4] 80	4	31
TOTAL	5,445	1,155	497	9	43

1. Does not include urban places served by State agencies except Polk-Hillsborough County, Fla., and the Boston metropolitan area. No consideration given to whether the agency is adequate to cope with the problem. Many are not.

2. Larger than number of agencies because some areas serve many urban places, e.g., Los Angeles County Air Pollution Control District.

3. Urban places with control agency and with major or moderate problem not necessarily the same. Percentages given in this column are too high by an unknown amount.

4. All but 3 of these urban places of less than 25,000 population are served by county or district programs.

tion. Part of this problem arises from the low salary schedules common in such agencies. A recent survey revealed the median annual salary for engineers in city air pollution control agencies to be $2,200 less than the median for all engineers, as reported by the National Science Foundation.

Since many local programs were originally directed only at

smoke control the personnel employed were often selected for their knowledge of fuel firing practices. The more diverse and complex sources which now present the major problems are often outside their area of competence. In such situations there may be a natural inclination for them to concentrate efforts on only those problems which are familiar.

It has been estimated that the number of personnel in local air pollution control agencies increased about one-third between 1952 and 1961. California agencies in 1961 employed about 3.6 times as many people as in 1952. In 1961, there were 37 more local agencies than there were in 1952, but outside of the new agencies in California, only 5 employ more than 2 people. Also, during this period five local agencies were discontinued. It is evident that, except in California, little or no headway was made to bring the resources of local air pollution control agencies more into line during the past decade, while the urban population was increasing by 30 percent.

Nongovernmental Activities

In addition to the programs of official agencies, work of one kind or another in the field of air pollution is carried on or sponsored by other organizations, such as technical societies, industry associations, universities, and research institutes.

The widespread interest in air pollution is demonstrated by the many organizations which have committees working on various aspects of the problem. The Air Pollution Control Association, American Society of Mechanical Engineers, American Society for Testing Materials, American Industrial Hygiene Association, American Public Health Association, American Medical Association, National Tuberculosis Association, American Society of Civil Engineers, and American Association for the Advancement of Science are examples of technical and professional groups which are concerned about air pollution. Some of these finance research in air pollution as well as contributing through committee work.

Research is also sponsored by industry associations, such as American Petroleum Institute, National Coal Association, American Iron & Steel Institute, National Association for Stream Improvement (a pulp and paper industry organization), Manufacturing Chemists' Association, Edison Electric Institute, and Automobile Manufacturers Association.

Several of these groups are presently conducting or sponsoring cooperative projects with the Division of Air Pollution of the Public Health Service. Among these are the Edison Electric Institute, Automobile Manufacturers Association, Manufacturing Chemists' Association, and American Public Works Association.

In addition to research sponsored by industry or government, universities utilize some of their own funds for air pollution research. Some research institutes may also do some self-financed work in this field.

Organizations sponsoring research reported the following amounts being devoted to the support of 347 research projects in 1962:

Organizations supporting air pollution research	Number of projects	Funding (dollars)	Per cent of total
Universities	17	548,000	4
Federal agencies	227	8,866,000	62
State agencies	18	1,027,000	7
Local agencies	11	640,000	5
Industrial organizations	38	1,890,000	13
Private (nonindustrial)	11	386,000	3
Not classified	25	799,000	6
TOTALS	347	14,156,000	100

A total of 466 projects was reported in the foregoing survey, indicating that the total amount actually being devoted to air pollution research in 1962 may have been as much as $20 million.

STATUS OF PRESENT TECHNOLOGY

The Measurement of Air Quality

During the past decade we have learned a great deal about the kinds and amounts of pollution in the air. More information is steadily being obtained as improved sampling and analytical equipment are developed and put into use. The National Air Sampling Network operated by the Public Health Service, as shown in figure 6 has accumulated extensive data concerning the amounts and chemical composition of particulates in the air in approximately 250 localities. Nonurban as well as urban sampling stations in all 50 States and Puerto Rico are included in this program. State and local agencies participate, operating the filter samplers and sending the samples to Cincinnati for analysis by the Public Health Service. Weight, radio-activity, and soiling measurements are made, as well as comprehensive chemical analyses.

Several common gaseous pollutants are measured at some 50 of the network stations. Included are nitrogen dioxide, sulfur dioxide and oxidants. More elaborate and extensive gas sampling is being done with automatic, continuous recording equipment at stations located in Chicago, Cincinnati, Detroit, Los Angeles, New Orleans, New York, Philadelphia, San Francisco, and Washington. In addition to the three contaminants just mentioned, these stations measure nitric oxide, carbon monoxide, ozone and total hydrocarbons. While there are many other sources of these gases, all of them, except sulfur dioxide, provide important information about pollution from motor vehicles. The sulfur dioxide is a particularly good indicator of pollution from stationary sources of fuel combustion, as well as from certain industrial processes.

A similar mobile sampling station has recently been put into operation by the Public Health Service. In addition to collecting data in various communities, it enables local officials to learn about the operation of such equipment. Because of the expense of the necessary equipment and lack of trained personnel very few localities have obtained comprehensive data on their air quality. While the number is comparatively small, regular air quality monitoring is done by air pollution control agencies of several States and communities. California has probably the most extensive programs of this type. These have been developed over a number of years by the various district programs as well as by the State.

The usefulness of such monitoring is illustrated by an oxidant sampling network operated by the Metropolitan Washington Council of Governments since the fall of 1961. Despite the absence of heavy industry sources, this network has confirmed that photochemical smog is occurring in objectionable amounts on frequent occasions. Until a satisfactory solution to the motor vehicle pollution problem is achieved, the frequency and severity of these smogs will increase just as they did in Los Angeles. The same conclusion can be applied, of course, to virtually every large urban area.

Monitoring programs serve a variety of purposes. A newly established sulfur dioxide measuring network in Chicago will provide local authorities with valuable information about specific sources, as well as about seasonal variations and the influence of other factors.

Some industrial establishments conduct air monitoring programs in the vicinities of their own operations, but data thus obtained are not always available for general use.

Expanding Our Knowledge of Weather Effects

Advances in meteorology have broadened understanding of the forces promoting or restricting the dispersal of contaminants, and

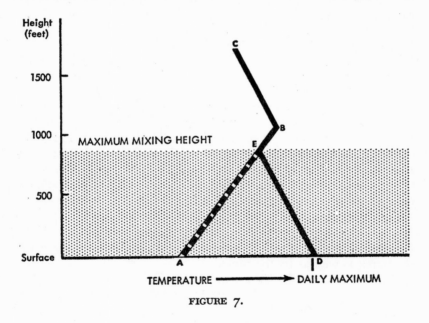

FIGURE 7.

have made it feasible to predict periods when these will accumulate in above normal amounts. Of vital significance, also, is the information which is being developed on the limitations of the atmosphere's ability to dilute pollution. The total mixing or absorptive capacity of the atmosphere over broad geographic regions is of great importance in determining the adequacy of pollution control. Such capacity has distinct limitations which may persist for long periods of time. For example, in January the maximum atmospheric mixing depth throughout the United States is generally between 650 and 2,000 feet.

The maximum mixing depth (or height), as illustrated by figure 7, can be explained as follows: The lines AB and BC indicate the temperature changes with height, as measured during early morning. The direction in which AB slants shows that the temperature increases with height up to about 1,000 feet. This means that an inversion is present. Above that, the temperature decreases with increasing height, as indicated by the slant of BC. The point D shows the maximum temperature occurring later that day. The line DE is drawn to show a decrease in temperature of 5.4° F. per 1,000 feet of height. If, as it does in this case, that line intersects the measured temperature profile, the point of intersection indicates the maximum height to which pollution can rise until the inversion disappears. In the example shown, the maximum mixing height is at E, approximately 850 feet above the ground.

Under these circumstances, it is the quantity of pollutant discharge which directly determines the ground-level pollutant concentration downwind after mixing in this layer.

For example, the use of tall stacks has been an accepted and widely used control procedure. The objective is to provide a means for adequate dilution and dispersion of the effluent pollution before it can return to ground level. The trend toward larger combustion and processing installations brings with it the production of larger volumes of waste products to be discharged. With the increasing population and its more extensive use of land, the distances from large pollution sources to urban concentrations of people become shorter or disappear entirely. To cope with this, stacks of ever-increasing height have been built. Some already exceed 600 feet, and there are proposals now under consideration for stacks 800 feet high for the dispersal of sulfur dioxide from large powerplants.

The cost of building stacks increases markedly with increasing size and height. Precise relationships cannot be presented because of many variables. However, a special report of the recent Federal Power Commission National Power Survey estimates that stack costs for projected very large conventional steam-electric generating stations might approach $3 per kilowatt as compared with an average cost of $0.70 per kilowatt for present conventional installations involving stacks of 450 to nearly 700 feet for plants of 1,200,000 to 1,500,000 kilowatt capacity. Based on these figures, while the stack for a 1,500,000-kilowatt plant might cost approximately $1 million the stack for a plant of twice this capacity could cost 5 to 10 times as much.

Unfortunately, even with such large expenditures, the high stack may not be successful in serving its purpose.

While plumes from such installations, under favorable atmospheric conditions, will rise high into the air and not return to the ground for long distances, there are prolonged periods of time during which the available volume of diluting air is simply insufficient to satisfy the need. Tall stacks can contribute little in dealing with this situation.

The point emphasized by this is that there is often a limit to the total mass of pollution that the atmosphere can dilute satisfactorily even with the use of stacks much higher than any yet built.

Unsolved Problems

A major unsolved technical problem is how to find an economical way to prevent the discharge of sulfur dioxide from fossil fuels. There are two approaches. One is to remove the sulfur dioxide from the stack gases. The other is to remove the sulfur from the fuel before use. Thus far, only partial success has been obtained by either avenue. It is for this reason that high stacks have been so extensively used. Even considering only the economic aspects, however, the grossly greater costs of higher stacks further emphasizes the importance of finding other ways to keep sulfur dioxide out of the air. The cost of preventing sulfur dioxide pollution may become an important factor in determining the extent to which nuclear powerplants will be able to compete with conventional plants during the coming decades.

Another major air pollution problem still lacking a satisfactory solution is emissions from motor vehicles. Despite accelerated research activities on the problem, stimulated by California legislation aimed at reducing vehicular pollution, fundamental technical questions need resolution before a satisfactory solution on a national basis is likely to be achieved.

What Can Be Done?

Despite these and other problems needing further research, our technology has reached the stage where widespread application of proven control principles could bring about a profound reduction of pollution from most of our problem sources, with a great improvement in the overall situation in many communities and areas.

Granting that further research will improve efficiencies and reduce costs, effective and reasonably economical control measures are available and in successful use for many types of pollution now being discharged. Particulate pollutant removal is accomplished by devices employing such principles as filtration, electrostatic precipitation, and centrifugal force. Liquid scrubbing, vapor recovery, combustion, and solid adsorption are examples of principles used for reducing gaseous pollution. Both gaseous and particulate pollution can sometimes be reduced through improved plant design, operating procedures, and proper maintenance of equipment.

Cost

At the 1962 National Conference on Air Pollution, figures were presented, table 5, showing examples of the cost of various types of air pollution controls which have been installed in Los Angeles County during the past few years. In some cases, the cost of control equipment was but a small fraction of the cost of the production equipment. In other instances, the cost of the control equipment was greater than the cost of the basic equipment.

TABLE 5. *Typical costs of basic and control equipment installed in Los Angeles County*

Source	Size of equipment	Cost of basic equipment	Type of control equipment	Cost of control equipment
Airblown asphalt system	500 barrels per batch	$10,500	Afterburner	$3,000
Asphalt concrete batching plant	200,000 pounds per hour	150,000	Scrubber	10,000

Source	Size of equipment	Cost of basic equipment	Type of control equipment	Cost of control equipment
Asphalt saturator	6 by 65 by 8 feet	40,000	Scrubber and electric precipitator	50,000
Asphalt tile production	5,000 pounds per hour	150,000	Baghouse	5,000
Borax drying and classifying	10,000 pounds per hour	1,000,000	Baghouse and scrubber	10,000
Bulk gasoline loading rack	667,000 gallons per day	88,000	Vapor control system	50,000
Carbon black plant	2,000 gallons per day	5,000	Baghouse	5,000
Catalytic reforming unit	2,400 barrels per day	265,000	Flare and sour water oxidizer	6,000
Ceramic tile production	8,000 pounds per hour	200,000	Scrubber	10,000
Chip dryer, aluminum	2,500 pounds per hour	3,000	Afterburner	3,000
Chrome plating	4 by 5 by 5 feet	2,000	Scrubber	800
Coffee roaster	3 tons per hour	35,000	Cyclone and afterburner	8,000
Concrete batching plant	900,000 pounds per hour	125,000	Baghouse	10,000
Core oven	8 by 8 by 12 feet	4,000	Afterburner	1,500
Crucible furnace, yellow brass	4 furnaces at 850 pounds each, heat	[1] 2,500	Baghouse	17,000
Crude oil distillation unit	37,000 barrels per hour	3,060,000	Vapor control system	10,000
Cupola, gray iron	48 inches inside diameter	40,000	Baghouse and quench tank	67,000
	27 inches inside diameter	25,000	do	32,000
Debonder	500 brake shoes per hour	1,800	Afterburner	300
Deep fat fryer, food	1,000 pounds per hour	15,000	do	1,500
Delayed coker unit	9,300 barrels per day	4,000,000	Scrubber (serving 3 cokers)	385,000
Drum reclamation incinerator	60 barrels per hour	10,000	Afterburner	2,000
	200 barrels per hour	25,000	do	5,000
Electric arc furnace, steel	18 tons, heat	75,000	Baghouse	45,000
Electric induction furnace, brass	2,000 pounds per hour	75,000	do	2,700
Enamel frit drying	1,500 pounds per hour	25,000	do	3,000

Source	Size of equipment	Cost of basic equipment	Type of control equipment	Cost of control equipment
Fiberboard produc-tion	32,000 pounds per hour	10,000	Electric pre-cipitator	15,000
Fire-retardant manu-facturing	1,000 pounds per	25,000	Baghouse	2,000
Fixed roof storage tank for gasoline	80,000 barrels	50,000	New floating roof tank	132,000
Flue-fed incinerator	Most sizes	4,000–7,000	Afterburner	2,500
Fluid catalytic crack-ing unit	40,000 barrels per day	7,460,000	Electric pre-cipitator	1,040,000
			CO boiler	1,770,000
			Cyclones	165,000
			Blowdown systems, vapor man-ifold, and flare	363,000
	7,400 barrels per day	1,747,500	Electric pre-cipitator, vapor mani-fold, and flare	131,000
Galvanizing kettle	4 by 30 by 4 feet	25,000	Baghouse	3,000
Gritblasting machine	6 cubic feet	9,300	do	1,700
Insecticide manu-facturing	1,000 pounds per hour	10,000	do	3,000
Insulation produc-tion, including cupola, blow chamber, and cur-ing oven	5,000 pounds per hour	13,000	Baghouse, scrubber, and after-burner	30,000
Liquid hydrogen manufacturing	32 tons per year	8,392,000	Flare	17,700
Lithographing oven	240 feet per min-ute	78,000	Afterburner	15,000
Multiple-chamber incinerator, indus-trial and commer-cial	50 pounds per hour	800		
	500 pounds per hour	6,500		
	6,000 pounds per hour	75,000		
Multiple-chamber incinerator, patho-logical	50 pounds per hour	1,000		
	200 pounds per hour	4,500		
Multiple-chamber incinerator, wire reclamation	100 pounds per hour	1,200		
	1,000 pounds per hour	15,000		

Source	Size of equipment	Cost of basic equipment	Type of control equipment	Cost of control equipment
Multiple-chamber incinerator, with continuous feed	250 pounds per hour	5,000		
bin	3,000 pounds per hour	45,000		
Natural gas plant	20,000,000 cubic feet per day	220,000	Vapor manifold and flare	5,000
Oil-water separator	300,000 barrels per day	170,000	Floating roof	80,000
	350 barrels per day	17,000	Cover	700
	3,500 barrels per day	32,000	Floating roof	8,000
Open hearth furnace, steel	60 tons, heat	200,000	Electric precipitator	150,000
Phosphate fertilizer production	2,000 pounds per hour	10,000	Baghouse	5,000
Phthalic anhydride manufacturing plant	25,000,000 pounds per year	1,200,000	Afterburner and baghouse	195,000
Pipe coating, including spinning, wrapping, and dipping	4–10 lengths per hour	23,500	Scrubbers	32,000
Pneumatic conveyors (minerals)	200 to 5,000 pounds per hour	2,000	Cyclone and baghouse	2,000
Pot furnace, type metal	16,000 pounds	9,000	Afterburner	3,000
Rendered grease processing	6 tons per day	10,000	Contact condenser and afterburner	2,500
Rendering cooker and drier (batch)	4 tons per batch	10,000	Surface condenser and afterburner	15,000
Rendering cooker system (continuous)	15 tons per hour	100,000	do	25,000
Rock crushing and sizing	300,000 pounds per hour	75,000	Scrubber	2,000
Rotogravure press	5-color, 44-inch web	340,000	Activated carbon filter	40,000
Rubber Banbury mixer	1,000 pounds per hour	25,000	Baghouse	3,000
Sandblast room	8 by 12 by 8 feet	1,600	do	3,000
Sewage treatment digestion	900,000 gallons per day	800,000	Water seals and flares	7,000
Sewage treatment headworks	250,000,000 gallons per day	550,000	Covers	20,000

Source	Size of equipment	Cost of basic equipment	Type of control equipment	Cost of control equipment
Sewage water reclamation	17,000,000 gallons per day	1,500,000	Covers and aeration tanks	25,000
Sewer pipe manufacturing	20,000 pounds per hour	1,000,000	Baghouse	10,000
Ship bulk loading	2,500 tons per hour	500,000	do	168,000
Smoke generator and smokehouse	11 by 14 by 11 feet	18,000	Precipitator, scrubber, and afterburner	42,000
Sulfuric acid plant	250 tons per day	1,900,000	Electrostatic precipitator	150,000
Sulfur recovery plant	2 parallel units, 65 tons per day, each	1,400,000	Incinerator	30,000
	10 tons per day	265,000	do	5,000
	2,840 pounds per day	30,000	do	1,000
	8,000 pounds per day	60,000	do	1,000
Sweat furnace, aluminum	3,000 pounds per hour	3,500	Afterburner and baghouse	3,500
Synthetic rubber manufacturing	30,000 tons per year	1,600,000	Vapor manifold and flare	250,000
Synthetic solvent dry cleaner	60 pounds per batch	14,000	Activated carbon and filter	3,000
Varnish cookers (2)	250 gallons each	4,000	Afterburner	5,500
Wallboard production	60,000 pounds per hour	1,500,000	Baghouse	100,000

1. Each.

The true price of control equipment is often difficult to determine. In some cases, the control system is tied into production changes. In others, the equipment serves to reclaim valuable materials which had been escaping. In still others, the controls are an integral part of a new installation and their cost cannot be accurately estimated.

Further research and experience with existing control systems will lead to greater collecting efficiencies and lower costs. The evidence is conclusive, however, that in the great majority of situations, where required, the technical know-how exists.

Solutions also exist for many important nonindustrial sources of air pollution. Open-burning dumps, the use of inadequate municipal incinerators, leaf burning, the open burning of scrapped automobiles, insulated wires, battery cases and tires—all of these can be controlled.

Increasingly widespread enforcement of smoke-abatement ordinances has proved that smoke pollution from domestic, commercial, and industrial incinerators, boilers, and heating systems can be largely eliminated. Accomplishing this may require limitations on permissible fuel quality, improved stoking and combustion equipment, and education as to proper firing practices.

STANDARDS FOR
AIR POLLUTION CONTROL

Attempts to set standards to limit the release of pollutants into the atmosphere have traditionally followed an empirical approach, based on the dual considerations of engineering feasibility and economic acceptability. Following this course, air pollution control programs in several of the larger American cities have developed emission limitations which affect for the most part the more obvious sources of smoke and, to a lesser degree, other sources of particulate pollution. Admittedly crude, but practical, techniques for measuring the output of visible pollutants were developed for purposes of enforcement—the most widely employed being the Ringelmann chart, a graduated spectrum against which the density of particulate pollution from a single source is estimated.

At the same time, standards were established to regulate the use of fuels to help curtail the release into the air of smoke, fly ash, and other particulate pollutants. To the extent that some of these regulations limited the use of fuels with high sulfur content, gaseous emissions in the form of oxides of sulfur were also somewhat curtailed.

These standards were applied to individual sources of pollution but, as sources multiplied and the entire picture of source emissions became more complex, it became apparent that emission limitations which were applied only to certain obvious sources were inadequate for effectively insuring the quality of the ambient air in an entire community.

In many cases the techniques and procedures employed to determine and enforce emission limitations were considered objectionable by the those officially responsible for the control of air pollution as well as by those responsible for the sources subject to such control.

These considerations have led to the recognition that an arbitrary approach to the development of air quality standards would have to give way to a rational approach that is based not only on the readily attainable but also—in terms of known and suspected effects of air pollution—on what is necessary for the protection of human health and welfare.

An organized scientific appraisal of the medical, social, and economic problems posed by air pollution has been underway for only about a decade. Most State and local control agencies have not yet determined the dimensions of their air pollution problems and have not adequately controlled many obvious sources of pollution. Nevertheless, the basic question of to what degree air must be cleaned must be answered. While the question is simple, the answer, which involves inevitably the promulgation of air quality standards, is complex.

Whether or not the lack of ambient air quality standards has seriously hindered the progress of control efforts, there is merit in the arguments of those who contend that, in the absence of standards, control programs are obliged to work partly in the dark and that those responsible for source emissions lack firm goals toward which to strive. The rational approach to air quality control would involve, first, a determination of the degree of ambient air quality desired; second, ambient air standards to determine the degree and kinds of control effort needed to insure adequate air quality; and, third, the development and enforcement of emission limitations to insure that individual sources are sufficiently curtailed so that emissions from the aggregate of sources do not exceed any provision of the ambient air standards.

Ambient air standards can most realistically be developed with reference to air quality guidelines in the form of air quality criteria, developed in the light of the best available technological and scientific judgments. In the development of air quality criteria, consideration is given to the dual factors of pollution concentrations and exposure times as these in combination cause specific effects on man, animals, vegetation, and other aspects of the environment. There are many kinds of such effects to be considered—including health, sensory irritation, and damage to animals, to ornamental plants, and to agricultural crops. In addition, consideration must be given to such matters as reduction of visibility, soiling and corrosion of fabrics, metals, and other materials, and possible effects on weather.

The same concentrations of specific biologically active pollutants are, in general, no less hazardous in one city than another, no matter to what extent the air pollution problems may differ in other aspects. Therefore, it is appropriate that State and local agencies look to the Federal Government for guidance which the Federal Government can provide by developing air quality criteria. The Federal air pollution program has the resources, the experience, and the perspective to provide national leadership in this area as it has in air pollution research, technical assistance, training, and information dissemination. The Federal program should develop and promulgate air quality criteria formulated upon the best knowledge available today and subject to review and modification as new knowledge dictates. These criteria would constitute comprehensive guides to which local and State agencies would refer in establishing their ambient air standards.

Standards for public protection have been successfully developed in many areas of modern industrialized life. Standards for the purity of foods and drugs and for water have resulted both from a recognized need and from the fact that these materials can be made safe for use before they reach the individual whose health depends upon their purity. While the need for standards in air has also recently become recognized, the fact that the community air cannot be treated or purified prior to use underscores the importance of the proper control of sources of pollution. Water taken from virtually any river would be dangerous to drink if it were not purified before use. The intake of air pollutants, on the other hand, which are present in the ambient atmosphere, cannot be avoided by the individual citizen.

The numbers, magnitudes, and types of sources, meteorological factors, and other variables affecting air quality in different geographic locations, vary considerably. These differences mean that emission limitations developed to insure air quality may differ somewhat from community to community and from State to State. For this reason, it is appropriate that local control agencies establish emission limitations in the light of local conditions.

In the case of interstate air pollution problems, ambient air quality standards developed by one community have a direct bearing on the quality of the air in an adjacent community located in another State.

In the event that standards established by a community are not sufficiently stringent to prevent damage to another community in a different State, it may be necessary to establish enforcement procedures to require compliance with adequate standards. In such cases the only recourse available in interstate pollution problems is through Federal legislation.

Because of imperfections in the status of scientific knowledge and changing technology ambient air standards should not be regarded as immutable. Control agencies will have to be sufficiently flexible in their regulatory activities to readily adapt to accepted air pollution criteria which will change in the light of new problems, new knowledge, and new opportunities for the control of air pollution.

There will be instances where some control agencies will find it desirable to establish ambient air standards that are considerably more stringent than those in other locations.

For example, a community in a resort area may determine that a degree of atmospheric clarity greater than that achieved by most cities is essential to its economic well-being. In such a case, it would no doubt establish emission limitations to insure a lower degree of visibility interference than might be required in other cities.

Only a small percentage of the States have statutory control programs, and most of these are very new and based on limited experience. With few exceptions—such as the States of California and Oregon, where a beginning has been made in the promulgation of air quality standards—most control programs are operating on a more or less arbitrary approach which tends to equate the acceptable with the readily attainable.

Air quality standards cannot be developed and applied effectively unless the control agency has detailed and continuing information about ambient air pollutant concentrations and about the sources of pollution in its area of jurisdiction. These data should be augmented by continuing information on the meteorology of the area. There are but few agencies currently able to arm themselves with such data because of budgetary and technical manpower insufficiencies. If the advantages of the rational approach to the control of air pollution are to be realized, these fundamental deficiencies in control agency financial support and staffing must be corrected.

A LOOK INTO THE FUTURE

It is obvious that current efforts are not on a scale adequate to contain air pollution even within its present unsatisfactory levels. The number of localities with significant problems, and the severity of such problems, are bound to increase with a steadily growing population, producing and consuming an ever-increasing amount of energy and products. The following table gives an estimate of the increase between 1950 and 1960 of the number of urban places with air pollution problems and of the population exposed.

Estimated increase in urban places with air pollution problems and people exposed to pollution (urban places of 2,500 or more population)

[Population in thousands]

Type of urban pollution problem and number of people exposed

Year	Major problem		Moderate problem		Minor problem		All problems	
	Number of places	Number of people	Number of places	Number of people	Number of places	Number of people	Number of places	Number of people
1950	224	36,710	636	22,450	1,407	21,920	2,267	81,080
1960	308	42,940	847	30,160	1,818	31,200	2,973	104,300
INCREASE, 1950–1960	84	6,230	211	7,710	411	9,280	706	23,220

The increase in population between 1960 and 1970 will be equal to the combined 1960 populations of the States of New York and California. At least 25 million more people, according to present trends, will be living in urban areas by 1970. The added pollution burden represented by this additional population, if inadequately controlled, could bring about a degeneration of air quality to the point where episodes of acute illness and even deaths were more than occasional. Accompanying this, undoubtedly, would be a continuation of the steadily increasing incidence of various types of chronic respiratory disease now being observed. Inevitably, the extent of damage to structures, crops, and other property would increase as well, with a decrease in area of land acceptable for residential, agricultural, or recreational use. This loss of land use is of great economic significance, since it increases the cost of the remaining acceptable land.

To prevent such a situation from developing, several courses of action merit consideration.

The expansion and acceleration of research efforts in all major aspects of the air pollution problem has been recommended as essential. Such recommendations have been recently emphasized in reports from several distinguished groups which have conducted detailed reviews and evaluations of national efforts to cope with the modern environment. Such groups, with representation from industry, State and local governments, and educational institutions, have included the National Academy of Sciences—National Research Council Committee on Atmospheric Sciences, the Surgeon General's Ad Hoc Task Group on Air Pollution Research Goals, and the Surgeon General's Committee on Environmental Health Problems. These reports point out the need and responsibilities for research by industry, and by States and communities, as well as by the Federal Government.

The development of air quality criteria deemed necessary to protect the public health and welfare is also required as a basis for selecting the standards to be employed. An important use of research findings will be in the formulation of such criteria.

In addition there is a need to strengthen the control programs of States and communities, since existing control authority rests solely with them. While there are exceptions, in general it can be said that such programs have three unsatisfied basic needs, which must be met in order to carry out their missions effectively: (1) sufficient funds and adequate salary scales, (2) appropriate adequate legal authority, and (3) public understanding and support.

Legislative proposals have been made to provide financial assistance to State and local air pollution control agencies through a Federal grants program. It is quite evident that budgetary support for the overwhelming majority of existing programs is completely inadequate. If the situation is allowed to deteriorate further the ultimate cost will be much greater.

Local jurisdictions do not always have the necessary authority to adopt such regulations as are needed to control pollution originating within their own boundaries. Even where they do, however, attainment of satisfactory air quality frequently requires control of pollution sources outside of the political boundaries of the community— sometimes even from another State. Solution of such problems requires, first and most importantly, a willingness to cooperate, on the part of the areas where such pollution arises, plus legal authority to establish necessary control powers in an existing agency or in a special one created for the desired purpose. The overall record, to date, on the control of multijurisdictional air pollution problems, has not been particularly encouraging.

Public understanding and support are essential for the successful control of the rapidly intensifying problems of air pollution. It was clearly demonstrated at the 1962 National Conference on Air Pollution that there is widespread concern about air pollution and a consensus that a greater control effort is needed now. The question to be resolved is how this should be accomplished.

SUMMARY

This report demonstrates that across the Nation, the problem of air pollution grows ever more serious. Current efforts by industry and Government to lift the curtains of smog which more and more frequently veil our cities, from coast to coast and border to border, are meeting with only limited success. The rapid deterioration of the quality of our air has reached the point at which more effective control measures can no longer be postponed. To underline this point, research continues to provide new evidence that air pollution is objectionable, not only for its aesthetic and nuisance efforts, which we can see and smell, and its economic damages, which are more varied and costly than we had supposed, but also because of its hazards to health and safety.

Pollution is increasing faster than our population increases, because our rising standard of living results in greater consumption of energy and goods per person, and our production and transportation activities increase on both accounts.

Technical procedures are available which can prevent the discharge of most contaminants to the air. The application of some of these procedures involves considerable cost. However, failure to use them is now costing the public far more in economic damages, even aside from the nuisances and hazards to health associated with air pollution.

Despite the lack of satisfactory answers to certain specific problems, such as motor vehicle pollution and sulfur oxides from fossil fuels, a significant reduction of pollution from most of our problem sources is now possible through more widespread application of proven control principles.

In this country, we have only begun to attack air pollution realistically. The Federal program of research and technical assistance has defined important facets of the problem and provided guidance to States and communities in assessing the nature of their local problem and demonstrating remedial measures.

One-third of the States have established programs to deal with air pollution, but most of these are, so far, quite limited in scope. Local government programs, where they exist, are generally understaffed and without sufficient financial and trained manpower resources to meet their needs properly. Only 34 local programs have annual budgets exceeding $25,000 and 7 of these are in California. Of the other 51 local air pollution control agencies, 21 try to function on less than $10,000 per year. In the past decade, despite a 30 per cent increase in urban population, there has been, outside of California, no overall increase in manpower to combat air pollution at the local level.

It has been estimated that in 1961 major air pollution problems existed in 308 urban places. This represents an increase of 84 in a decade. About 7,300 places, housing 60 percent of the population, are confronted with air pollution problems of one kind or another.

The American public looks forward to a growing population, an expanding economy, and an improving state of well-being. Essential to this is clean air. To compensate for past neglect of air quality conservation, a greater effort is required now, by the public, by industry, and by governmental agencies at all levels. The nationwide character of the air pollution problem requires an adequate Federal program to lend assistance, support, and stimulus to State and community programs.

There is a need for the establishment of air quality standards in terms of known and suspected effects on what is necessary for the protection of human health and welfare, agriculture, and property.

A number of States do not have air pollution control laws; others have laws which have control authority only, or no control authority, but local option legislation and research and technical assistance authority.

It is quite evident that an aggressive program of research needs to be directed toward providing assistance in developing appropriate State and local air pollution control laws and standards. There is also a need for nationwide enforcement and standards and in addition consideration needs to be given to the international aspect of air pollution.

NOTE

1. Los Angeles County Air Pollution Control District.

SUPPLEMENT

Supplement I

SUMMARY OF RESPONSES BY STATES TO MAIL QUESTIONNAIRE OF APRIL 30, 1963, ON AIR POLLUTION SENT BY SENATOR MCNAMARA, CHAIRMAN, SENATE PUBLIC WORKS COMMITTEE

I. Introduction · On April 30, Senator Pat McNamara, chairman of the Senate Public Works Committee, sent letters to the Governors of all the States and territories requesting them to answer a set of seven questions on the status of air pollution control legislation in their respective jurisdictions and soliciting their opinions on certain proposed Federal activities in the field, the answers to be used in preparing a staff report on the subject of air pollution control. By August 15 replies had been received from 51 of the States and territories; only Kansas, Louisiana, and Minnesota had not yet replied.

II. Question-by-Question Analysis ·

1) "Does your State have air pollution control laws? If so, would you give a brief digest of their principal provisions?"

Thirty-three of the responding units had such laws; 18 did not. Five States, Connecticut, Colorado, Maryland, North Carolina, and

Utah, had passed significant air pollution control legislation during their 1963 legislative sessions.

The responses to the second half of this question (i.e., give a brief digest) varied greatly in approach and content. For purposes of analysis, States having laws were placed into three categories:

(1) Control authority, with or without other provisions (15 (States);

(2) No control authority, but local option legislation, with or without research and technical assistance authority (12 States);

(3) Research and technical assistance authority only (6 States). (See tables for breakdown.)

2) "If your State does not have air pollution control laws, is it contemplated that such laws may be enacted?"

Of the 18 units having no air pollution control laws, 10 (Arkansas, Georgia, Maine, Michigan, Montana, New Mexico, Texas, Virginia, Puerto Rico, and the Virgin Islands) indicated some interest in promoting such legislation. Three States (Arkansas, Montana, Virginia) reported having studies of the problem underway, with a view to eventual framing of appropriate laws. Five (Georgia, Maine, Michigan, New Mexico, Texas) related previous, unsuccessful attempts to pass air pollution legislation, but added that efforts in this direction continue.

Eighteen of the thirty-three units already having air pollution laws followed the instructions and ignored question 2. Of the other 14, 5 asserted satisfaction with their present laws; 3, having at present control authority, are engaged in critically reviewing existing legislation; 4 have local option laws at present, and of these, 2 (Illinois, Kentucky) expressed real optimism concerning the passage of control legislation; 1 (Colorado) has a research law and is studying the need for more general legislation in the field.

3) "Do you have air quality standards and emission standards? If so, what measures are taken to obtain enforcement or compliance?"

California has established statewide air quality standards, enforcible by local districts, and motor vehicle emission standards enforcible at the State level; Oregon has quality and emission standards enforced through hearings before the State sanitary authority; New York is in the process of establishing air quality standards. No other States have gone as far in this field, although the establishment of such standards is reported to be authorized by statute in Alaska,

Colorado, Indiana, Washington, and West Virginia (and for quality only in Maryland and Pennsylvania).

Several units have emission standards for one or a few pollutants:

District of Columbia: Prohibits automobile exhaust emissions as dark or darker than Ringelmann No. 2 and enforces this by periodic inspection;

Florida: Limits smoke emission density to Ringelmann No. 2 and has limits for fluoride emission;

Hawaii: Has standards for visible emissions, enforcible through legal proceedings;

New Jersey: Limits smoke density to Ringelmann No. 2, and in addition has standards for permissible levels of fly ash emission, stated in pounds per hour.

4) "Do you have air pollution problems in your State which arise from sources outside your State? If so, do you have agreements with neighboring State or States to deal with the problem, and what provisions are made to handle the matter?"

Nineteen units reported air pollution problems originating outside their jurisdiction, while 29 said they had none. Generally, the States with such problems tended also to have control authority of their own. Six States reported the existence of formal or semiformal mechanisms dealing with interstate air pollution problems:

New Jersey and New York work toward the solution of their joint problems through the air pollution branch of the Interstate Sanitation Commission, which makes technical studies and recommends action to the Governors and legislatures, and through the New York-New Jersey Cooperative Committee for the Control of Interstate Air Polution, which is designed to "discuss and plan activities for the control of interstate air pollution."

Michigan noted the existence of the United States-Canada International Joint Commission as a medium for discussion of air pollution problems in the Detroit River area.

District of Columbia participates with nearby local governments in Maryland and Virginia in special air pollution committees of the Metropolitan Washington Council of Governments.

Five States (Indiana, Ohio, Oregon, Vermont, Washington) reported having made some attempt to cope with this problem by working along more informal, cooperative lines. Delaware, which has an unresolved interstate problem with Maryland, suggested that "when interstate problems occur and one State has no air pollution control power it would appear that Federal legislation should be available so that either State may apply through its Governor for assistance in the solution of such a problem."

5) "Does your State have a State-financed program of air pollution control research?"

Ten States have legislation authorizing air pollution control research, but only three, California (which spends $800,000 a year for this purpose), New Jersey (which has spent $250,000 over the past 9 years), and New York reported conducting fairly extensive programs. Many replies mentioned the need for Federal leadership in research; those from California, Delaware, Iowa, Massachusetts, West Virginia, and Wisconsin especially stressed this aspect of the Federal role in the field of air pollution.

6) "Would it be helpful to your State if the Department of Health, Education, and Welfare would recommend air quality standards and emission standards and assist in obtaining compliance with such standards?"

This is a three-part question. With respect to air quality standards, 37 units said "Yes," 1 said "Yes" with qualifications, and only 12 "No." Concerning emission standards, 35 said "Yes," 1 "Yes" with qualifications, and 12 "No." All but two of the units responding to both parts either favored both proposals or rejected both. New York, a State with comprehensive control programs, said "Yes" to quality standards and "No" to emission standards, stating that State-to-State variation in pollution levels makes the establishment of emission standards more properly a local function; Virginia, which has no law at all, said exactly the reverse, without giving reasons. Here again the importance of the Federal role in research was stressed; several letters suggested that the United States concentrate on developing criteria for evaluating air pollution and leave the actual standard setting to the States. Among these were California, Massachusetts, Ohio, Oregon, Texas, and Washington.

The replies were less receptive to the suggestion of Federal participation in the enforcement of air pollution control standards. Of those responding, 19 said "Yes," but 9 of these had more or less extensive qualifications, and 23 said "No." An interesting aspect of the response to this part of the question is the fact that units already having control authority of their own were generally less receptive to Federal aid in enforcement than the units without such laws.

7) "General suggestions on how to cope with air pollution."

The responses to this question were generally not very extensive, but some did provide interesting insights into State thinking on various aspects of air pollution control.

Some of the more interesting suggestions were:

Alaska: [1] Federal assistance along lines of water pollution would be beneficial.

Arizona (and Michigan and Nebraska): [1] Praises free cooperation approach to control.

Arkansas: [2] Primary control authority should rest with States; air pollution program should be in State health agency.

California: [1] Motor vehicle emission control should receive highest priority from Federal Government: Control emissions from present-day automobiles, but long-range objective to design pollution-free engines, use rapid transit systems, and proper city planning.

Colorado: [2] All Federal-local negotiations and activity should be through State health department.

Connecticut: [2] Federal grants to States should be on a formula, rather than a project basis, so as to avoid "grantsmanship" and tailoring one's program to meet the whims and fashions of Federal grant administrators.

Florida: [2] Interested in research on removal of sulfur from fuels, and in the development of inexpensive sampling and analytic equipment. Feels that all grants to localities should be processed through State air pollution agency.

Hawaii: [1] Desire Federal program and training grants to States and stronger emphasis on research on Federal level.

Indiana: [1] Should require approval of State air pollution agency before grants are made to localities.

Iowa: [2] For local or interlocal control; State control action only on request or where local government fails to act; Federal control action only when requested by State or in interstate problems after consultation with offending State.

Kentucky: [3] Encourages extension of Federal program of grants for program establishment, training, and research.

Maine: [1] For interstate cooperation; Federal role should be research and technical assistance.

Maryland: [3] Doubts that universally satisfactory air quality will ever be achieved; for application of controls, where economic conditions permit, to obtain a reasonable air quality level.

Michigan: [1] For cooperative efforts between State and local units of government and industrial sources.

Missouri: [2] Air quality and emission standards should be set at the local level.

Nebraska: [1] With reasonable amount of encouragement, industry will fulfill its obligations.

New Hampshire: [2] Federal Government should limit itself to a research and advisory role.

New Jersey: [1] Research directed toward technical and rulemaking methodology most essential; cost should primarily fall on Federal Government.

New Mexico: [1] Essential to learn more about effects and control; standards should be developed and adopted by all States; looks forward to State legislation to control present air pollution situation before it becomes a statewide problem.

New York: [3] Air pollution is a national problem only in that such problems are found nationwide; but they differ in cause and effect.

North Carolina: [2] For local control with technical guidance from State and Federal Government and Federal financial assistance.

Oregon: [1] Great need is to awake people to the problem and make them realize its control is a community function. Stimulate local action by program grants and better definition and publicizing of the actual economic costs of air pollution.

Pennsylvania: [1] Federal Government can assist States through technical and financial assistance and research (especially burning culm piles).

Rhode Island: [3] Air pollution not well understood; need more research.

South Dakota: [2] Air pollution in State does not warrant full-time staff at State level; welcomes specialist consultation for isolated problems.

Tennessee: [2] Impressed with complaints from rural areas or small towns about point sources; application of controls and how they are to be financed is the problem.

Texas: [2] Need for research on standards and on biological effects of air pollution stressed.

Utah: [1] State and local efforts sufficient to control air pollution;

no need for Federal participation in enforcement.

Vermont: [1] Wants technical assistance to aid local solving of local problems, and recommendation of methods for obtaining compliance.

Virginia: [2] Problem of inability of State to provide technical assistance to communities with air pollution problem since no statutory responsibility exists.

Wisconsin: [1] Advises Federal loans for the construction of control facilities, and tax amortization acceleration for such facilities.

III. Conclusion · Most States seem to be wary of direct Federal action in air pollution control but admit their own inadequacy in the fields of research, including the development of criteria for standards of air quality, and seem to favor expanded Federal action in these areas.

---

1. Reply signed by Governor.
2. Reply signed by State health officer.
3. Reply signed by other State official.

Summary of responses by States to mail questionnaire of Apr. 30, 1963, on pollution sent by Senator McNamara, Chairman, Senate Public Works Committee

GENERAL COMPILATION TABLES

			Replies to questions [4]		
State [1]	Officer responding [2]	Type of air pollution law [3]	New air pollution legislation planned	Existing air quality and emission standards	Interstate air pollution problems
Alabama	HO	0	N	N	N.
Alaska	G	1	Y	N	N.
Arizona	G	2	NA	N	N.
Arkansas	HO	0	Y	N	N.
California	G	1	NA	Y	N.
Colorado	G	3	Y	N	NA.
Connecticut	HO	3	N	N	N.
Delaware	HO	1	NA	N	Y.
District of Columbia	G	1	Y	Y	Y.
Florida	HO	1	NA	Y	N.
Georgia	HO	0	Y	N	N.
Hawaii	G	1	NA	Y	N.
Idaho	HO	1	NA	N	N.
Illinois	HO	2	Y	N	Y.

State	Officer responding	Type of air pollution law	Replies to questions		
			New air pollution legislation planned	Existing air quality and emission standards	Interstate air pollution problems
Indiana	G	1	NA	N	Y.
Iowa	HO	2	N	N	N.
Kentucky	O	2	Y	N	Y.
Maine	G	0	Y	N	Y.
Maryland	O	1	NA	N	Y.
Massachusetts	O	1	NA	Y	N.
Michigan	G	0	Y	N	Y.
Mississippi	HO	0	N	N	N.
Missouri	HO	2	N	N	Y.
Montana	G	0	Y	N	N.
Nebraska	G	2	Y	N	N.
Nevada	G	2	N	N	N.
New Hampshire	HO	0	N	N	N.
New Jersey	G	1	NA	Y	Y.
New Mexico	G	0	Y	N	Y.
New York	O	1	NA	Y	Y.
North Carolina	HO	3	NA	N	NA.
North Dakota	O	0	N	N	N.
Ohio	O	3	NA	N	Y.
Oklahoma	O	3	N	N	N.
Oregon	G	1	NA	Y	Y.
Pennsylvania	G	1	Y	N	Y.
Rhode Island	O	2	Y	N	N.
South Carolina	HO	2	Y	N	N.A.
South Dakota	HO	0	N	N	N.
Tennessee	HO	3	NA	N	N.
Texas	HO	0	Y	N	N.
Utah	G	2	NA	N	Y.
Vermont	G	0	N	N	Y.
Virginia	HO	0	Y	N	Y.
Washington	HO	2	NA	N	Y.
West Virginia	G	1	NA	N	Y.
Wisconsin	G	2	N	N	N.
Wyoming	O	0	N	N	N.
Guam	G	0	N	N	N.
Puerto Rico	HO	0	Y	N	N.
Virgin Islands	G	0	Y	N	N.

1. States not replying were: Kansas, Louisiana, Minnesota.

2. Key: G—Governor; HO—State health officer; O—Other official.

3. Key: 0—no State air pollution laws; 1—control authority, with or without local option and research and technical assistance authority; 2—no control authority but local option legislation, with or without research and technical assistance authority; 3—research and technical assistance authority only.

4. Key: Y—yes; N—no; NA—no answer.

Summary of responses by States to mail questionnaire of Apr. 30, 1963, on air pollution sent by Senator McNamara, Chairman, Senate Public Works Committee—Continued

| | | Replies to questions: HEW assistance desirable in— | | |
State	Research program authorized	Formulation of air quality standards	Formulation of emission standards	Obtaining compliance with standards
Alabama	N	Y	Y	NA.
Alaska	N	Y	Y	Y.
Arizona	Y	N	N	N.
Arkansas	N	N	N	N.
California	Y	N	N	N.
Colorado	Y	Y	Y	N.
Connecticut	N	Y	Y	Y.
Delaware	N	Y	Y	Y.
District of Columbia	N	Y	Y	Y.
Florida	N	Y	Y	NA.
Georgia	N	Y	Y	N.
Hawaii	N	N	N	N.
Idaho	N	Y	Y	NA.
Illinois	N	N	N	N.
Indiana	N	Y	Y	N.
Iowa	N	Y	Y	Y.
Kentucky	N	N	N	N.
Maine	N	Y	Y	Y.
Maryland	Y	Y	Y	Y.
Massachusetts	N	N	N	N.
Michigan	N	N	N	N.
Mississippi	N	Y	Y	Y.
Missouri	N	Y	Y	NA.
Montana	N	Y	Y	Y.
Nebraska	N	Y	Y	NA.
Nevada	N	Y	Y	Y.
New Hampshire	N	Y	Y	NA.
New Jersey	Y	Y	Y	N.
New Mexico	N	Y	Y	Y.
New York	Y	Y	N	Y.
North Carolina	N	Y	NA	NA.
North Dakota	N	NA	NA	NA.
Ohio	Y	N	N	N.
Oklahoma	N	Y	Y	Y.
Oregon	Y	Y	Y	N.
Pennsylvania	N	Y	Y	N.
Rhode Island	N	Y	Y	N.
South Carolina	N	Y	NA	NA.
South Dakota	N	Y	Y	Y.
Tennessee	N	Y	Y	Y.
Texas	N	N	N	N.

State	Research program authorized	Replies to questions: HEW assistance desirable in—		
		Formulation of air quality standards	Formulation of emission standards	Obtaining compliance with standards
Utah	N	Y	Y	N.
Vermont	N	Y	Y	Y.
Virginia	N	N	Y	N.
Washington	Y	N	N	N.
West Virginia	N	Y	Y	N.
Wisconsin	Y	Y	Y	N.
Wyoming	N	Y	Y	N.
Guam	N	Y	Y	Y.
Puerto Rico	N	Y	Y	Y.
Virgin Islands	N	Y	Y	Y.

NOTE.—N—No.
   Y—Yes.
   NA—No answer.

Supplement II

BRIEF DIGEST OF STATE AIR POLLUTION LAWS

Introduction · Legislation enacted by the various States to meet the air pollution problem presents a broad range of approaches. In most cases where the State has actual control authority, there is provision in the legislation which recognizes local interests and responsibilities and permits local governments to enact more stringent requirements. Thus far there are 15 States which have legislation of this type. In addition, 12 States have enacted enabling legislation, which although variable in detail and extent, permits the establishment of programs for control at a local level of government. At least six States have provided the mechanism for conducting research and making technical assistance available to the local governments. A growing number of States have recognized the financial burden placed on industry in meeting the requirements for air pollution control and six states have either exempted such facilities from taxation or have provided for rapid tax amortization. The development of standards for either emissions or ambient air quality is gathering considerable momentum and at least 14 States have such authority in their legislation. However, widespread progress in this area is quite limited at this time. A review of existing State air pollution legislation does reveal general similarities in objectives, but considerable variation in the means of attaining them, either through content, organizational structure, or procedure.

Alaska.—Under the general enabling statute for the department of health and welfare, Alaska has developed a more detailed administrative code relative to air pollution. The commissioner of health and welfare is empowered to establish air quality standards, conduct enforcement proceedings, and institute legal proceedings to compel compliance with his orders, grant (and revoke) permits to potential air pollution-creating installations, require the submission of plans for air pollution control by any industrial establishment or property development, engage in cooperative activities, and represent Alaska for the receipt of moneys for air pollution control.

Arizona.—A county board of supervisors has authority to investigate and control air pollution within its jurisdiction, including the authority to adopt rules and regulations and to establish an air pollution control district for this purpose if it so desires.

California.—Enabling laws have been passed that permit the formation of air pollution control districts in all counties and establish a regional air pollution control district in the San Francisco Bay area. Local districts of this kind are given broad powers to adopt and enforce rules and regulations on the control of pollutants from stationary sources.

The State department of public health is authorized to study the health effects and the nature and occurrence of air pollution, assist local agencies, monitor air pollutants, and adopt standards for air quality and for motor vehicle emissions.

The State motor vehicle pollution control board has the responsibility for testing devices, approving those found to meet the standards established by the department of public health, and setting up schedules for the adoption of any such device when two or more of the same type have been approved.

The department of motor vehicles is authorized to license and supervise the operation of motor vehicle pollution control device inspection stations.

Cost of equipment installed for the purpose of controlling air pollution may be deducted from income for tax purposes, and the cost of such equipment may be amortized over a 60-month period.

Colorado.—The two primary objectives of the Colorado law are:

(1) The development by early 1964 of standards of air quality and standards for motor vehicle pollution control devices; and

(2) The identification of the geographic areas in which air pollution is occurring. The State board of public health, aided by the advice of air pollution advisory committee appointed by the Governor, is charged with the primary responsibility for meeting the objectives.

Connecticut.—The commissioner of health is empowered to engage in research and in cooperative and educational activities relative to the control of air pollution, and to accept and administer Federal grants and other gifts.

Delaware.—The air pollution authority, administered by the State board of health, is empowered to develop a comprehensive pollution control program, conduct studies, investigations, and research relating to air pollution and its causes, promulgate rules and regulations and issue orders, encourage voluntary action to control air pollution, and represent the State in dealings relative to interstate compacts for air pollution control.

District of Columbia.—There now exist scattered laws and regulations relative to the control of emissions from motor vehicles, smoke emission, dusts, and noxious odors and gases. Further, responsibility for the coordination and development of a comprehensive air pollution control program has been placed, by a recent reorganization order, on the Director of Public Health.

Florida.—The air pollution control commission, established in the State board of health, is empowered to promulgate rules and regulations for the control of air pollution, establish air pollution control districts within the State, and provide technical services. The State board of health is authorized to enforce the commission's rules and regulations and to engage in research and educational and cooperative activities. Alachua, Broward, Brevard, St. Lucie, and Sarasota Counties have air pollution control authority established by specific State laws.

Hawaii.—The State director of health is authorized to adopt rules and regulations controlling air pollution, designate specific geographical areas to which these will apply, establish a section of air pollution control in the State department of health, conduct and supervise research programs on air pollution, authorize the issuance of permits to control pollution, enter and inspect premises to conduct tests, hold hearings on air pollution complaints, organize county advisory air pollution associations, and conduct programs on air pollution control education.

Idaho.—The air pollution control commission in the State board of health has authority to engage in research and educational and cooperative activities, to adopt and enforce rules and regulations relative to air pollution, and to organize county units for the local study of air pollution problems. The board of health is required to cooperate with the commission and to police air pollution pursuant to its rules and regulations.

Facilities or equipment used to control air pollution, in such proportion as they have no other beneficial purposes, are exempted from taxation.

Illinois.—Cities and counties have authority to pass ordinances regulating air pollution within their jurisdictions, including authority to abate any active pollution and to specify the use and design of equipment which emits air contaminants.

The air pollution control board may pass rules and regulations, including the regulation of new equipment potentially productive of air pollution, and may act to enforce them, by making investigations, holding hearings, and instituting legal proceedings. The board is directed to encourage voluntary cooperation with its air pollution control goals, and to offer and render technical assistance to lower level control agencies. Further, it is empowered to engage in research and educational and cooperative activities, to grant variances, and to grant certificates of exemption from State enforcement authority to those localities which have air pollution control programs not inconsistent in intent and operation with those of the State.

Indiana.—The air pollution control board within the State board of health is empowered to adopt and promulgate reasonable rules and regulations, make investigations, enter orders to abate air pollution, and bring appropriate legal action to enforce its final orders or determinations. The State board of health is directed to provide the staff for the air pollution control board, promote air pollution control ordinances and activities in local communities, provide technical assistance, provide assistance to areas unable to afford an air pollution control program, and resolve cases outside the jurisdiction of local control agencies. State enforcement authority does not extend to those areas which already have effective laws of their own that are consistent with the requirements of the State law.

Iowa.—Statutes provide for limited air pollution control by municipalities, but not by any State agency.

Kentucky.—Air pollution control districts, activated by resolution of the appropriate county fiscal court, are empowered to make rules and regulations for the control of air pollution within their boundaries, and to enforce them with the help of their appointed officers and a hearing board. A district may require permits for all potentially pollution-creating operations.

Maryland.—The State board of health and mental hygiene is authorized to adopt rules and regulations and to enforce them, and to engage in educational, cooperative, and research activities. The air pollution control council is primarily advisory to the board but is also specifically directed to make recommendations for adoption of rules and regulations and changes therein, to conduct hearings prior to the adoption of such rules, and to prepare recommendations for individual exceptions thereto.

Massachusetts.—City authorities may pass air pollution control regulations, subject to approval by the State department of health, which may also adopt and amend regulations and assume direct jurisdiction in the case of intercity air pollution.

A metropolitan air pollution control district which comprises Boston and contiguous towns controls air pollution with its borders, as agent of the department, by establishing and enforcing rules and conducting field studies. Other similar districts may be formed by two or more contiguous political units on joint application to, and approval by, the department.

Equipment on real property used to control air pollution is exempt from taxation.

Missouri.—The powers delegated by the legislature to municipalities include the authority to control, and require the abatement of, nuisances and to control the emission of smoke.

Montana.—An interim air pollution investigating committee composed of seven Montana residents appointed by the Governor, established in 1963, is directed to study the nature, character, and extent of air pollution in the State and in its various communities, and to report, without recommendation, to the 1965 session of the legislature.

Nebraska.—The State authorizes cities of 150,000 or more inhabitants to provide by ordinance for smoke abatement.

Nevada.—Boards of county commissioners and cities within the county may cooperate for the control of air pollution through joint use of personnel, equipment, and facilities.

New Hampshire.—The State provides a limited tax exemption for devices and installations put in operation for the purpose of controlling air pollution.

New Jersey.—The air pollution control commission has responsibility for developing rules and regulations for the control of air pollution. The State department of health is authorized to enforce these, and is further empowered to engage in research and educational and cooperative activities, to require the registration of potential air pollution-creating operations and the filing of reports, to inspect buildings other than private residences, to process complaints, to hold hearings, and to institute legal proceedings. Penalties are provided for violations.

New York.—The air pollution control board in the State department of health is empowered to adopt and enforce rules and regulations, promulgate quality standards, conduct research, cooperate with other appropriate agencies, encourage voluntary adoption of good air pollution practices, conduct programs of air pollution control education, supply technical assistance, and develop a comprehensive plan for the control of air pollution in the State. Penalties and variance procedures are also provided.

New York and New Jersey cooperate in the interstate sanitation commission, which conducts research and field studies on air pollution, aids the State air pollution enforcement agencies, and makes recommendations to the Governors and legislatures.

North Carolina.—The State air hygiene service in the State board of health is authorized to participate in cooperative, educational, and technical assistance activities and to conduct research on air quality standards.

Ohio.—The director of health is authorized to conduct research and educational and cooperative activities relative to air pollution.

A pollution control certificate, granted upon application to and approval by the tax commissioner, exempts all, or any specified part, of the pollution control facility to which it applies from several kinds of State and local taxes.

Oklahoma.—The State department of health is empowered to conduct research, training, and demonstrations relative to air pollution and its control, and to cooperate with the Public Health Service in administering air pollution control programs.

Oregon.—The sanitary authority is directed to develop a comprehensive plan for air pollution control and prevention; to cooperate with appropriate agencies, Federal and others; to conduct programs of research and education; and to establish and enforce rules, regulations, and air quality standards.

Counties and cities are authorized to enact air pollution ordinances, and to act cooperatively for establishing an air pollution program, setting up if they so desire a board empowered to issue and enforce regulations.

Pennsylvania.—The air pollution commission is authorized to adopt rules and regulations for air pollution control, and to adjudicate alleged violations thereof. The department of health is directed to enforce these regulations and also to carry on research, technical assistance, and cooperative and educational activities. Regional air pollution associations are authorized to act as liaison between the commission and the inhabitants of their regions.

Rhode Island.—State law provides for smoke control in cities of 150,000 or more, and allows it at local option in smaller cities.

South Carolina.—Statute prohibits the emission of untreated gaseous wastes from certain industrial processes in counties containing cities of more than 65,000 inhabitants.

Tennessee.—The air pollution control service in the State department of public health is authorized to cooperate with other air pollution authorities, conduct research, and provide technical assistance to subordinate units.

Utah.—A board of county commissioners is empowered to pass ordinances to control air pollution. The causing of air pollution shall constitute a misdemeanor.

Washington.—Cities, towns, and counties, and districts formed by combinations of these, are authorized to control air pollution within their boundaries by developing and implementing a comprehensive program, including enforcement, research, and cooperative activities. Districts are governed by boards representing their constituent parts, and are supported by county tax contributions. A State air pollution control board, in the department of health, is authorized to approve research and standard development activities which are carried out by the director of health.

West Virginia.—An air pollution control commission is authorized to adopt and enforce regulations, conduct research, give technical assistance, appoint technical advisory councils for various areas of the State, accept money and aid from the Federal Government, and cooperate with it and other appropriate groups and agencies.

Wisconsin.—Counties are empowered to regulate air pollution by prescribing rules and regulations, setting fees for permits, providing for an appeal board, an advisory board, and/or a county department of air pollution control, and prescribing penalties.

Pollution control installations required or recommended by a local governmental body shall be exempt from local taxation for 5 years, if no net income is created by the installations. Also, such property may be amortized on the basis of a 60-month estimated life for purposes of State income taxation.

Appendixes

Clean Air Act—Public Law 88—206

1965 Amendment of Clean Air Act

Clean Air Act—Public Law 88-206.

88th Congress H. R. 6518 December 17, 1963

An Act to improve, strengthen, and accelerate programs for the prevention and abatement of air pollution

Be it enacted by the Senate and House of Representatives of the United States of America in Congress assembled, That the Act of July 14, 1955, as amended (42 U.S.C. 1857–1857g), is hereby amended to read as follows:

"FINDINGS AND PURPOSES

"SECTION 1. (a) The Congress finds—

"(1) that the predominant part of the Nation's population is located in its rapidly expanding metropolitan and other urban areas, which generally cross the boundary lines of local jurisdictions and often extend into two or more States;

"(2) that the growth in the amount and complexity of air pollution brought about by urbanization, industrial development, and the increasing use of motor vehicles, has resulted in mounting dangers to the public health and welfare, including injury to agricultural crops and livestock, damage to and the deterioration of property, and hazards to air and ground transportation;

"(3) that the prevention and control of air pollution at its source is the primary responsibility of States and local governments; and

"(4) that Federal financial assistance and leadership is essential for the development of cooperative Federal, State, regional, and local programs to prevent and control air pollution.

"(b) The purposes of this Act are—

"(1) to protect the Nation's air resources so as to promote the public health and welfare and the productive capacity of its population;

"(2) to initiate and accelerate a national research and development program to achieve the prevention and control of air pollution;

"(3) to provide technical and financial assistance to State and local governments in connection with the development and execution of their air pollution prevention and control programs; and

"(4) to encourage and assist the development and operation of regional air pollution control programs.

"COOPERATIVE ACTIVITIES AND UNIFORM LAWS

"SEC. 2. (a) The Secretary shall encourage cooperative activities by the States and local governments for the prevention and control of air pollution; encourage the enactment of improved and, so far as practicable in the light of varying conditions and needs, uniform State and local laws relating to the prevention and control of air pollution; and encourage the making of agreements and compacts between States for the prevention and control of air pollution.

"(b) The Secretary shall cooperate with and encourage cooperative activities by all Federal departments and agencies having functions relating to the prevention and control of air pollution, so as to assure the utilization in the Federal air pollution control program of all appropriate and available facilities and resources within the Federal Government.

"(c) The consent of the Congress is hereby given to two or more States to negotiate and enter into agreements or compacts, not in conflict with any law or treaty of the United States, for (1) cooperative effort and mutual assistance for the prevention and control of air pollution and the enforcement of their respective laws relating thereto, and (2) the establishment of such agencies, joint or otherwise, as they may deem desirable for making effective such agreements or compacts. No such agreement or compact shall be binding or obligatory upon any State a party thereto unless and until it has been approved by Congress.

"RESEARCH, INVESTIGATIONS, TRAINING, AND OTHER ACTIVITIES

"SEC. 3. (a) The Secretary shall establish a national research and development program for the prevention and control of air pollution and as part of such program shall—

"(1) conduct, and promote the coordination and acceleration of, research, investigations, experiments, training, demonstrations, surveys, and studies relating to the causes, effects, extent, prevention, and control of air pollution; and

"(2) encourage, cooperate with, and render technical services and provide financial assistance to air pollution control agencies and other appropriate public or private agencies, institutions, and organizations, and individuals in the conduct of such activities; and

"(3) conduct investigations and research and make surveys concerning any specific problem of air pollution in cooperation with any air pollution control agency with a view to recommending a solution of such problem, if he is requested to do so by such agency or if, in his judgment, such problem may affect any community or communities in a State other than that in which the source of the matter causing or contributing to the pollution is located; and

"(4) initiate and conduct a program of research directed toward the development of improved, low-cost techniques for extracting sulfur from fuels.

"(b) In carrying out the provisions of the preceding subsection the Secretary is authorized to—

"(1) collect and make available, through publications and other appropriate means, the results of and other information, including appropriate recommendations by him in connection therewith, pertaining to such research and other activities;

"(2) cooperate with other Federal departments and agencies, with air pollution control agencies, with other public and private agencies, institutions, and organizations, and with any industries involved, in the preparation and conduct of such research and other activities;

"(3) make grants to air pollution control agencies, to other public or nonprofit private agencies, institutions, and organizations, and to individuals, for purposes stated in subsection (a) (1) of this section;

"(4) contract with public or private agencies, institutions, and organizations, and with individuals, without regard to sections 3648 and 3709 of the Revised Statutes (31 U.S.C. 529; 41 U.S.C. 5);

"(5) provide training for, and make training grants to, personnel of air pollution control agencies and other persons with suitable qualifications;

"(6) establish and maintain research fellowships, in the Department of Health, Education, and Welfare and at public or nonprofit private educational institutions or research organizations;

"(7) collect and disseminate, in cooperation with other Federal departments and agencies, and with other public or private agencies, institutions, and organizations having related responsibilities, basic data on chemical, physical, and biological effects of varying air quality and other information pertaining to air pollution and the prevention and control thereof; and

"(8) develop effective and practical processes, methods, and prototype devices for the prevention or control of air pollution.

"(c) (1) In carrying out the provisions of subsection (a) of this section the Secretary shall conduct research on, and survey the results of other scientific studies on, the harmful effects on the health or welfare of persons by the various known air pollution agents (or combinations of agents).

"(2) Whenever he determines that there is a particular air pollution agent (or combination of agents), present in the air in certain quantities, producing effects harmful to the health or welfare of persons, the Secretary shall compile and publish criteria reflecting accurately the latest scientific knowledge useful in indicating the kind and extent of such effects which may be expected from the presence of such air pollution agent (or combination of agents) in the air in varying quantities. Any such criteria shall be published for informational purposes and made available to municipal, State, and interstate air pollution control agencies. He shall revise and add to such criteria whenever necessary to reflect accurately developing scientific knowledge.

"(3) The Secretary may recommend to such air pollution control agencies and to other appropriate organizations such criteria of air quality as in his judgment may be necessary to protect the public health and welfare.

"GRANTS FOR SUPPORT OF AIR POLLUTION CONTROL PROGRAMS

"SEC. 4. (a) From the sums appropriated annually for the purposes of this Act but not to exceed 20 per centum of any such appropriation, the Secretary is authorized to make grants to air pollution control agencies in an amount up to two-thirds of the cost of developing, establishing, or improving programs for the prevention and control of air pollution: *Provided,* That the Secretary is authorized to make grants to intermunicipal or interstate air pollution control agencies (described in section 9 (b) (2) and (4)) in an amount up to three-fourths of the cost of developing, establishing, or improving, regional air pollution programs. As used in this subsection, the term 'regional air pollution control program' means a program for the prevention and control of air pollution in an area that includes the areas of two or more municipalities, whether in the same or different States.

"(b) From the sums available under subsection (a) of this section for any fiscal year the Secretary shall from time to time make grants to air pollution control agencies upon such terms and conditions as the Secretary may find necessary to carry out the purpose of this section. In establishing regulations for the granting of such funds the Secretary shall, so far as practicable, give due consideration to (1) the population, (2) the extent of the actual or potential air pollution problem, and (3) the financial need of the respective agencies. No agency shall receive any grant under this section during any fiscal year when its expenditures of non-Federal funds for air pollution programs will be less than its expenditures were for such programs during the preceding fiscal year. No grant shall be made under this section until the Secretary has consulted with the appropriate official as designated by the Governor or Governors of the State or States affected.

"(c) Not more than 12½ per centum of the grant funds available under subsection (a) of this section shall be expended in any one State.

"ABATEMENT OF AIR POLLUTION

"SEC. 5. (a) The pollution of the air in any State or States which endangers the health of welfare of any persons, shall be subject to abatement as provided in this section.

"(b) Consistent with the policy declaration of this Act, municipal, State, and interstate action to abate air pollution shall be encouraged and shall not be displaced by Federal enforcement action except as otherwise provided by or pursuant to a court order under subsection (g).

"(c) (1) (A) Whenever requested by the Governor of any State, a State air pollution control agency, or (with the concurrence of the Governor and the State air pollution control agency for the State in which the municipality is situated) the governing body of any municipality, the Secretary shall, if such request refers to air pollution which is alleged to endanger the health or welfare of persons in a State other than that in which the discharge or discharges (causing or contributing to such pollution) originate, give formal notification thereof to the air pollution control agency of the municipality where such discharge or discharges originate, to the air pollution control agency of the State in which such municipality is located, and to the interstate air pollution control agency, if any, in whose jurisdictional area such municipality is located, and shall call promptly a conference of such agency or agencies and of the air pollution control agencies of the municipalities which may be adversely affected by such pollution, and the air pollution control agency, if any, of each State, or for each area, in which any such municipality is located.

"(B) Whenever requested by the Governor of any State, a State air pollution control agency, or (with the concurrence of the Governor and the State air pollution control agency for the State in which the municipality is situated) the governing body of any municipality, the Secretary shall, if such request refers to alleged air pollution which is endangering the health or welfare of persons only in the State in which the discharge or discharges (causing or contributing to such pollution) originate and if a municipality affected by such air pollution, or the municipality in which such pollution originates, has either made or concurred in such request, give formal notification thereof to the State air pollution control agency, to the air pollution control agencies of the municipality where such discharge or discharges originate and of the municipality or municipalities alleged to be adversely affected thereby, and to any interstate air pollution control agency, whose jurisdictional area includes any such municipality and shall promptly call a conference of such agency or agencies, unless, in the judgment of the Secretary, the effect of such pollution is not of such significance as to warrant exercise of Federal jurisdiction under this section.

"(C) The Secretary may, after consultation with State officials of all affected States, also call such a conference whenever, on the basis of reports, surveys, or studies, he has reason to believe that any pollution referred to in subsection (a) is occurring and is endangering the health and welfare of persons in a State other than that in which the discharge or discharges originate. The Secretary shall invite the cooperation of any municipal, State, or interstate air pollution control agencies having jurisdiction in the affected area on any surveys or studies forming the basis of conference action.

"(2) The agencies called to attend such conference may bring such persons as they desire to the conference. Not less than three weeks' prior notice of the conference date shall be given to such agencies.

"(3) Following this conference, the Secretary shall prepare and forward to all air pollution control agencies attending the conference a summary of conference discussions including (A) occurrence of air pollution subject to abatement under this Act; (B) adequacy of measures taken toward abatement of the pollution; and (C) nature of delays, if any, being encountered in abating the pollution.

"(d) If the Secretary believes, upon the conclusion of the conference or thereafter, that effective progress toward abatement of such pollution is not being made and that the health or welfare of any persons is being endangered, he shall recommend to the appropriate State, interstate, or municipal air pollution control agency (or to all such agencies) that the necessary remedial action be taken. The Secretary shall allow at least six months from the date he makes such recommendations for the taking of such recommended action.

"(e) (1) If, at the conclusion of the period so allowed, such remedial action or other action which in the judgment of the Secretary is reasonably calculated to secure abatement of such pollution has not been taken, the Secretary shall call a public hearing, to be held in or near one or more of the places where the discharge or discharges causing or contributing to such pollution originated, before a hearing board of five or more persons appointed by the Secretary. Each State in which any discharge causing or contributing to such pollution originates and each State claiming to be adversely affected by such pollution shall be given an opportunity to select one member of such hearing board and each Federal department, agency, or instrumentality having a substantial interest in the subject matter as determined by the Secretary shall be given an opportunity to select one member of such hearing board, and one member shall be a representative of the appropriate interstate air pollution agency if one exists, and not less than a majority of such hearing board shall be persons other than officers or employees of the Department of Health, Education, and Welfare. At least three weeks' prior notice of such hearing shall be given to the State, interstate, and municipal air pollution control agencies called to attend such hearing and to the alleged polluter or polluters.

"(2) On the basis of evidence presented at such hearing, the hearing board shall make findings as to whether pollution referred to in subsection (a) is occurring and whether effective progress toward abatement thereof is being made. If the hearing board finds such pollution is occurring and effective progress toward abatement thereof is not being made it shall make recommendations to the Secretary concerning the measures, if any, which it finds to be reasonable and suitable to secure abatement of such pollution.

"(3) The Secretary shall send such findings and recommendations to the person or persons discharging any matter causing or contributing to such pollution; to air pollution control agencies of the State or States and of the municipality or municipalities where such discharge or discharges originate; and to any interstate air pollution control agency whose jurisdictional area includes any such municipality, together with a notice specifying a reasonable time (not less than six months) to secure abatement of such pollution.

"(f) If action reasonably calculated to secure abatement of the pollution within the time specified in the notice following the public hearing is not taken, the Secretary—

"(1) in the case of pollution of air which is endangering the health or welfare of persons in a State other than that in which the discharge or discharges (causing or contributing to such pollution) originate, may request the Attorney General to bring a suit on behalf of the United States to secure abatement of pollution, and

"(2) in the case of pollution of air which is endangering the health or welfare of persons only in the State in which the discharge or discharges (causing or contributing to such pollution) originate, at the request of the Governor of such State, shall provide such technical and other assistance as in his judgment is necessary to assist the State in judicial proceedings to secure abatement of the pollution under State or local law or, at the request of the Governor of such State, shall request the Attorney General to bring suit on behalf of the United States to secure abatement of the pollution.

"(g) The court shall receive in evidence in any suit brought in a United States court under subsection (f) of this section a transcript of the proceedings before the board and a copy of the board's recommendations and shall receive such further evidence as the court in its discretion deems proper. The court, giving due consideration to the practicability of complying with such standards as may be applicable and to the physical and economic feasibility of securing abatement of any pollution proved, shall have jurisdiction to enter such judgment, and others enforcing such judgment, as the public interest and the equities of the case may require.

"(h) Members of any hearing board appointed pursuant to subsection (e) who are not regular full-time officers or employees of the United States shall, while participating in the hearing conducted by such board or otherwise engaged on the work of such board, be entitled to receive compensation at a rate fixed by the Secretary, but not exceeding $50 per diem, including travel time, and while away from their homes or regular places of business they may be allowed travel expenses, including per diem in lieu of subsistence, as authorized by law (5 U.S.C. 73b-2) for persons in the Government service employed intermittently.

"(i) (1) In connection with any conference called under this section, the Secretary is authorized to require any person whose activities result in the emission of air pollutants causing or contributing to air pollution to file with him, in such form as he may prescribe, a report, based on existing data, furnishing to the Secretary such information as may reasonably be required as to the character, kind, and quantity of pollutants discharged, and the use of devices or other means to prevent or reduce the emission of pollutants by the person filing such a report. After a conference has been held with respect to any such pollution the Secretary shall require such reports from the person whose activities result in such pollution only to the extent recommended by such conference. Such report shall be made under oath or otherwise, as the Secretary may prescribe, and shall be filed with the Secretary within such reasonable period as the Secretary may prescribe, unless additional time be granted by the Secretary. No person shall be required in such report to divulge trade secrets or secret processes and all information reported shall be considered confidential for the purposes of section 1905 of title 18 of the United States Code.

"(2) If any person required to file any report under this subsection shall fail to do so within the time fixed by the Secretary for filing the same, and such failure shall continue for thirty days after notice of such default, such person shall forfeit to the United States the sum of $100 for each and every day of the continuance of such failure, which forfeiture shall be payable into the Treasury of the United States, and shall be recoverable in a civil suit in the name of the United States brought in the district where such person has his principal office or in any district in which he does business: *Provided*, That the Secretary may upon application therefor remit or mitigate any forfeiture provided for under this subsection and he shall have authority to determine the facts upon all such applications.

"(3) It shall be the duty of the various United States attorneys, under the direction of the Attorney General of the United States, to prosecute for the recovery of such forfeitures.

"AUTOMOTIVE VEHICLE AND FUEL POLLUTION

"SEC. 6. (a) The Secretary shall encourage the continued efforts on the part of the automotive and fuel industries to develop devices and fuels to prevent pollutants from being discharged from the exhaust of automotive vehicles, and to this end shall maintain liaison with automotive vehicle, exhaust control device, and fuel manufacturers. For this purpose, he shall appoint a technical committee, whose membership shall consist of an equal number of representatives of the Department and of automotive vehicle, exhaust control device, and fuel manufacturers. The committee shall meet from time to time at the call of the Secretary to evaluate progress in the development of such devices and fuels and to develop and recommend research programs which could lead to the development of such devices and fuels.

"(b) One year after enactment of this section, and semi-annually thereafter, the Secretary shall report to the Congress on measures taken toward the resolution of the vehicle exhaust pollution problem and efforts to improve fuels including (A) occurrence of pollution as a result of discharge of pollutants from automotive exhaust; (B) progress of research into development of devices and fuels to reduce pollution from exhaust to automotive vehicles; (C) criteria on degree of pollutant matter discharged from automotive exhausts; (D) efforts to improve fuels so as to reduce emission of exhaust pollutants and (E) his recommendations for additional legislation, if necessary, to regulate the discharge of pollutants from automotive exhausts.

"COOPERATION BY FEDERAL AGENCIES TO CONTROL AIR POLLUTION FROM FEDERAL FACILITIES

"SEC. 7. (a) It is hereby declared to be the intent of Congress that any Federal department or agency having jurisdiction over any building, installation, or other property shall, to the extent practicable and consistent with the interests of the United States and within any available appropriations, cooperate with the Department of Health, Education, and Welfare and with any air pollution control agency in preventing and controlling the pollution of the air in any area insofar as the discharge of any matter from or by such building, installation, or other property may cause or contribute to pollution of the air in such area.

"(b) In order to control air pollution which may endanger the health or welfare of any persons, the Secretary may establish classes of potential pollution sources for which any Federal department or agency having jurisdiction over any building, installation, or other property shall, before discharging any matter into the air of the United States, obtain a permit from the Secretary for such discharge, such permits to be issued for a specified period of time to be determined by the Secretary and subject to revocation if the Secretary finds pollution is endangering the health and welfare of any persons. In connection with the issuance of such permits, there shall be submitted to the Secretary such plans, specifications, and other information as he deems relevant thereto and under such conditions as he may prescribe. The Secretary shall report each January to the Congress the status of such permits and compliance therewith.

"ADMINISTRATION

"SEC. 8. (a) The Secretary is authorized to prescribe such regulations as are necessary to carry out his functions under this Act. The Secretary may delegate to any officer or employee of the Department of Health, Education, and Welfare such of his powers and duties under this Act, except the making of regulations, as he may deem necessary or expedient.

"(b) Upon the request of an air pollution control agency, personnel of the Public Health Service may be detailed to such agency for the purpose of carrying out the provisions of this Act. The provisions of section 214 (d) of the Public Health Service Act shall be applicable with respect to any personnel so detailed to the same extent as if such personnel had been detailed under section 214 (b) of that Act.

"(c) Payments under grants made under this Act may be made in installments, and in advance or by way of reimbursement, as may be determined by the Secretary.

"DEFINITIONS

"SEC. 9. When used in this Act—

"(a) The term 'Secretary' means the Secretary of Health, Education, and Welfare.

"(b) The term 'air pollution control agency' means any of the following:

"(1) A single State agency designated by the Governor of that State as the official State air pollution control agency for purposes of this Act;

"(2) An agency established by two or more States and having substantial powers or duties pertaining to the prevention and control of air pollution;

"(3) A city, county, or other local government health authority, or, in the case of any city, county, or other local government in which there is an agency other than the health authority charged with responsibility for enforcing ordinances or laws relating to the prevention and control of air pollution, such other agency; or

"(4) An agency of two or more municipalities located in the same State or in different States and having substantial powers or duties pertaining to the prevention and control of air pollution.

"(c) The term 'interstate air pollution control agency' means—

"(1) an air pollution control agency established by two or more States, or

"(2) an air pollution control agency of two or more municipalities located in different States.

"(d) The term 'State' means a State, the District of Columbia, the Commonwealth of Puerto Rico, the Virgin Islands, Guam, and American Samoa.

"(e) The term 'person' includes an individual, corporation, partnership, association, State, municipality, and political subdivision of a State.

"(f) The term 'municipality' means a city, town, borough, county, parish, district, or other public body created by or pursuant to State law.

"(g) All language referring to adverse effects on welfare shall include but not be limited to injury to agricultural crops and livestock, damage to and the deterioration of property, and hazards to transportation.

"OTHER AUTHORITY NOT AFFECTED

"SEC. 10. (a) Except as provided in subsection (b) of this section, this Act shall not be construed as superseding or limiting the authorities and responsibilities, under any other provision of law, of the Secretary or any other Federal officer, department, or agency.

"(b) No appropriation shall be authorized or made under section 301, 311, or 314 (c) of the Public Health Service Act for any fiscal year after the fiscal year ending June 30, 1964, for any purpose for which appropriations may be made under authority of this Act.

"RECORDS AND AUDIT

"SEC. 11. (a) Each recipient of assistance under this Act shall keep such records as the Secretary shall prescribe, including records which fully disclose the amount and disposition by such recipient of the proceeds of such assistance, the total cost of the project or undertaking in connection with which such assistance is given or used, and the amount of that portion of the cost of the project or undertaking supplied by other sources, and such other records as will facilitate an effective audit.

"(b) The Secretary of Health, Education, and Welfare and the Comptroller General of the United States, or any of their duly authorized representatives, shall have access for the purpose of audit and examinations to any books, documents, papers, and records of the recipients that are pertinent to the grants received under this Act.

"SEPARABILITY

"SEC. 12. If any provision of this Act, or the application of any provision of this Act to any person or circumstance, is held invalid, the application of such provision to other persons or circumstances, and the remainder of this Act, shall not be affected thereby.

"APPROPRIATIONS

"SEC. 13. (a) There is hereby authorized to be appropriated to carry out section 4 of this Act for the fiscal year ending June 30, 1964, not to exceed $5,000,000.

"(b) There is hereby authorized to be appropriated to carry out this Act not to exceed $25,000,000 for the fiscal year ending June 30,

1965, not to exceed $300,000,000 for the fiscal year ending June 30, 1966, and not to exceed $35,000,000 for the fiscal year ending June 30, 1967.

"SHORT TITLE

"SEC. 14. This Act may be cited as the 'Clean Air Act.'"

SEC. 2. The title of such Act of July 14, 1955, is amended to read "An Act to provide for air pollution prevention and control activities of the Department of Health, Education, and Welfare, and for other purposes."

Approved December 17, 1963.

LEGISLATIVE HISTORY

HOUSE REPORTS No. 508 (Comm. on Interstate and Foreign Commerce),

No. 1003 (Comm. of Conference).

SENATE REPORT No. 638 accompanying S. 432 (Comm. on Public Works).

CONGRESSIONAL RECORD, Vol. 109 (1963):

July 24: Considered and passed House.

Nov. 19: Considered and passed Senate, amended, in lieu of S. 432.

Dec. 10: House and Senate agreed to conference report.

1965 Amendment of Clean Air Act

SEC. 101. The Clean Air Act is amended (1) by inserting immediately above the heading of section 1: "TITLE I—AIR POLLUTION PREVENTION AND CONTROL"; (2) by changing the words "this Act" wherever they appear in sections 1 through 7 to "this title"; (3) by redesignating sections 1 through 7 and references thereto as sections 101 through 107; (4) by redesignating sections 8 through 14 and references thereto as sections 301 through 307; (5) by inserting immediately above the heading of the so redesignated section 301: "TITLE III—GENERAL"; (6) by striking out subsection (a) of the so redesignated section 306 and striking out the letter (b) at the beginning of subsection (b) in the so redesignated section 306; (7) by striking out "this Act" in the so redesignated section 306 and inserting in lieu thereof "title I"; and (8) by inserting after the so redesignated section 107 and before the heading of such title III the following new title:

"TITLE II—CONTROL OF AIR POLLUTION FROM MOTOR VEHICLES

"Short title

"SEC. 201. This title may be cited as the 'Motor Vehicle Air Pollution Control Act.'

"Establishment of standards

"SEC. 202. (a) The Secretary shall by regulation, giving appropriate consideration to technological feasibility and economic costs, prescribe as soon as practicable standards, applicable to the emission of any kind of substance, from any class or classes of new motor vehicles or new motor vehicle engines, which in his judgment cause or contribute to, or are likely to cause or to contribute to, air pollution which endangers the health or welfare of any persons, and such standards shall apply to such vehicles or engines whether they are designed as complete systems or incorporate other devices to prevent or control such pollution.

"(b) Any regulations initially prescribed under this section, and amendments thereto, with respect to any class of new motor vehicles or new motor vehicle engines shall become effective on the effective date specified in the order promulgating such regulations which date shall be determined by the Secretary after consideraton of the period reasonably necessary for industry compliance.

"Prohibited acts

"SEC. 203. (a) The following acts and the causing thereof are prohibited—

"(1) in the case of a manufacturer of new motor vehicles or new motor vehicle engines for distribution in commerce, the manufacture for sale, the sale, or the offering for sale, or the introduction or delivery for introduction into commerce, or the importation into the United States for sale or resale, of any new motor vehicle or new motor vehicle engine, manufactured after the effective date of regulations under this title which are applicable to such vehicle or engine unless it is in conformity with regulations prescribed under section 202 (except as provided in subsection (b));

"(2) for any person to fail or refuse to permit access to or copying of records or to fail to make reports or provide information, required under section 207; or

"(3) for any person to remove or render inoperative any device or element of design installed on or in a motor vehicle or motor vehicle engine in compliance with regulations under this title prior to its sale and delivery to the ultimate purchaser.

"(b) (1) The Secretary may exempt any new motor vehicle or new motor vehicle engine, or class thereof, from subsection (a), upon such terms and conditions as he may find necessary to protect the public health or welfare, for the purpose of research, investigations, studies, demonstrations, or training, or for reasons of national security.

"(2) A new motor vehicle or new motor vehicle engine offered for importation by a manufacturer in violation of subsection (a) shall be refused admission into the United States, but the Secretary of the Treasury and the Secretary of Health, Education, and Welfare may, be joint regulation, provide for deferring final determination as to admission and authorizing the delivery of such a motor vehicle or engine offered for import to the owner or consignee thereof upon such terms and conditions (including the furnishing of a bond) as may appear to them appropriate to insure that any such motor vehicle or engine will be brought into conformity with the standards, requirements, and limitations applicable to it under this title. The Secretary of the Treasury shall, if a motor vehicle or engine is finally refused admission under this paragraph, cause disposition thereof in accordance with the customs laws unless it is exported, under regulations prescribed by such Secretary, within ninety days of the date of notice of such refusal or such additional time as may be permitted pursuant to such regulations, except that disposition in accordance with the customs laws may not be made in such manner as may result, directly or indirectly, in the date, to the ultimate consumer, of a new motor vehicle or new motor vehicle engine that fails to comply with applicable standards of the Secretary of Health, Education, and Welfare under this title.

"(3) A new motor vehicle or new motor vehicle engine intended solely for export, and so labeled or tagged on the outside of the container and on the vehicle or engine itself, shall not be subject to the provisions of subsection (a).

"Injunction proceedings

"SEC. 204. (a) The district courts of the United States shall have jurisdiction to restrain violations of paragraph (1), (2), or (3) of section 203 (a).

"(b) Actions to restrain such violations shall be brought by and in the name of the United States. In any such action, subpenas for witnesses who are required to attend a district court in any district may run into any other district.

"Penalties

"SEC. 205. Any person who violates paragraph (1), (2), or (3) of section 203 (a) shall be subject to a fine or not more than $1,000. Such violation with respect to section 203 (a) (1) and 203 (a) (3) shall constitute a separate offense with respect to each new motor vehicle or new motor vehicle engine.

"Certification

"SEC. 206. (a) Upon application of the manufacturer, the Secretary shall test, or require to be tested, in such manner as he deems appropriate, any new motor vehicle or new motor vehicle engine submitted by such manufacturer to determine whether such vehicle or engine conforms with the regulations prescribed under section

202 of this title. If such vehicle or engine conforms to such regulations the Secretary shall issue a certificate of conformity, upon such terms, and for such period not less than one year, as he may prescribe.

"(b) Any new motor vehicle or any motor vehicle engine sold by such manufacturer which is in all material respects substantially the same construction as the test vehicle or engine for which a certificate has been issued under subsection (a), shall for the purposes of this Act be deemed to be in conformity with the regulations issued under section 202 of this title.

"Records and reports

"SEC. 207. (a) Every manufacturer shall establish and maintain such records, make such reports, and provide such information, as the Secretary may reasonably require to enable him to determine whether such manufacturer has acted or is acting in compliance with this title and regulations thereunder and shall, upon request of an officer or employee duly designated by the Secretary, permit such officer or employee at reasonable times, to have access to and copy such records.

"(b) All information reported or otherwise obtained by the Secretary or his representative pursuant to subsection (a), which information contains or relates to a trade secret of other matter referred to in section 1905 of title 18 of the United States Code, shall be considered confidential for the purpose of such section 1905, except that such information may be disclosed to other officers or employees concerned with carrying out this Act or when relevant in any proceeding under this Act. Nothing in this section shall authorize the withholding of information by the Secretary or any officer or employee under his control, from the duly authorized committees of the Congress.

"Definitions for title II

"SEC. 208. As used in this title—

"(1) The term 'manufacturer' means any person engaged in the manufacturing or assembling of new motor vehicles or new motor vehicle engines, or importing such vehicles or engines for resale, or who acts for and is under the control of any such person in connection with the distribution of new motor vehicles or new motor vehicle engines, but shall not include any dealer with respect to new motor vehicles or new motor vehicle engines received by him in commerce.

"(2) The term 'motor vehicle' means any self-propelled vehicle designed for transporting persons or property on a street or highway.

"(3) The term 'new motor vehicle' means a motor vehicle the equitable or legal title to which has never been transferred to an ultimate purchaser; and the term 'new motor vehicle engine' means an engine in a new motor vehicle or a motor vehicle engine the equitable or legal title to which has never been transferred to the ultimate purchaser.

"(4) The term 'dealer' means any person who is engaged in the sale or the distribution of new motor vehicles or new motor vehicle engines to the ultimate purchaser.

"(5) The term 'ultimate purchaser' means, with respect to any new motor vehicle or new motor vehicle engine, the first person who in good faith purchases such new motor vehicle or new engine for purposes other than resale.

"(6) The term 'commerce' means (A) commerce between any place in any State and any place outside thereof; and (B) commerce wholly within the District of Columbia.

"*Appropriations*

"SEC. 209. There is hereby authorized to be appropriated to carry out this title II, not to exceed $470,000 for the fiscal year ending June 30, 1966, not to exceed $845,000 for the fiscal year ending June 30, 1967, not to exceed $1,195,000 for the fiscal year ending June 30, 1968, and not to exceed $1,470,000 for the fiscal year ending June 30, 1969."

SEC. 102. (a) Paragraph (1) of subsection (c) of the redesignated section 105 of the Clean Air Act (which relates to abatement of air pollution) is amended by adding at the end thereof the following new subparagraph:

"(D) Whenever the Secretary, upon receipt of reports, surveys, or studies from any duly constituted international agency, has reason to believe that any pollution referred to in subsection (a) which endangers the health or welfare of persons in a foreign country is occurring, or whenever the Secretary of State requests him to do so with respect to such pollution which the Secretary of State alleges is of such a nature, the Secretary of Health, Education, and Welfare shall give formal notification thereof to the air pollution control agency of the municipality where such discharge or discharges originate, to the air pollution control agency of the State in which such municipality is located, and to the interstate air pollution control agency, if any, in the jurisdictional area of which such municipality is located, and shall call promptly a conference of such agency or agencies. The Secretary shall invite the foreign country which may be adversely affected by the pollution to attend and participate in the conference, and the representative of such country shall, for the purpose of the conference and any further proceeding resulting from such conference, have all the rights of a State air pollution control agency. This subparagraph shall apply only to a foreign country which the Secretary determines has given the United States essentially the same rights with respect to the prevention or control of air pollution occurring in that country as is given that country by this subparagraph."

(b) So much of subsection (f) of such redesignated section 105 as precedes clause (2) of such subsection is amended to read as follows:

"(f) If action reasonably calculated to secure abatement of the pollution within the time specified in the notice following the public hearing is not taken, the Secretary—

"(1) in the case of pollution of air which is endangering the health or welfare of persons (A) in a State other than that in which the discharge or discharges (causing or contributing to such pollution) originate, or (B) in a foreign country which has participated in a conference called under subparagraph (D) of subsection (c) of this section and in all proceedings under this section resulting from such conference, may request the Attorney General to bring a suit on behalf of the United States to secure abatement of the pollution and."

SEC. 103. Redesignated section 103 of the Clean Air Act (which relates to research, investigations, and training) is amended—

(1) by striking out the word "and" at the end of paragraphs (1), (2), and (3) of subsection (a) thereof;

(2) by striking out the period at the end of paragraph (4) of subsection (a) thereof and inserting in lieu thereof"; and";

(3) by adding after paragraph (4) of subsection (a) thereof the following new paragraph (5):

"(5) conduct and accelerate research programs (A) relating to the means of controlling hydrocarbon emissions resulting from the evaporation of gasoline in carburetors and fuel tanks, and the means of controlling emissions of oxides of nitrogen and aldehydes from gasoline-powered or diesel-powered vehicles, and to carry out such research the Secretary shall consult with the technical committee established under section 106 of this Act, and for research concerning diesel-powered vehicles he may add to such committee such representatives from the diesel-powered vehicle industry as he deems appropriate; and (B) directed toward the development of improved low-cost techniques designed to reduce emissions of oxides of sulfur produced by the combustion of sulfur-containing fuels."; and

(4) by adding at the end of such section the following new subsections:

"(d) The Secretary is authorized to construct such facilities and staff and equip them as he determines to be necessary to carry out his functions under this Act.

"(e) If, in the judgment of the Secretary, an air pollution problem of substantial significance may result from discharge or discharges into the atmosphere, he may call a conference concerning this potential air pollution problem to be held in or near one or more of the places where such discharge or discharges are occurring or will occur. All interested persons shall be given an opportunity to be heard at such conference, either orally or in writing, and shall be permitted to appear in person or by representative in accordance with procedures prescribed by the Secretary. If the Secretary finds, on the basis of the evidence presented at such conference, that the discharge or discharges if permitted to take place or continue are likely to cause or contribute to air pollution subject to abatement under section 105 (a), he shall send such findings, together with recommendations concerning the measures which he finds reasonable and suitable to prevent such pollution, to the person or persons whose actions will result in the discharge or discharges involved; to air pollution agencies of the State or States and of the municipality or municipalities where such discharge or discharges will originate; and to the interstate air pollution control agency, if any, in the jurisdictional area of which any such municipality is located. Such findings and recommendations shall be advisory only, but shall be admitted, together with the record of the conference, as part of the record of proceedings under subsections (c), (d), and (e) of section 105."

TITLE II—SOLID WASTE DISPOSAL

Short title

SEC. 201. This title (hereinafter referred to as "this Act") may be cited as the "Solid Waste Disposal Act".

Findings and purposes

SEC. 202. (a) The Congress finds—

(1) that the continuing technological progress and improvement in methods of manufacture, packaging, and marketing of consumer products has resulted in an ever-mounting increase, and in a change in the characteristics, of the mass of material discarded by the purchaser of such products;

(2) that the economic and population growth of our Nation, and the improvements in the standard of living enjoyed by our population, have required increased industrial production to meet our needs, and have made necessary the demolition of old buildings, the construction of new buildings, and the provision of highways and other avenues of transportation, which, together with related industrial, commercial, and agricultural operations, have resulted in a rising tide of scrap, discarded, and waste materials;

(3) that the continuing concentration of our population in expanding metropolitan and other urban areas has presented these communities with serious financial, management, intergovernmental, and technical problems in the disposal of solid wastes resulting from the industrial, commercial, domestic, and other activities carried on in such areas;

(4) that inefficient and improper methods of disposal of solid wastes result in scenic blights, create serious hazards to the public health, including pollution of air and water resources, accident hazards, and increase in rodent and insect vectors of disease, have an adverse effect on the land values, create public nuisances, otherwise interfere with community life and development;

(5) that the failure or inability to salvage and reuse such materials economically results in the unnecessary waste and depletion of our natural resources; and

(6) that while the collection and disposal of solid wastes should continue to be primarily the function of State, regional, and local agencies, the problems of waste disposal as set forth above have become a matter national in scope and in concern and necessitate

Federal action through financial and technical assistance and leadership in the development, demonstration, and application of new and improved methods and processes to reduce the amount of waste and unsalvageable materials and to provide for proper and economical solid-waste disposal practices.

(b) the purposes of this Act therefore are—

(1) to initiate and accelerate a national research and development program for new and improved methods of proper and economic solid-waste disposal, including studies directed toward the conservation of natural resources by reducing the amount of waste and unsalvageable materials and by recovery and utilization of potential resources in solid wastes; and

(2) to provide technical and financial assistance to State and local governments and interstate agencies in the planning, development, and conduct of solid-waste disposal programs.

Definitions

SEC. 203. When used in this Act—

(1) The term "Secretary" means the Secretary of Health, Education, and Welfare; except that such term means the Secretary of the Interior with respect to problems of solid waste resulting from the extraction, processing, or utilization of minerals or fossil fuels where the generation, production, or reuse of such waste is or may be controlled within the extraction, processing, or utilization facility or facilities and where such control is a feature of the technology or economy of the operation of such facility or facilities.

(2) The term "State" means a State, the District of Columbia, the Commonwealth of Puerto Rico, the Virgin Islands, Guam, and American Samoa.

(3) The term "interstate agency" means an agency of two or more municipalities in different States, or an agency established by two or more States, with authority to provide for the disposal of solid wastes and serving two or more municipalities located in different States.

(4) The term "solid waste" means garbage, refuse, and other discarded solid materials, including solid-waste materials resulting from industrial, commercial, and agricultural operations, and from community activities, but does not include solids or dissolved material in domestic sewage or other significant pollutants in water resources, such as silt, dissolved or suspended solids in industrial waste

water effluents, dissolved materials in irrigation return flows or other common water pollutants.

(5) The term "solid-waste disposal" means the collection, storage, treatment, utilization, processing, or final disposal of solid waste.

(6) The term "construction", with respect to any project of construction under this Act, means (A) the erection or building of new structures and acquisition of lands or interests therein, or the acquisition, replacement, expansion, remodeling, alteration, modernization, or extension of existing structures, and (B) the acquisition and installation of initial equipment of, or required in connection with, new or newly acquired structures or the expanded, remodeled, altered, modernized or extended part of existing structures (including trucks and other motor vehicles, and tractors, cranes, and other machinery) necessary for the proper utilization and operation of the facility after completion of the project; and includes preliminary planning to determine the economic and engineering feasibility and the public health and safety aspects of the project, the engineering, architectural, legal, fiscal, and economic investigations and studies, and any surveys, designs, plans, working drawings, specifications, and other action necessary for the carrying out of the project, and (C) the inspection and supervision of the process carrying out the project to completion.

Research, demonstrations, training, and other activities

SEC. 204. (a) The Secretary shall conduct, and encourage, cooperate with, and render financial and other assistance to appropriate public (whether Federal, State, Interstate, or local) authorities, agencies, and institutions, private agencies and institutions, and individuals in the conduct of, and promote the coordination of, research, investigations, experiments, training, demonstrations, surveys, and studies relating to the operation and financing of solid-waste disposal programs, the development and application of new and improved methods of solid-waste disposal (including devices and facilities therefore), and the reduction of the amount of such waste and unsalvageable waste materials.

(b) In carrying out the provisions of the preceding subsection, the Secretary is authorized to—

(1) collect and make available, through publications and other appropriate means, the results of, and other information pertaining

to, such research and other activities, including appropriate recommendations in connection therewith;

(2) cooperate with public and private agencies, institutions, and organizations, and with any industries involved in the preparation and the conduct of such research and other activities; and

(3) make grants-in-aid to public or private agencies and institutions and to individuals for research, training projects, surveys, and demonstrations (including construction of facilities), and provide for the conduct of research, training, surveys, and demonstrations by contract with public or private agencies and institutions and with individuals; and such contracts for research or demonstrations or both (including contracts for construction) may be made in accordance with and subject to the limitations provided with respect to research contracts of the military departments in title 10, United States Code, section 2353, except that the determination, approval, and certification required thereby shall be made by the Secretary.

(c) Any grant, agreement, or contract made or entered into under this section shall contain provisions effective to insure that all information, uses, processes, patents and other developments resulting from any activity undertaken pursuant to such grant, agreement, or contract will be made readily available on fair and equitable terms to industries utilizing methods of solid-waste disposal and industries engaging in furnishing devices, facilities, equipment, and supplies to be used in connection with solid-waste disposal. In carrying out the provisions of this section, the Secretary and each department, agency, and officer of the Federal Government having functions or duties under this Act shall make use of and adhere to the Statement of Government Patent Policy which was promulgated by the President in his memorandum of October 10, 1963. (3 CFR, 1963 Supp., p. 238.)

(d) Notwithstanding any other provision of this Act, the United States shall not make any grant to pay more than two-thirds of the cost of construction of any facility under this Act.

Interstate and interlocal cooperation

SEC. 205. The Secretary shall encourage cooperative activities by the States and local governments in connection with solid-waste disposal programs; encourage, when practicable, interstate, interlocal, and regional planning for, and the conduct of, interstate, interlocal, and regional solid-waste disposal programs; and encourage the enactment of improved and, so far as practicable, uniform State and local laws governing solid-waste disposal.

Grants for State and interstate planning

Sec. 206. (a) The Secretary may from time to time, upon such terms and conditions consistent with this section as he finds appropriate to carry out the purposes of this Act, make grants to State and interstate agencies of not to exceed 50 per centum of the cost of making surveys of solid-waste disposal practices and problems within the jurisdictional areas of such States or agencies, and of developing solid-waste disposal plans for such areas.

(b) In order to be eligible for a grant under this section the State, or the interstate agency, must submit an application therefore which—

(1) designates or establishes a single State agency (which may be an interdepartmental agency) or, in the case of an interstate agency, such interstate agency, as the sole agency for carrying out the purposes of this section;

(2) indicates the manner in which provision will be made to assure full consideration of all aspects of planning essential to statewide planning (or in the case of an interstate agency jurisdiction-wide planning) for proper and effective solid-waste disposal consistent with the protection of the public health, including such factors as population growth, urban and metropolitan development, land use planning, water pollution control, air pollution control, and the feasibility of regional disposal programs;

(3) sets forth its plans for expenditure of such grant, which plans provide reasonable assurance of carrying out the purposes of this section;

(4) provides for submission of a final report of the activities of the State or interstate agency in carrying out the purposes of this section, and for the submission of such other reports, in such form and containing such information, as the Secretary may from time to time find necessary for carrying out the purposes of this section and for keeping such records and affording such access thereto as he may find necessary to assure the correctness and verification of such reports; and

(5) provides for such fiscal-control and fund-accounting procedures as may be necessary to assure proper disbursement of and accounting for funds paid to the State or interstate agency under this

section.

(c) The Secretary shall make a grant under this section only if he finds that there is satisfactory assurance that the planning of solid-waste disposal will be coordinated, so far as practicable, with other related State, interstate, regional, and local planning activities, including those financed in part with funds pursuant to section 701 of the Housing Act of 1954.

Labor standards

SEC. 207. No grant for a project of construction under this Act shall be made unless the Secretary finds that the application contains or is supported by reasonable assurance that all laborers and mechanics employed by contractors or subcontractors on projects of the type covered by the Davis-Bacon Act, as amended (40 U.S.C. 276a—276a-5), will be paid wages at rates not less than those prevailing on similar work in the locality as determined by the Secretary of Labor in accordance with that Act; and the Secretary of Labor shall have with respect to the labor standards specified in this section the authority and functions set forth in Reorganization Plan Numbered 14 of 1950 (15 F.R. 3176; 5 U.S.C. 133z-15) and section 2 of the Act of June 13, 1934, as amended (40 U.S.C. 276c).

Other authority not affected

SEC. 208. This Act shall not be construed as superseding or limiting the authorities and responsibilities, under any other provisions of law, of the Secretary of Health, Education, and Welfare, the Secretary of the Interior, or any other Federal officer, department, or agency.

Payments

SEC. 209. Payments of grants under this Act may be made (after necessary adjustment on account of previously made underpayments or overpayments) in advance or by way of reimbursement, and in such installments and on such conditions as the Secretary may determine.

Appropriations

SEC. 210. (a) There is hereby authorized to be appropriated to the Secretary of Health, Education, and Welfare, to carry out this Act, not to exceed $7,000,000 for the fiscal year ending June 30, 1966, not to exceed $14,000,000 for the fiscal year ending June 30,

1967, not to exceed $19,200,000 for the fiscal year ending June 30, 1963, and not to exceed $20,000,000 for the fiscal year ending June 30, 1969:

(b) There is hereby authorized to be appropriated to the Secretary of the Interior, to carry out this Act, not to exceed $3,000,000 for the fiscal year ending June 30, 1966, not to exceed $6,000,000 for the fiscal year ending June 30, 1967, not to exceed $10,800,000 for the fiscal year ending June 30, 1968, and not to exceed $12,500,000 for the fiscal year ending June 30, 1969.

Bibliography [1]

THE FOLLOWING is an annotated selective bibliography of books, journal articles, monographs, and related papers concerned with air pollution and economics.

"APCA Abstracts," *Journal of the Air Pollution Control Association,* Vol. 15 (September, 1965).

American Society of Planning Officials, Planning Advisory Service, *New Techniques for Shaping Urban Expansion* (Information Report No. 160), Chicago, July, 1962. *Contains recommendations regarding the location of industrial activities in an urban area.*

Arrow, Kenneth J., *Social Choice and Individual Values* (Cowles Commission Monograph No. 12), New York, John Wiley & Sons, 1951. Second edition, 1963. *Arrow's fundamental work, deriving the social welfare function.*

Bailey, M. C., "Analytical Framework for Measuring Social Costs," *Journal of Farm Economics,* Vol. 44 (May, 1962), pp. 564–74. *Indicates the possibility of measuring social costs in certain areas of agriculture; most of the costs measured, however, can be found in market and, therefore, have established market values.*

Bain, Joe S., "Criteria for Undertaking Water-Resource Developments," *American Economic Review,* Vol. 50 (March–May, 1960), pp. 310–20. *Analysis of criteria for water resources in the framework of benefit-cost analysis.*

Baumol, William, "Activity Analysis," *American Economic Review,* Vol. 48 (June–December, 1958), pp. 837–73.

Brownlee, O. H., "The Economics of Government Expenditures: Using Market Mechanisms in Making Government Expenditure Decisions," *American Economic Review,* Vol. 49 (March–May, 1959), pp. 359–67.

Burkhead, Jesse, Reviews of *Water Resource Development* and of *Multiple Purpose River Development,* in *Review of Economics*

---

1. Mr. Ivars Gutmanis, of the Division of Air Pollution, U.S. Public Health Service, compiled the greater part of this bibliography.

and Statistics, Vol. 42 (May, 1960), pp. 237–9.

Carr, Donald E., *The Breath of Life,* New York, W. W. Norton & Company, Inc., 1965.

Council of Europe, European Conference on Air Pollution, *Economic Effects of Air Pollution,* Strasbourg, July, 1963. (Mimeographed.) *Contains a summary of air pollution in various countries in Europe, with some very preliminary estimates of the costs of air pollution.*

Davis, A. L., "Site Selection and Metropolitan Control," University of Florida, Florida Engineering and Experiment Station, Gainsville. "Atmospheric Pollution," Bulletin Series No. 38 (September, 1956), pp. 33–8. *Advocates site selection of industrial activities as a means to control air pollution.*

Davis, Otto A., and Whinston, Andrew, "Externalities, Welfare, and the Theory of Games," *Journal of Political Economy,* Vol. 70 (June, 1962), pp. 241–62. *A highly developed paper on measurement of externalities. The authors advocate administrative processes for adjustment of welfare losses due to externalities.*

Dorfman, Robert, ed., *Measuring Benefits of Government Investments,* Washington, D.C., The Brookings Institution, 1963. *A volume containing a number of individual approaches to benefit-cost measurement in various public-expenditure areas, such as urban renewal, education, public health, aviation, and others.*

Eckstein, Otto, "A Survey of the Theory of Public Expenditure Criteria," in *Public Finances: Needs, Sources, and Utilization,* Conference of the Universities National Bureau Committee for Economic Research, Princeton, Princeton University Press, 1961. *Analysis by Dr. Eckstein of the public-expenditure criteria now partly implemented by the Bureau of the Budget.*

——— *Water Resource Development,* Cambridge, Mass., Harvard University Press, 1958.

Economic Studies of Outdoor Recreation (Reports to the Outdoor Resources Review Commission), Washington, D.C., 1962.

Edelman, Sidney, *Legal Problems of Interjurisdictional Air Pollution Control* (Paper 62-93), Washington, D.C., U.S. Department of Health, Education, and Welfare, Public Health Service, Division of Air Pollution, 1962. (Mimeographed.) *Considers the alternatives needed to handle interjurisdictional air pollution control problems.*

Forte, Francesco, and Buchanan, James M., "The Evaluation of

Public Services," *Journal of Political Economy*, Vol. 69 (April, 1961), pp. 107–21.

Gutmanis, Ivars, and Goldner, Lester, "Welfare Economics and Public Policy: Parallels in the Analysis of the Impact of Air Pollution and Weather Modification." A paper prepared for the Symposium on the Economic and Social Aspects of Weather Modification, Boulder, Colorado, July 1–3, 1965.

Hammond, Richard J., Review of *Multiple Purpose River Development*, in *Journal of Political Economy*, Vol. 67 (June, 1959), pp. 314–5.

Herfindahl, Orris C., and Kneese, Allen V., *Quality of the Environment: An Economic Approach to Some Problems in Using Land, Water, and Air*, Baltimore, Johns Hopkins Press, 1965.

Hicks, J. R., "The Foundations of Welfare Economics," *Economic Journal*, Vol. 49 (December, 1939), pp. 696–712.

Hirshleifer, J., "Comment," in *Public Finances: Needs, Sources, and Utilization*, Conference of the Universities National Bureau Committee for Economic Research, Princeton, Princeton University Press, 1961.

Hitch, Charles, "Suboptimization in Operations Problems," *Journal of the Operations Research Society of America*, Vol. 1 (May, 1953), pp. 87–99. *A development and evaluation of suboptimal goals with regard to economic policy.*

Holland, W. D., and others, "Industrial Zoning as a Means of Controlling Area Source Air Pollution," *Journal of the Air Pollution Control Association*, Vol. 10 (April, 1960), pp. 147–55. (Also found in Air Pollution Control Association Abstract No. 2990, June, 1959, p. 22.) *Advocates zoning as a means of controlling air pollution, a concept initially developed in the Soviet Union and not used extensively in the United States.*

Ingram, William T., "Place of Performance Standards in Planning and Zoning Regulations," *Journal of the Air Pollution Control Association*, Vol. 12 (February, 1962), pp. 62–3. *Describes performance standards in manufacturing industries as related to air-pollution emissions and zoning.*

Johnson, Lyndon B., "Advancing the Nation's Health," January 7, 1965. *A message from the President of the United States.*

Joint Economic Committee, Congress of the U.S., *The Federal Budget as an Economic Document*, Washington, D.C., 1962.

Kneese, Allen V., *Water Pollution—Economic Aspects and Research*

Needs, Washington, D.C., Resources for the Future, Inc., 1962. *A blueprint for economic analysis of water pollution, which has been subsequently carried out as proposed by Resources for the Future, Inc.*

Krutilla, John V., "Welfare Aspects of Benefit-Cost Analysis," *Journal of Political Economy,* Vol. 69 (June, 1961), pp. 226–35. *An excellent summary of the applicability of welfare economics to benefit-cost analysis. The author argues that in most projects to which benefit-cost analysis is applied, the application of welfare-economics criteria is not significant, because of small redistribution effects.*

Lange, O., "The Foundations of Welfare Economics," *Econometrica,* Vol. 10 (July–October, 1942), pp. 215–28.

Lipsey, R. G., and Lancaster, Kelvin, "The General Theory of the Second Best," *Review of Economic Studies,* Vol. 24 (1956–57), pp. 11–32. *An early attempt to assign priorities and evaluate these in terms of economic criteria for public and private expenditures, with special emphasis on the possibilities for obtaining the best return on the investment under given constraints.*

Little, I. M. D., *A Critique of Welfare Economics,* New York and London, Oxford University Press, 1957.

———— "The Foundations of Welfare Economics," *Oxford Economics Papers,* New Series (June, 1949). *Classic work on modern welfare economics.*

Marglin, Stephen A., "The Social Rate of Discount and the Optimal Rate of Investment," *Quarterly Journal of Economics,* Vol. 77 (February, 1963), pp. 95–111.

Margolis, Julius, "A Comment on the Pure Theory of Public Expenditure," *Review of Economics and Statistics,* Vol. 37 (November, 1955), pp. 347–9.

———— "The Economic Evaluation of Federal Water Resource Development," *American Economic Review,* Vol. 49 (March–May, 1959), pp. 96–111. *A critical review, analyzing the research used for the development of water resources.*

McKean, Roland N., *Efficiency in Government Through Systems Analysis, with Emphasis on Water Resources Development,* New York, John Wiley & Sons, 1958. *An excellent volume on benefit-cost analysis. The author indicates the most common pitfalls of economic analysis and advocates new approaches to the development of criteria for public expenditure.*

Mellon, W. Giles, An Approach to a General Theory of Priorities: An Outline of Problems and Methods (Memorandum No. 42, Princeton University Econometric Research Program), July, 1962. A comprehensive attempt to evaluate the problems and methods relating to public policies.

Musgrave, Richard A., The Theory of Public Finance, New York, McGraw-Hill, 1959. A standard text on the theory of public finance.

Peacock, Alan T., and Robertson, D. J., Public Expenditure: Appraisal and Control, Edinburgh, Oliver and Boyd, 1963. A thorough analysis of public expenditures, including administrative procedures employed for control of such expenditures.

Proposed Practices for Economic Analysis of River Basin Projects (Report to the Inter-Agency Committee on Water Resources), May, 1958.

Reder, Melvin Warren, Studies in the Theory of Welfare Economics, New York, Columbia University Press, 1947.

Renshaw, E., "A Note on the Measurement of the Benefits from Public Investment in Navigation Projects," American Economic Review, Vol. 47 (June–December, 1957), pp. 652–62.

——— Review of Design of Water-Resource Systems, in Journal of Political Economy, Vol. 70 (October, 1962), p. 516.

——— Review of Efficiency in Government Through Systems Analysis, with Emphasis on Water Resources Development, in Journal of Political Economy, Vol. 68 (February, 1960), pp. 99–100.

Robinson, Joan, Economic Philosophy, Chicago, Aldine Press, 1962.

Samuelson, Paul A., "Aspects of Public Expenditure Theories," Review of Economics and Statistics, Vol. 40 (November, 1958), pp. 332–8.

——— "Diagrammatic Exposition of a Theory of Public Expenditures," Review of Economics and Statistics, Vol. 37 (November, 1955), pp. 350–6. A classic article on public-expenditure criteria.

——— "Further Comment on Welfare Economics," American Economic Review, Vol. 33 (September, 1943), pp. 604–7.

——— "The Pure Theory of Public Expenditures," Review of Economics and Statistics, Vol. 36 (November, 1954), pp. 387–9.

Schueneman, J. J., High, M. D., and Bye, W. E., Air Pollution Aspects of the Iron and Steel Industry, Cincinnati, June, 1963. (Mimeographed.) Describes air pollution resulting from iron and steel manufacturing processes.

Scott, Anthony, Review of *Water Resource Development*, in *Journal of Political Economy*, Vol. 68 (February, 1960), pp. 98–9. *A critical evaluation of benefit-cost analysis as applied to water-resource development.*

Secretary of Health, Education, and Welfare, *Automotive Air Pollution* (Report to the U.S. Congress), Washington, D.C., U.S. Government Printing Office, 1965.

Southern Illinois University, Public Administration and Metropolitan Affairs Program, *Public Awareness and Concern with Air Pollution in the St. Louis Metropolitan Area*, Washington, D.C., U.S. Department of Health, Education, and Welfare, Public Health Service, Division of Air Pollution, 1965.

Steiner, Peter O., "Choosing Among Alternative Public Investments in the Water Resource Field," *American Economic Review*, Vol. 49 (June–December, 1959), pp. 893–916.

Stern, A. C., ed., *Air Pollution*, New York, Academic Press, 1961. *A most comprehensive work on various aspects of air pollution. Economic aspects, however, are not discussed in any detail.*

Stigler, G. J., "The New Welfare Economics," *American Economic Review*, Vol. 33 (June, 1943), pp. 355–9.

The Surgeon General's Ad Hoc Task Group on Air Pollution Research Goals, *National Goals in Air Pollution Research*, Washington, D.C., U.S. Department of Health, Education, and Welfare, Public Health Service, Division of Air Pollution, 1960. *Concerned with the nationwide needs within the ten years 1960–1970 for research on the growing problems of community air pollution.*

Tolley, G. S., "McKean on Government Efficiency," *Review of Economics and Statistics*, Vol. 41 (November, 1959), pp. 446–8.

———Review of *Water Supply: Economics, Technology, and Policy*, in *Journal of Political Economy*, Vol. 70 (June, 1962), pp. 303–4.

——— and Harrell, Cleon, "Extensions of Benefit-Cost Analysis," *American Economic Review*, Vol. 52 (March–May, 1962), pp. 459–68.

——— and Hastings, V. S., "Optimal Water Allocation: the North Platte River," *Quarterly Journal of Economics*, Vol. 74 (May, 1960), pp. 279–95.

U.S. Department of Agriculture, *Land and Water Resources: A Policy Guide*, Washington, D.C., 1962.

U.S. Department of Health, Education, and Welfare, *Measuring Air Quality*, Washington, D.C., U.S. Government Printing Office, 1964.

―――― Public Health Service, *Atmospheric Emissions from Sulfuric Acid Manufacturing Processes* (Public Health Service Publication No. 999-AP-13), Washington, D.C., U.S. Government Printing Office, 1965. *Emissions to the atmosphere from the manufacture of sulfuric acid were investigated jointly by the Manufacturing Chemists' Association, Inc., and the U.S. Public Health Service; the study was the first in a cooperative program for evaluation of emissions from selected chemical manufacturing processes.*

―――― *Digest of State Air Pollution Laws* (Public Health Service Publication No. 711), Washington, D.C., U.S. Government Printing Office, 1963. Supplement published in 1964.

―――― Division of Air Pollution, *Engineering Research in Air Pollution*, Cincinnati, 1963. *Gives a summary and analysis of engineering research related to air pollution.*

―――― *Motor Vehicles, Air Pollution, and Health* (Report of the Surgeon General to the U.S. Congress in compliance with Public Law 86—493, the Schenck Act), Washington, D.C., U.S. Government Printing Office, 1962.

U.S. House of Representatives, Committee on Interstate and Foreign Commerce, *Clean Air Act Amendments* (Hearings before the Subcommittee on Public Health and Welfare, 89th Congress, First Session), Washington, D.C., U.S. Government Printing Office, 1965.

U.S. Senate, Committee on Public Works, *Air Pollution Control* (Hearings before the Subcommittee on Air and Water Pollution, 89th Congress, First Session), Washington, D.C., U.S. Government Printing Office, 1965.

U.S. Senate, Subcommittee on Air and Water Pollution, *Steps Toward Clean Air* (Report to the Committee on Public Works), Washington, D.C., U.S. Government Printing Office, 1964.

Vickrey, William, Review of *Public Finances: Needs, Sources, and Utilization*, in *Journal of Political Economy*, Vol. 70 (April, 1962), p. 201.

Wallace, T. D., "Measures of Social Costs of Agricultural Programs," *Journal of Farm Economics*, Vol. 44 (May, 1962), pp. 580–95.

Wantrup, Siegfried von Ciriacy, "Benefit-Cost Analysis and Public

Resource Development," *Journal of Farm Economics,* Vol. 37 (November, 1955), pp. 676–89.

World Health Organization, *Air Pollution,* Geneva, 1961. *A general and comprehensive work, discussing various aspects of air pollution and its effect upon human environment.*

Special Bibliographies

Gibson, J. R., Culver, W. E., and Kurz, M. E., *The Air Pollution Bibliography,* Washington, D.C., Library of Congress Technical Information Division, 1959. Compiled for the Public Health Service, U.S. Department of Health, Education, and Welfare. *A comprehensive work listing most of the important works in the area of air-pollution research up to the time of publication.*

Isabella, Santina M., *Index to Air Pollution Research,* University Park, Pennsylvania, The Pennsylvania State University, 1965. *Government-sponsored research activity is included, but there are some notable omissions.*

Jacobius, A. J., and others, *The Air Pollution Bibliography,* Vol. II, Washington, D.C., Library of Congress Technical Information Division, 1959. Compiled for the Public Health Service, U.S. Department of Health, Education, and Welfare. *Very similar to the Gibson, Culver, and Kurz bibliography noted above.*

Peele, William J., *Annotated Bibliography on the Planning Aspects of Air Pollution Control,* U.S. Department of Health, Education, and Welfare, Public Health Service, March 15, 1965. (Mimeographed.)

U.S. Department of Health, Education, and Welfare, *Air Pollution Publications: A Selected Bibliography, 1955–1963,* Washington, D.C., U.S. Government Printing Office, 1964. *A very comprehensive bibliography on air pollution.*

Index